The 2014

First

Bus Handbook

British Bus Publishing

Body codes used in the Bus Handbook series:

Type:
A	Articulated vehicle
B	Bus, either single-deck or double-deck
BC	Interurban - high-back seated bus
C	Coach
M	Minibus with design capacity of 16 seats or less
N	Low-floor bus (Niederflur), either single-deck or double-deck
O	Open-top bus (CO = convertible - PO = partial open-top)

Seating capacity is then shown. For double-decks the upper deck quantity is followed by the lower deck.

Please note that seating capacities shown are generally those provided by the operator. It is common practice, however, for some vehicles to operate at different capacities when on certain duties.

Door position:-
C	Centre entrance/exit
D	Dual doorway.
F	Front entrance/exit
R	Rear entrance/exit (no distinction between doored and open)
T	Three or more access points

Equipment:-
T	Toilet	TV	Training vehicle.
M	Mail compartment	RV	Used as tow bus or engineers' vehicle.

Allocation:-
s	Ancillary vehicle
t	Training bus
u	out of service or strategic reserve; refurbishment or seasonal requirement
w	Vehicle is withdrawn and awaiting disposal.

e.g. - B32/28F is a double-deck bus with thirty-two seats upstairs, twenty-eight down and a front entrance/exit., N43D is a low-floor bus with two or more doorways.

Re-registrations:-
Where a vehicle has gained new index marks the details are listed at the end of each fleet showing the current mark, followed in sequence by those previously carried starting with the original mark.

Annual books are produced for the major groups:
The Stagecoach Bus Handbook
The First Bus Handbook
The Arriva Bus Handbook
The Go-Ahead Bus Handbook
The National Express Coach Handbook

Regional books in the series:
The Scottish Bus Handbook
The Welsh Bus Handbook
The Ireland & Islands Bus Handbook
English Bus Handbook: Smaller Groups
English Bus Handbook: Notable Independents
English Bus Handbook: Coaches

Associated series:
The Hong Kong Bus Handbook
The Malta Bus Handbook
The Leyland Lynx Handbook
The Postbus Handbook
The Mailvan Handbook
The Toy & Model Bus Handbook - Volume 1 - Early Diecasts
The Fire Brigade Handbook (fleet list of each local authority fire brigade)
The Police Range Rover Handbook

Some earlier editions of these books are still available. Please contact the publisher on 01952 255669.

The 2014 FirstBus Handbook

The 2014 First Bus Handbook is part of the Bus Handbook series that details the fleets of selected bus and coach operators. These Bus Handbooks are published by British Bus Publishing. Although this book has been produced with the encouragement of and in co-operation with Firstgroup, it is not an official publication. The vehicles included are subject to variation, particularly as new vehicle deliveries lead to older vehicles being withdrawn. The contents are correct to March 2014.

Quality photographs for inclusion in the series are welcome, for which a fee is paid. High-resolution digital images are also welcome on CD or DVD. Unfortunately the publishers cannot accept responsibility for any loss and they require that you show your name on each disc.

To keep the fleet information up to date we recommend the publication, Buses, published monthly by Key Publications, or for more detailed information, the PSV Circle monthly news sheets. The writer and publisher would be glad to hear from readers should any information be available which corrects or enhances that given in this publication.

Editorial team: Stuart Martin and Bill Potter

Acknowledgments:
We are grateful to John Birtwistle, Tom Johnson, Steve Richmond, the PSV Circle and the management and officials of First companies for their kind assistance and co-operation in the compilation of this book. The front and rear cover views are by Dave Heath while the frontispiece is by Richard Godfrey.

Earlier editions are available from the orderline, 01952 255669 or our web site.

1994 Badgerline Bus Handbook	1-897990-26-X	2004 First Bus Handbook	1-897990-91-X
1996 FirstBus Handbook	1-897990-27-8	2005 First Bus Handbook	1-904875-15-7
1997 FirstBus Handbook	1-897990-28-6	2006 First Bus Handbook	1-904875-16-5
1998 FirstBus Handbook	1-897990-29-4	2007 First Bus Handbook	1-904875-17-3
1999 First Bus Handbook	1-897990-86-3	2008 First Bus Handbook	8971904875185
2000 First Bus Handbook	1-897990-87-1	2009 First Bus Handbook	8971904875192
2001 First Bus Handbook	1-897990-88-X	2010 First Bus Handbook	8971904875208
2002 First Bus Handbook	1-897990-89-8	2011 First Bus Handbook	8971904875215
2003 First Bus Handbook	1-897990-90-1	2012 First Bus Handbook	9781904875222

2013 First Bus Handbook ISBN 9781904875239

ISBN 9781904875246

© Published by British Bus Publishing Ltd, March 2014

British Bus Publishing Ltd, 16 St Margaret's Drive, Telford, TF1 3PH

Telephone: 01952 255669

web; www.britishbuspublishing.co.uk
e-mail: sales@britishbuspublishing.co.uk

Contents

Introduction 5
Depots and codes 9

Fleet at February 2014 12

Allocations:
Aberdeen 86
Scotland East 86
Glasgow 88
West Yorkshire 91
York 94
South Yorkshire 94
Manchester 96
Midlands 98
Eastern Counties 99
Essex 101
Hampshire, Dorset & Berkshire 102
West of England 105
South West 107
Cymru 108
Aircoach 110

Vehicle Index 111

First's marketing introduced The Star name for the new bus service designed to transport passengers around Portsmouth and Southsea, a name which also encompasses the area's naval history. Twenty six Streetlite buses have been named after ships, including the *Mary Rose, HMS Warrior* and the *Victory,* while the remainder are named after other naval vessels that currently operate from Portsmouth Naval Base. Seen on the network is 63065, SK63KKF. *Mark Lyons*

Introduction

FirstGroup plc is the UK's largest surface transportation company with a turnover of over six billion pounds, employing over 120,000 staff in Europe and North America. First runs local bus services throughout the UK outside London, and these currently carry some 2.3 million passengers per day in more than forty major towns and cities from Aberdeen to Penzance, with express coach services also operated in Ireland. Full details of First's operations can be found at www.firstgroup.com.

First is also the UK's largest train operator, with four passenger franchises: First Great Western, First Capital Connect, First TransPennine Express and First ScotRail. First also owns Hull Trains, an "open access" operator. Between them these companies operate one quarter of the UK passenger rail network with a balanced portfolio of intercity, commuter and regional services, and carry over 310 million passengers per year. The Croydon Tramlink operated by First on behalf of Transport for London carries twenty-nine million passengers per year.

First's North American business is split into First Student (yellow school buses), First Transit (local bus service operations) and Greyhound. In addition to the iconic Greyhound brand, market segmentation has seen the introduction of Bolt Bus and Yo! Bus for long distance coaching in recent years. All three divisions provide services across Canada and North America. First Student alone carries over four million passengers daily with a fleet of over 60,000 school buses.

First was formed in 1995 from the merger of the Badgerline Group plc based in Weston-super-Mare, and GRT Bus Group plc based in Aberdeen. Badgerline had its roots in the former National Bus Company subsidiary of the same name which was formed in 1986 from the country operations of Bristol Omnibus. As a result of acquisitions, the Badgerline company grew and at the time of the merger comprised the former National Bus Companies Western National, Midland Red West, Bristol Omnibus, Eastern National/ Thamesway, Eastern Counties and South Wales Transport, along with the former West Yorkshire passenger transport executive operation privatised as Yorkshire Rider. GRT was originally Grampian Regional Transport, the municipal operation in Aberdeen privatised under the 1985 Transport Act. GRT had also grown by acquisition and comprised the former Leicester and Northampton municipal operations, together with the Alexander (Midland) and Eastern Scottish former Scottish Bus Group fleets.

The new company was named FirstBus plc, this changing to FirstGroup plc in December 1997 to reflect the diversification of the business into rail and airport management. First soon acquired the former passenger transport executive operations in South Yorkshire (Mainline) and the southern part of the Greater Manchester Transport operations. Other operators acquired comprised the former Strathclyde Passenger Transport Executive operations and adjacent Kelvin Central (former Scottish Bus Group), former NBC companies Potteries, North Devon, Southern National, BeeLine (previously Alder Valley) and Provincial, and the Southampton municipal operation. A new corporate livery was soon introduced, initially on low-floor vehicles. The final components of the UK Bus operations were the privatised London Buses subsidiary Centrewest and on the opposite side of London the recently established Capital Citybus. Smaller operators subsequently bought included Chester City Transport, Hutchisons of Overtown and Truronian of Truro.

The Overground concept of simplified networks with clear, colour-coded route branding, launched in 1999, was the first such unified marketing application within the bus industry. Overground rapidly spread from its Glasgow origin to cover many of First's urban operations, based on frequent, reliable bus services provided by low-floor vehicles at a time when these were relatively uncommon.

The American-style Yellow School Bus concept was introduced to the UK by First in 2002, with the first scheme being in Hebden Bridge in West Yorkshire. First now operates a fleet of over 200 such vehicles in the UK on both its own and local authority sponsored schools services. These services have the same driver every day, the driver having a list of passengers who are to use the service. The same safety and security features are employed as in the vast US schoolbus fleet, and some of the drivers have been recruited from the parents of the schoolchildren. The ftr concept with the Streetcar vehicle introduced in 2007 in York, Leeds and Swansea has been refreshed, with many of these high-quality articulated buses, for example, now operating on the "Hyperlink" branded high frequency shuttle between Leeds and Bradford.

The unified Group livery was refined over the years to encompass specific variations for interurban (Excel and AirCoach) services, Park & Ride services and RailLink services. A new livery for the UK bus fleet was unveiled in 2012, based on the strong brand image generated since 1998. This initially received considerable exposure through the deployment of two hundred new vehicles to transport visitors to the Olympic Games in London. Now visible throughout First's operations, the new livery reintroduced local branding, emphasising local accountability for the provision of a high-quality local service network. Each bus identifies its operating depot and the region, or group of services, where it operates. Examples can be seen in the following pages. The accelerated repaint programme which commenced in 2012 has made the new First livery a common sight across the UK.

Tim O'Toole became the Chief Executive of FirstGroup plc in 2010, when the founder of the Group, Moir Lockhead retired. Tim brought a wealth of experience to the Group from both the USA and UK along with a new approach to the business. Through its "Better Journeys for Life" programme, the UK Bus Division is at the forefront of developments to create a new vision for bus services across the UK and to generate sustained passenger satisfaction and volume growth. Essential components of this programme include public consultation, staff communications and working closely with Governments, local authorities and other local stakeholders to develop partnerships and sustainable transport policies.

Building upon First's early involvement in guided busways, with four of these currently in operation in Leeds, Bradford and Ipswich, a new

Operating the MetroRapid 801 service between Tech Ridge and Southpark Meadows, which started public service on 26th January 2014, is New Flyer 5014 in the First Transit Capital Metro fleet serving Austin Texas. Austin is one of the USA cities pioneering Bus Rapid Transit type services and a second route using non articulated single deckers is to start in August 2014. *John Birtwistle*

busway scheme linking Gosport with Fareham in Hampshire was opened in April 2012, branded as the Eclipse system and developed in partnership with Hampshire County Council. The first route combines segregated busway, traffic signal priority and bus lanes, together with major improvements to passenger infrastructure to bring passengers to their destination on time every time, using a new fleet of high-quality dedicated vehicles. This concept of Bus Rapid Transit is under consideration for other parts of the UK and is growing in popularity in First's USA operations.

During 2012, First launched the Sheffield Bus Partnership with South Yorkshire PTE, Sheffield City Council and the other operators in the city. First considers strategic partnerships with local authorities to be the way forward, and this approach is being used to introduce significant improvements to the bus networks in West Yorkshire and Greater Bristol amongst many others. The Glasgow network was re-launched as SimpliCity in 2013 with a rationalised and simplified network offering improved services and frequencies over an easily assimilated system of routes, accompanied by major investment in new vehicles.

Fares were also reviewed in many areas in 2013, with the objective of providing value for money products. Operations in Greater Manchester, West and South Yorkshire all saw significant reductions in the price of period tickets with resultant increases in bus use. A more radical approach was taken in Bristol where an extensive public consultation exercise was undertaken, the results of which were evaluated and resulted in a much simplified fares structure for City services and improved discounts for young people. This was introduced in late 2013 and has resulted in dramatic increases in bus patronage in the Greater Bristol area. A follow up consultation relating to bus services in the former county of Avon outside Bristol is underway in early 2014.

Investment in both vehicles and technology continues. Not only is all First's bus ticketing equipment compatible with ITSO Smartcards, but mobile ticketing and contactless technology are also in development. Full smart ticketing systems are being rolled out in West and South Yorkshire, Greater Bristol and Hampshire during 2014 with additional schemes already in the pipeline.

Having previously trialled LPG, CNG, fuel cell and battery electric vehicles, together with experimental hybrids, all First buses run on ultra-low sulphur diesel. The use of more fuel-efficient and less polluting hybrid vehicles continues to grow, with these vehicles now in service in London, Leeds, Manchester, Bath, Chelmsford, Heathrow and Glasgow. In partnership with City of York Council, electric vehicles are being introduced to the York Park & Ride services in 2014, and hybrid vehicles will also be drafted in to City services. Meanwhile, in Aberdeen a partnership with the City Council will see the first UK use of hydrogen fuel cell buses outside London, these being introduced during 2014.

Successful evaluation of the lightweight Wrightbus Streetlite vehicle has led to significant orders for these vehicles in 2013 and 2014. The original design has been developed to a full-size single-deck vehicle and the latest "micro hybrid" variant, which uses waste energy from braking to power vehicle ancillary systems, has helped to cut fuel use and emissions still further. The first production "micro hybrid" Streetlites will enter service in 2014 across First's operations.

First is committed to reducing its fuel use, and significant driver training, education and feedback programmes have been rolled out to assist in achieving this aim. The GreenRoad system monitors each driver's braking, acceleration and cornering forces, and, by highlighting where the normal limits of these are exceeded, is used to provide ongoing education and training of drivers, improving fuel economy, road safety and passenger comfort. This alone resulted in fuel savings of over 5% across the board.

First's UK Bus operations have recently gone through a period of consolidation. In 2013 the disposal of the London operations was completed with the sales to Tower Transit and Metroline. The final London operations in Dagenham were taken over by Stagecoach later in the year. First has now focussed its attention and investment on its operations outside London and 2014 sees the biggest single investment in new vehicles in the deregulated market yet.

Spring 2014 sees the commencement of services on the busy Wilmslow Road corridor in Manchester, following the acquisition of Finglands Coachways from the EYMS Group. A new fleet of vehicles will be used to develop services in this area.

Depots and Codes

Company legal name as holder of O licence	Registered operating centres	Code
Aberdeen		
First Aberdeen Ltd	King Street, Aberdeen	AB
Scotland East		
Midland Bluebird Ltd	Dunmore Street, Balfron	BF
Midland Bluebird Ltd	Cowie Road, Bannockburn	BK
Midland Bluebird Ltd	Stirling Road, Larbert	LT
Midland Bluebird Ltd	Stirling Street, Galashiels	GS
First Edinburgh Ltd	The Mall, Musselburgh	MU
First Edinburgh Ltd	Deans Road, Livingston	LV
Glasgow		
First Glasgow (No 1) Ltd	South Street, Scotstoun, Glasgow	SN
First Glasgow (No 1) Ltd	Victoria Road, Glasgow (Larkfield)	LF
First Glasgow (No 1) Ltd	Tollcross Road, Glasgow (Parkhead)	PH
First Glasgow (No 2) Ltd	Glasgow Road, Blantyre	B
First Glasgow (No 2) Ltd	Birch Road, Dumbarton	DU
First Glasgow (No 2) Ltd	Glencryan Road, Cumbernauld	CD
First Glasgow (No 2) Ltd	Castlehill Road, Overtown	O
West Yorkshire		
First West Yorkshire Ltd	Hunslet Park, Leeds	HP
First West Yorkshire Ltd	Headconner Lane, Bramley, Leeds	BM
First West Yorkshire Ltd	Bowling Back Lane, Bradford	BD
First West Yorkshire Ltd	Old Fieldhouse Lane, Huddersfield	HU
First West Yorkshire Ltd	Skircoat Lane, Halifax	HX
York		
First York Ltd	James Street, York	YK
South Yorkshire		
First South Yorkshire Ltd	Midland Road, Rotherham	RO
First South Yorkshire Ltd	Olive Grove, Sheffield	OG
First South Yorkshire Ltd	Duke Street, Doncaster	DN
Manchester		
First Manchester Ltd	Weston Street, Bolton	BN
First Manchester Ltd	Rochdale Road, Bury	BY
First Manchester Ltd	Queen's Road, Manchester	QS
First Manchester Ltd	Wallshaw Street, Oldham	OM
First Manchester Ltd	Oxford Road, Fallowfield	OX
First Manchester Ltd	Broadway, Dukinfield, Tameside	TE
Midlands		
First Potteries Ltd	Dividy Road, Adderley Green	AG
First Potteries Ltd	Liverpool Road, Newcastle-under-Lyme	NE
Leicester CityBus Ltd	Abbey Lane, Leicester	LE
First Midland Red Buses Ltd	Friar Street, Hereford	HD
First Midland Red Buses Ltd	Padmore Street, Worcester	WR
Eastern Counties		
First Eastern Counties Buses Ltd	Vancouver Avenue, King's Lynn	KL
First Eastern Counties Buses Ltd	Caister Road, Great Yarmouth	YA
First Eastern Counties Buses Ltd	Foundation Street, Ipswich	IP
First Eastern Counties Buses Ltd	Gas Works Road, Lowestoft	LO
First Eastern Counties Buses Ltd	Vulcan Road, Norwich	VN

First has introduced a new livery and local name for *the buses of Somerset* **which are allocated to Taunton and Bridgwater. This incorporates a green-based scheme as shown by TransBus Trident 33380, LK53EYZ.**
Steve Rice

Essex

First Essex Buses Ltd	Westway, Chelmsford	CM
First Essex Buses Ltd	Queen Street, Colchester	CO
First Essex Buses Ltd	Telford Road, Clacton	CN
First Essex Buses Ltd	Springfield Industrial Estate, Braintree	BR
First Essex Buses Ltd	Cherrydown East, Basildon	BS
First Essex Buses Ltd	London Road, Hadleigh	HH
First Essex Buses Ltd	Luton Airport	LN

Hampshire and Berkshire

First Beeline Buses Ltd	Market Street, Bracknell	BL
First Beeline Buses Ltd	Stoke Road, Slough	SH
First Beeline Buses Ltd	Reading Transport Ltd	RG
First Hampshire & Dorset Ltd	London Road, Hilsea, Portsmouth	HI
First Hampshire & Dorset Ltd	Gosport Road, Hoeford, Fareham	HO
First Hampshire & Dorset Ltd	Empress Road, Southampton	SO
First Hampshire & Dorset Ltd	Edward Street, Weymouth	WH
First Hampshire & Dorset Ltd	West Street, Bridport	BP

West of England

First Bristol Ltd	Lawrence Hill, Bristol	LH
First Bristol Ltd	Hengrove, Bristol	HG
First Somerset & Avon Ltd	Marlborough Street, Bristol	MS
First Somerset & Avon Ltd	Searle Crescent, Weston-super-Mare	WS
First Somerset & Avon Ltd	Weston Island, Bath	BA

Devon & Cornwall

First Devon & Cornwall Ltd	East Quay, Bridgwater	BW
First Devon & Cornwall Ltd	Hamilton Road, Taunton	TN
First Devon & Cornwall Ltd	Chelson Meadow, Plymouth	PL
First Devon & Cornwall Ltd	Union Street, Camborne	CE

Cymru

First Cymru Buses Ltd	Bridgend	BG
First Cymru Buses Ltd	Cardiff	CF
First Cymru Buses Ltd	Pentregethin Road, Ravenhill, Swansea	RA
First Cymru Buses Ltd	Swansea coaching unit	RAC
First Cymru Buses Ltd	Inkerman Street, Llanelli	LL
First Cymru Buses Ltd	Withybush Industrial Est, Haverfordwest	HV
First Cymru Buses Ltd	Acacia Avenue, Sandfields, Port Talbot	PT

Aircoach

Aircoach Ltd	Great Northern Mall, Belfast	BT
Aircoach Ltd	Airport Business Park, Dublin Airport	D

Depot Codes

AB	King Street, Aberdeen	IP	Foundation Street, Ipswich
AG	Dividy Road, Adderley Green	KL	Vancouver Avenue, King's Lynn
B	Glasgow Road, Blantyre	LE	Abbey Lane, Leicester
BA	Weston Island, Bath	LF	Victoria Road, Larkfield, Glasgow
BD	Bowling Back Lane, Bradford	LH	Lawrence Hill, Bristol
BF	Dunmore Street, Balfron	LL	Inkerman Street, Llanelli
BG	Bridgend	LN	Luton Airport
BK	Cowie Road, Bannockburn	LO	Gas Works Road, Lowestoft
BL	Market Street, Bracknell	LT	Stirling Road, Larbert
BM	Headconner Lane, Bramley, Leeds	LV	Deans Road, Livingston
BN	Weston Street, Bolton	MS	Marlborough Street, Bristol
BP	West Street, Bridport	MU	The Mall, Musselburgh
BR	Springfield Industrial Estate, Braintree	NE	Liverpool Road, Newcastle-under-Lyme
BS	Cherrydown East, Basildon	O	Castlehill Road, Overtown
BT	Great Northern Mall, Belfast	OG	Olive Grove, Sheffield
BW	East Quay, Bridgwater	OM	Wallshaw Street, Oldham
BY	Rochdale Road, Bury	OX	Oxford Road, Manchester
CD	Glencryan Road, Cumbernauld	PH	Tollcross Road, Parkhead, Glasgow
CE	Union Street, Camborne	PL	Chelson Meadow, Plymouth
CF	Cardiff	PT	Acacia Avenue, Sandfields, Port Talbot
CM	Westway, Chelmsford	QS	Queen's Road, Manchester
CN	Telford Road, Clacton	RA	Pentregethin Road, Ravenhill, Swansea
CO	Queen Street, Colchester	RAC	Swansea coaching unit
D	Airport Business Park, Dublin	RG	Reading Transport Ltd
DN	Duke Street, Doncaster	RO	Midland Road, Rotherham
DU	Birch Road, Dumbarton	SH	Stoke Road, Slough
GS	Stirling Street, Galashiels	SN	South Street, Scotstoun
HD	Friar Street, Hereford	SO	Portswood Road, Southampton
HG	Hengrove, Bristol	TE	Broadway, Dukinfield, Tameside
HH	London Road, Hadleigh	TN	Hamilton Road, Taunton
HI	London Road, Hilsea, Portsmouth	VN	Vulcan Road, Norwich
HO	Gosport Road, Hoeford, Fareham	WH	Edward Street, Weymouth
HP	Hunslet Park, Leeds	WR	Padmore Street, Worcester
HU	Old Fieldhouse Lane, Huddersfield	WS	Searle Crescent, Weston-super-Mare
HV	Withybush Ind Est, Haverfordwest	YA	Caister Road, Great Yarmouth
HX	Skircoat Lane, Halifax	YK	James Street, York

A new operational location since the last edition is Luton Airport where three articulated buses are based for the link with Luton's Parkway station. Showing the livery used is 10181, T4FCC. *John Birtwistle*

Fleet at February 2014

10017	BY	X401CSG	Scania L94UA			Wrightbus Solar Fusion		AN58D	2001		

10035-10043			Volvo B7LA			Wright Eclipse Fusion		AN56D	2000		
10035	BA	W118CWR	**10038**	HP	W127DWX	**10040**	HP	W128DWX	**10042**	HP	W129DWX
10036	BA	W119CWR	**10039**	HP	W122DWX	**10041**	HP	W124DWX	**10043**	HP	W126DWX
10037	BA	W122CWR									

10044	ABu	V601GGB	Volvo B10BLA			Wright Fusion		AN53D	1999		
10045	AB	V602GGB	Volvo B10BLA			Wright Fusion		AN53D	1999		

10047-10052			Volvo B7LA			Wright Eclipse Fusion		AN56D	2000		
10047	AB	W2FAL	**10049**	AB	W4FAL	**10051**	AB	W6FAL	**10052**	AB	W7FAL
10048	AB	W3FAL	**10050**	AB	W5FAL						

10103-10110			Volvo B10BLA			Wright Fusion		AN55D	1999		
10103	SNu	V603GGB	**10105**	SNu	V605GGB	**10107**	SNu	V607GGB	**10109**	SNu	V609GGB
10104	SNu	V604GGB	**10106**	SNu	V606GGB	**10108**	SNu	V608GGB	**10110**	SNu	V610GGB

10133-10148			Volvo B7LA			Wrightbus Eclipse Fusion		AN56D	2000-01		
10133	SNu	W133WPO	**10138**	AB	X138FPO	**10144**	AB	X144FPO	**10148**	AB	Y148ROT
10136	AB	X136FPO	**10141**	AB	X141FPO						

10154-10173			Volvo B7LA			Wrightbus Eclipse Fusion		AN56D	2005		
10154	AB	SV05DXA	**10159**	AB	SV05DXG	**10164**	AB	SV05DXM	**10169**	AB	SV05DXT
10155	AB	SV05DXC	**10160**	AB	SV05DXH	**10165**	AB	SV05DXO	**10170**	AB	SV05DXU
10156	AB	SV05DXD	**10161**	AB	SV05DXJ	**10166**	AB	SV05DXP	**10171**	AB	SV05DXW
10157	AB	SV05DXE	**10162**	AB	SV05DXK	**10167**	AB	SV05DXR	**10172**	AB	SV05DXX
10158	AB	SV05DXF	**10163**	AB	SV05DXL	**10168**	AB	SV05DXS	**10173**	AB	SV05DXY

10174-10183			Volvo B7LA			Wrightbus Eclipse Fusion		AN56D	2005	10180-2 are AN50D	
10174	BA	WX55HVZ	**10177**	BA	WX55HWC	**10180**	LN	T3FCC	**10182**	LN	T5FCC
10175	BA	WX55HWA	**10178**	BA	AN02EDN	**10181**	LN	T4FCC	**10183**	AB	SF05KUH
10176	BA	WX55HWB	**10179**	BA	BN02EDN						

11035-11038			Mercedes-Benz O530 Citaro G		Mercedes-Benz			AN49T	2002-04		
11035	u	KR52ZSW	**11036**	CE	SN04XYA	**11037**	CE	SN04XXY	**11038**	CE	SN04XXZ

11073-11083			Mercedes-Benz O530 Citaro G		Mercedes-Benz			AN29D	2008-09		
11073	D	08D67693	**11076**	D	08D69040	**11079**	D	08D69972	**11082**	D	09D5300
11074	D	08D67694	**11077**	D	08D69043	**11080**	D	08D69973	**11083**	D	09D5303
11075	D	08D67697	**11078**	D	08D69070	**11081**	D	08D69974			

11101-11115			Mercedes-Benz O530 Citaro G		Mercedes-Benz			AN52T	2009		
11101	YK	BG58OLR	**11105**	YK	BG58OLX	**11109**	YK	BG58OMD	**11113**	YK	BG58OMJ
11102	YK	BG58OLT	**11106**	YK	BG58OMA	**11110**	YK	BG58OME	**11114**	YK	BG58OMK
11103	YK	BG58OLU	**11107**	YK	BG58OMB	**11111**	YK	BG58OMF	**11115**	YK	BG58OML
11104	YK	BG58OLV	**11108**	YK	BG58OMC	**11112**	YK	BG58OMH			

12001-12018			Scania OmniCity CN94UA		Scania			AN58D	2005		
12001	BY	YN05GYA	**12006**	BY	YN05GYD	**12011**	BY	YN05GYO	**12015**	BY	YN05GYR
12002	BY	YN05GYB	**12007**	BY	YN05GYE	**12012**	BY	YN05GYV	**12016**	BY	YN05GYS
12003	BY	YN05GYH	**12008**	BY	YN05GYF	**12013**	BY	YN05GYU	**12017**	BY	YN05GYT
12004	BY	YN05GYJ	**12009**	BY	YN05GYG	**12014**	BY	YN05GYP	**12018**	BY	YN05GYW
12005	BY	YN05GYC	**12010**	BY	YN05GYK						

19000	RA	S90FTR	Volvo B7LA			Wrightbus StreetCar		AN37D	2005		

First continues to operate articulated buses in certain areas, notably, Leeds, Bury, Aberdeen and Bath. Seen in June 2013 is 10178, AN02EDN, which carries a livery for the Eden Project. *Richard Godfrey*

19001-19038

			Volvo B7LA			Wrightbus StreetCar		AN37D	2006-07		
19001	BM	YK06AOU	19011	BM	YK06AUC	19021	BM	YJ07LVN	19030	RA	S10FTR
19002	BM	YK06ATV	19012	BM	YJ06XLR	19022	BM	YJ07LVO	19031	LN	T6FCC
19003	BM	YK06ATU	19013	BM	YJ06XLS	19023	BM	YJ07LVR	19032	RA	S20FTR
19004	BM	MH06ZSW	19014	BM	YJ56EAA	19024	BM	YJ07LVS	19033	RA	S80FTR
19005	BM	YK06ATX	19015	BM	YJ56EAC	19025	BM	YJ07LVT	19034	RA	S30FTR
19006	BM	MH06ZSP	19016	BM	YJ56EAE	19026	BM	YJ07LVU	19035	RA	S40FTR
19007	BM	YK06ATY	19017	BM	YJ56EAF	19027	BM	YJ07LVV	19036	RA	S50FTR
19008	BM	YK06ATZ	19018	BM	YJ56EAG	19028	BM	YJ07LVW	19037	RA	S60FTR
19009	BM	YK06AUL	19019	BM	YJ07LVL	19029	RA	S100FTR	19038	RA	S70FTR
19010	BM	YK06AUA	19020	BM	YJ07LVM						

20021	AB	FC52AFC	Volvo B12B	Jonckheere Mistral	C53F	2003
20108	CE	WSV409	Volvo B10M-62	Plaxton Première 320	C53F	1996
20109	YAt	N609APU	Volvo B10M-62	Plaxton Première 320	C53F	1996
20122	VNt	P732NVG	Volvo B10M-62	Plaxton Première 320	C53F	1996
20128	CMt	P768XHS	Volvo B10M-62	Plaxton Première 320	C55F	1997

20201-20207

			Volvo B12T			Plaxton Excalibur		C53F	1999		
20201	WR	T701JLD	20202	WR	T702JLD	20205	AB	WSU489	20207	AB	FSU382

20300	GS	WX54ZHM	Volvo B7R	Plaxton Profile	C53F	2005
20301	GS	WX54ZHN	Volvo B7R	Plaxton Profile	C53F	2005
20302	LT	WX54ZHO	Volvo B7R	Plaxton Profile	C53F	2005
20307	LT	WX05OZF	Volvo B7R	Plaxton Profile	C53F	2005

20321-20327

			Volvo B7R			Plaxton Profile		C70F	2007		
20321	RAC	YN57BVU	20323	CF	YN57BVW	20325	CF	YN57BVY	20327	GS	YN57BWU
20322	RAC	YN57BVV	20324	CF	YN57BVX	20326	GS	YN57BVZ			

20351-20374

			Volvo B7R			Plaxton Profile		C45F	2005		
20351	AB	WA05UNG	20357	MU	CV55ABK	20363	LV	CV55ACZ	20369	LT	CV55AMU
20352	AB	WA05UNE	20358	BK	CV55ACO	20364	LV	CV55AFE	20370	LV	CV55AGY
20353	AB	WA05UNF	20359	LV	CV55ACU	20365	MU	CV55AHA	20371	GS	CV55AMX
20354	LV	CU05LGJ	20360	LT	CV55ACX	20366	LV	CV55AFF	20372	AB	CV55ANF
20355	BK	CU05LGK	20361	LV	CV55ACY	20367	AB	CV55AGX	20373	AB	CV55ANP
20356	LV	CV55ABN	20362	LV	CV55AFA	20368	GS	CV55AGZ	20374	AB	CV55AOO

Pictured operating the Lanarkshire Express is 20505, AO02RCV, a Volvo B12M with Plaxton Paragon bodywork. Allocated to Blantyre when pictured in June 2013, the coach has since moved further north and is now based at Aberdeen. *Mark Doggett*

20405	LVw	R305JAF	Volvo B10M-62	Plaxton Expressliner 2	C49FT	1998	
20408	PLst	R308JAF	Volvo B10M-62	Plaxton Expressliner 2	C49FT	1998	
20412	CE	S312SCV	Volvo B10M-62	Plaxton Expressliner 2	C49FT	1998	
20416	HGt	WSV408	Volvo B10M-62	Plaxton Expressliner 2	C44FT	1999	
20417	HOt	P177NAK	Volvo B10M-62	Plaxton Première 350	C53F	1997	Waugh, Greenhead, 1998
20418	HOt	P176NAK	Volvo B10M-62	Plaxton Première 350	C49FT	1997	Waugh, Greenhead, 1998
20457	HOt	R813HWS	Volvo B10M-62	Plaxton Expressliner 2	C44FT	1997	
20460	HGt	T310AHY	Volvo B10M-62	Plaxton Expressliner 2	C44FT	1999	
20461	BWt	X191HFB	Volvo B10M-62	Plaxton Expressliner 2	C44FT	2000	
20463	CM	X193HFB	Volvo B10M-62	Plaxton Expressliner 2	C44FT	2000	

20500-20509   Volvo B12M   Plaxton Paragon   C53F   2002

20500	CM	AO02RBX	20503	DU	AO02RCF	20506	Bu	AO02RCX	20508	DU	AO02RCZ
20501	CM	AO02RBY	20504	DU	AO02RCU	20507	ABu	AO02RCY	20509	DU	AO02RDU
20502	DU	AO02RBZ	20505	AB	AO02RCV						

20514	YA	WV02EUP	Volvo B12M 12.8m	Plaxton Paragon	C50FT	2002	
20515	YA	WV02EUR	Volvo B12M 12.8m	Plaxton Paragon	C50FT	2002	
20550	SO	CU04AYP	Volvo B12B	TransBus Paragon	C49FT	2004	
20551	SO	CU04AYS	Volvo B12B	TransBus Paragon	C49FT	2004	
20556	CE	TT04TRU	Volvo B12B	Plaxton Panther	C49FT	2004	Truronian, 2008
20557	CE	TT05TRU	Volvo B12B	Plaxton Panther	C48FT	2005	Truronian, 2008
20558	CE	TT55TRU	Volvo B12B 12.8m	Plaxton Panther	C49FT	2005	Truronian, 2008
20559	CE	TT06NEX	Volvo B12B	Plaxton Panther	C49FT	2006	Truronian, 2008
20560	CE	TX06NEX	Volvo B12B	Plaxton Panther	C49FT	2006	Truronian, 2008
20561	CE	TT07TRU	Volvo B12B	Plaxton Panther	C49FT	2007	Truronian, 2008
20611	RG	LK07CDE	Volvo B12B 12.8m	Plaxton Panther	C53F	2007	
20612	RG	LK07CDF	Volvo B12B 12.8m	Plaxton Panther	C53F	2007	
20613	RG	LK07CDN	Volvo B12B 12.8m	Plaxton Panther	C53F	2007	

20651-20669   Volvo B12BT   Jonckheere JSV   C51FT   2008-09

20651	D	08D69442	20656	D	08D70357	20661	D	09D2773	20666	D	09D3708
20652	D	08D70256	20657	D	08D70459	20662	D	09D2774	20667	D	09D4282
20653	D	08D70351	20658	D	08D70460	20663	D	09D2777	20668	D	09D4649
20654	D	08D70352	20659	D	08D70461	20664	D	09D3364	20669	D	09D4276
20655	D	08D70354	20660	D	08D70462	20665	D	09D3365			

Chelmsford bus station is the location for this view of 20801, YN08OWO, one of five Volvo B9R coaches used on route X30 that links Southend with Stansted Airport. *Richard Godfrey*

20801-20805

			Volvo B9R			Plaxton Panther		C43FT	2008		
20801	CM	YN08OWO	**20803**	CM	YN08OWR	**20804**	CM	YN08OWU	**20805**	CM	YN08OWV
20802	CM	YN08OWP									

20806	RG	YX11HPO	Volvo B9R		Plaxton Panther	C49F	2011		
20807	RG	YX11HPP	Volvo B9R		Plaxton Panther	C49F	2011		
20808	RG	YN62GYR	Volvo B9R		Plaxton Panther	C49F	2013		
20809	RG	YN62GXS	Volvo B9R		Plaxton Panther	C49F	2013		
20810	RG	YY63WBT	Volvo B9R		Plaxton Panther	C49F	2014		
20811	RG	YY63WBU	Volvo B9R		Plaxton Panther	C49F	2014		

20901-20910

			Volvo B11R			Plaxton Panther		C49FT	2014		
20901	D	141D24	**20904**	D	141D27	**20907**	D	141D30	**20909**	D	141D32
20902	D	141D26	**20905**	D	141D28	**20908**	D	141D31	**20910**	D	141D34
20903	D	141D25	**20906**	D	141D29						

21032	BWt	J732KBC	Dennis Javelin 11m	Plaxton Paramount 3200 III	tv	1992	Jones, Login, 1998,
21145	RAu	R175VWN	Dennis Javelin GX	Plaxton Première 350	BC70F	1998	

23008-23015

			Scania K114IB			Irizar Century Capacity 12.35	C53F		2003-04		
23008	CE	YV03UBA	**23010**	CE	YV03UBC	**23012**	CE	YV03UBE	**23014**	CE	YN04AJX
23009	CE	YV03UBB	**23011**	CE	YV03UBD	**23013**	CE	YN04AJU	**23015**	RG	YN04AJV

23016-23021

			Scania K114IB			Irizar Century Capacity 12.35	C49FT		2004		
23016	D	04D74499	**23018**	D	04D74479	**23020**	RACu	YN54APK	**23021**	AB	YN54APF
23017	D	04D72883	**23019**	CEu	YN54APX						

23201	CEu	YN04YHY	Scania K114IB	Irizar Century 12.35	C49F	2004
23202	CEu	YN04YHW	Scania K114IB	Irizar Century 12.35	C49F	2004
23204	RAu	YN04YHZ	Scania K114IB	Irizar Century 12.35	C49F	2004
23208	CE	WM04NZU	Volvo B12B	Plaxton Panther	C49FT	2004

First operates the Greyhound network in North America and introduced the name and distinctive livery to some coach routes in England and Wales. Illustrating the scheme is Irizar PB 23316, YN55PXG, allocated to the coaching based in Swansea. *John Birtwistle*

23302-23314
Scania K114 EB — Irizar PB — C49FT — 2004

23302	RACu	YN54NXU	23306	AB	PSU629	23309	CF	YN54NXR	23312	RAC	YN54NYT
23303	RACu	YN54NXV	23307	CF	YN54NXZ	23310	RAu	YN54NXT	23313	CE	YN54NYU
23304	RA	YN54NXW	23308	CF	YN54NXO	23311	RAC	YN54NYR	23314	RAC	YN54NYV
23305	AB	PSU628									

23315-23320
Scania K114 EB — Irizar PB — C41FT — 2005

23315	RAC	YN55PXF	23317	RAC	YN55PXH	23319	RAC	YN55PXK	23320	CF	YN55PXL
23316	RAC	YN55PXG	23318	RAC	YN55PXJ						

23321-23325
Scania K114 EB — Irizar PB — C41FT — 2006

23321	CF	YN06CGU	23323	CF	YN06CGX	23324	CF	YN06CGY	23325	RAC	YN06CGZ
23322	CF	YN06CGV									

23330	AB	SV58ASZ	Scania K340 EB	Irizar PB		C49FT	2008
23401	AB	LSK570	Scania K114EB	Irizar Century 12.35		C49FT	2004
23402	AB	LSK571	Scania K114EB	Irizar Century 12.35		C49FT	2004

23501-23504
Scania K340EB — Caetano Levanté — C49FT — 2006

23501	D	06D120305	23502	D	06D120303	23503	D	06D120304	23504	D	06D120368

24000	D	05D62327	Setra S315 GT-HD	Setra		C49F	2005 Evobus, 2006

24029-24047
Setra S415HD — Setra — C44F — 2004

24029	w	04D22632	24033	BT	KFZ4663	24036	D	04D22822	24043	D	04D22845
24030	BT	KFZ4654	24034	BT	KFZ4662	24038	D	04D22824	24044	D	04D22855
24031	BT	KFZ4652	24035	BT	KFZ4661	24041	D	04D22843	24047	D	04D34313
24032	BT	KFZ4653									

29004	AB	YJ61FAF	Temsa Safari HD	Temsa		C49FT	2011
29005	AB	YJ61FAA	Temsa Safari HD	Temsa		C49FT	2011
29006	AB	YJ13GUE	Temsa Safari HD	Temsa		C53F	2013
29007	AB	YJ13GUF	Temsa Safari HD	Temsa		C53F	2013

Four Temsa Safari coaches are now allocated to Aberdeen with 29006, YJ13GUE, shown while undertaking touring duties at Inveraray. The Temsa Safari is aimed at the European coach market and manufactured at Temsa's Adana plant in Turkey. *Murdoch Currie*

30031	NE	G755XRE	Leyland Olympian ONCL10/1RZ	Leyland	B47/29F	1989
30033	NE	G757XRE	Leyland Olympian ONCL10/1RZ	Leyland	BC43/29F	1989
30038	NEu	G762XRE	Leyland Olympian ONCL10/1RZ	Leyland	BC43/29F	1989
30107	PHu	K174EUX	Volvo Olympian	Alexander RH	B42/28F	1994
30239	BM	S655NUG	Volvo Olympian	Alexander Royale	B42/29F	1998
30560	BK	P190TGD	Volvo Olympian	Alexander RL	B47/32F	1996
30561	RO	X856UOK	Volvo B7TL	Alexander ALX400	N47/29F	2001
30562	RO	X857UOK	Volvo B7TL	Alexander ALX400	N47/29F	2001
30563	RO	X858UOK	Volvo B7TL	Alexander ALX400	N47/29F	2001

30564-30578 — Volvo B7TL — Alexander ALX400 — N49/27F — 2002

30564	RO	WU02KVE	30569	RO	WU02KVK	30573	OG	WU02KVP	30576	OG	WU02KVT
30565	RO	WU02KVF	30570	RO	WU02KVL	30574	OG	WU02KVR	30577	RO	WU02KVV
30567	RO	WU02KVH	30571	OG	WU02KVM	30575	RO	WU02KVS	30578	RO	WU02KVW
30568	RO	WU02KVJ	30572	OG	WU02KVO						

| 30722 | HXs | B49PJA | Leyland Olympian ONLXB/1R | Northern Counties | B43/30F | 1985 |

30740-30751 — Volvo Olympian — Alexander RL — B47/32F — 1996

30740	BK	P192TGD	30744	BK	P196TGD	30748	BF	P201TGD	30750	BF	P203TGD
30741	LTu	P193TGD	30745	BF	P197TGD	30749	BF	P202TGD	30751	BK	P204TGD
30743	BK	P195TGD	30746	BF	P198TGD						

30790-30815 — Volvo Olympian — Alexander Royale — B43/29F — 1997-98

30790	BM	R610JUB	30802	HX	R622JUB	30809	HX	R629JUB	30813	HX	R633JUB
30791	BD	R611JUB	30805	HX	R625JUB	30810	HX	R630JUB	30814	HU	R634JUB
30796	BD	R616JUB	30806	HX	R626JUB	30811	HX	R631JUB	30815	HU	R636JUB
30800	HX	R620JUB	30808	HX	R176HUG	30812	HX	R632JUB			

30816-30834 — Volvo Olympian — Alexander Royale — B43/29F — 1998-99

30816	HU	R636HYG	30821	HU	R641HYG	30826	LT	R646HYG	30829	LT	R649HYG
30817	BD	R637HYG	30822	HU	R642HYG	30827	LT	R647HYG	30832	MU	R652HYG
30818	HU	R638HYG	30823	HU	R643HYG	30828	LT	R648HYG	30834	BD	S654FWY

30840-30845

Volvo Olympian — Alexander Royale — B43/29F — 1999

30840	HU	T660VWU	30843	HU	T663VWU	30844	HX	T664VWU	30845	HX	T665VWU
30841	HU	T661VWU									

30846-30870

Volvo B7TL — Alexander ALX400 — N49/29F — 2000

30846	OG	W701CWR	30853	HU	W708CWR	30859	HX	W714CWR	30865	HU	W668CWT
30847	HU	W702CWR	30854	HU	W709CWR	30860	HX	W715CWR	30866	BD	W721CWR
30848	HU	W703CWR	30855	HX	W667CWT	30861	OG	W716CWR	30867	BD	W722CWR
30849	HX	W704CWR	30856	HX	W711CWR	30862	OG	W717CWR	30868	BD	W723CWR
30850	HU	W705CWR	30857	BD	W712CWR	30863	HU	W718CWR	30869	BD	W724CWR
30851	HU	W706CWR	30858	HX	W713CWR	30864	HU	W719CWR	30870	BD	W726CWR
30852	HU	W707CWR									

30871-30915

Volvo B7TL — Alexander ALX400 — N49/29F — 2000

30871	BY	W726DWX	30883	DN	W738DWX	30894	BD	X749VUA	30905	DN	W776DWX
30872	BY	W727DWX	30884	DN	W739DWX	30895	BD	W773DWX	30906	DN	W761DWX
30873	BY	W728DWX	30885	DN	W772DWX	30896	BD	W751DWX	30907	DN	W762DWX
30874	BN	W729DWX	30886	LO	W741DWX	30897	BD	W752DWX	30908	BD	X763VUA
30875	BN	W771DWX	30887	BR	W742DWX	30898	DN	W753DWX	30909	BD	X764VUA
30876	BY	W731DWX	30888	YA	W743DWX	30899	DN	W754DWX	30910	BD	W778DWX
30877	BY	W732DWX	30889	LO	W744DWX	30900	LO	W774DWX	30911	BD	X766VUA
30878	BN	W733DWX	30890	BD	W745DWX	30901	LO	W756DWX	30912	BD	X767VUA
30879	BY	W734DWX	30891	BD	W746DWX	30902	BR	W757DWX	30913	BD	W768DWX
30880	BY	W735DWX	30892	BD	W747DWX	30903	BR	W758DWX	30914	BD	W769DWX
30881	DN	W736DWX	30893	BD	W748DWX	30904	DN	W759DWX	30915	BD	X779VUA
30882	DN	W737DWX									

30916-30938

Volvo B7TL — Alexander ALX400 — N49/29F — 2000

30916	HU	W771KBT	30922	BM	W788KBT	30928	BM	X796NWR	30934	BM	X354VWT
30917	HU	W772KBT	30923	BM	X791NWR	30929	BM	X797NWR	30935	HU	X356VWT
30918	HU	W773KBT	30924	BM	X792NWR	30930	BM	X798NWR	30936	HU	X357VWT
30919	HU	W774KBT	30925	BM	X793NWR	30931	BM	X351VWT	30937	OG	X358VWT
30920	HU	W787KBT	30926	BM	X794NWR	30932	BM	X352VWT	30938	OG	X359VWT
30921	HU	W776KBT	30927	BM	X795NWR	30933	BM	X353VWT			

30939-30965

Volvo B7TL — Alexander ALX400 — N49/27F — 2001-02

30939	BD	Y794XNW	30946	HU	YJ51RRO	30953	HU	YJ51RSU	30960	BN	YJ51RDU
30940	BD	Y795XNW	30947	HU	YJ51RRU	30954	YK	YJ51RDO	30961	OX	YJ51RDV
30941	HU	Y796XNW	30948	HU	YJ51RRV	30955	YK	YJ51RCU	30962	OX	YJ51RDX
30942	HU	Y797XNW	30949	HU	YJ51RRX	30956	OX	YJ51RCV	30963	BN	YJ51RDY
30943	HU	Y798XNW	30950	HU	YJ51RRY	30957	OX	YJ51RCX	30964	OX	YJ51RAU
30944	HU	YJ51RPY	30951	HU	YJ51RRZ	30958	OX	YJ51RCZ	30965	YK	YJ51RAX
30945	HU	YJ51RPZ	30952	HU	YJ51RSO	30959	YK	YJ51RCO			

31129-31148

Volvo B7TL — Alexander ALX400 — N49/27F — 2003

31129	OG	YU52VYE	31134	OG	YU52VYK	31140	OG	YU52VYR	31145	RO	YU52VYX
31130	OG	YU52VYF	31135	OG	YU52VYL	31141	OG	YU52VYS	31146	HU	YU52VYY
31131	OG	YU52VYG	31137	OG	YU52VYN	31142	RO	YU52VYT	31147	HU	YU52VYZ
31132	OG	YU52VYH	31138	OG	YU52VYO	31143	HU	YU52VYV	31148	DN	YU52VZA
31133	OG	YU52VYJ	31139	OG	YU52VYP	31144	RO	YU52VYW			

31200	CDu	R152EHS	Volvo Olympian	Alexander Royale	B42/29F	1997	

31435-31461

Volvo Olympian — Alexander RL — B47/32F — 1996

31435	LF	N946SOS	31442	DUu	N953SOS	31446	GS	N957SOS	31457	CE	N968SOS
31438	DUu	N949SOS	31443	LFu	N954SOS	31447	GS	N958SOS	31458	CE	N969SOS
31440	LT	N951SOS	31444	DU	N955SOS	31448	DUu	N959SOS	31461	CE	N972SOS
31441	LT	N952SOS	31445	LT	N956SOS	31449	LF	N960SOS			

31469-31492

Volvo Olympian — Alexander Royale — B42/29F — 1997

31469	CDu	P596WSU	31481	CDu	P617WSU	31486	Bu	R143EHS	31491	CDu	R148EHS
31477	CDu	P605WSU	31483	CDu	P619WSU	31489	CDu	R146EHS	31492	CDu	R149EHS
31478	PHu	P606WSU									

31497	BK	R655DUS	Volvo Olympian	Northern Counties Palatine II	B43/29F	1997
31518	NE	M847DUS	Leyland Olympian	Alexander Royale	BC47/28F	1994
31528	ABs	URS318X	Leyland Atlantean AN68C/1R	Alexander AL	O45/29D	1982
31529	ABs	CRG325C	Daimler CVG6	Alexander B	B37/29R	1965

Leonard Street in Sheffield provides the background to this view of Volvo B7TL 31139, YU52VYP, one of twelve from the batch to be allocated to Olive Grove depot. *Mark Lyons*

31558-31563

		Volvo B7TL			Alexander ALX400			N49/29F	2001	
31558	LT	X132NSS	31560	LT	X103NSS	31562	LT	X136NSS	31563	LT	X137NSS
31559	LT	X771NSO	31561	LT	X104NSS					

31572	LTu	P594WSU	Volvo Olympian	Alexander Royale	B42/29F	1997
31577	ABt	XSS344Y	Leyland Atlantean AN68D/1R	Alexander AL	tv	1983

31642-31669

		Volvo Olympian			Alexander Royale			B42/29F	1998-99	
31642	BF	R310LKS	31656	LT	S925AKS	31663	LTu	S932AKS	31667	LTu	S936AKS
31646	LT	R314LKS	31660	LTu	S929AKS	31666	LTu	S935AKS	31669	LTu	S938AKS

31677	BD	P613WSU	Volvo Olympian	Alexander Royale	B42/29F	1997
31684	GS	P588WSU	Volvo Olympian	Alexander Royale	B42/29F	1997
31687	GS	P592WSU	Volvo Olympian	Alexander Royale	B42/29F	1997
31688	GS	P593WSU	Volvo Olympian	Alexander Royale	B42/29F	1997

31760-31775

		Volvo Olympian			Alexander RH			B47/29F	1997-98	London United, 2003
31760	BD	R921WOE	31764	BD	R925WOE	31768	BD	R932YOV	31773	HPu	R938YOV
31761	BD	R922WOE	31765	BD	R926WOE	31769	BD	R933YOV	31774	HX	R939YOV
31762	BD	R923WOE	31766	BD	R930WOE	31770	BD	R934YOV	31775	HX	R940YOV
31763	BD	R924WOE	31767	BD	R931WOE	31771	HPu	R935YOV			

31776-31786

		Volvo B7TL			TransBus ALX400			N49/27F	2003	
31776	DN	YN53EOA	31779	DN	YN53EOD	31782	DN	YN53EOG	31785	DN	YN53EOK
31777	DN	YN53EOB	31780	DN	YN53EOE	31783	DN	YN53EOH	31786	DN	YN53EOL
31778	DN	YN53EOC	31781	DN	YN53EOF	31784	DN	YN53EOJ			

31787-31804

		Volvo B7TL			Wrightbus Eclipse Gemini			N45/29F	2003	
31787	B	YN53EFE	31792	GS	YN53EFK	31797	B	YN53EFR	31801	B	YN53EFW
31788	B	YN53EFF	31793	B	YN53EFL	31798	B	YN53EFT	31802	B	YN53EFX
31789	B	YN53EFG	31794	B	YN53EFM	31799	B	YN53EFU	31803	B	YN53EFZ
31790	GS	YN53EFH	31795	B	YN53EFO	31800	B	YN53EFV	31804	B	YN53EGC
31791	GS	YN53EFJ	31796	B	YN53EFP						

Alexander's ALX400 was popular with many operators, especially for buses allocated to London duties. Now converted to single-door and seen working through Southampton on Park and Ride duties is 32255, **LT52WWA**. *Dave Heath*

31806	BMu	R928WOE	Volvo Olympian	Alexander RH	B47/29F	1997	London United, 2003
31807	HX	R929WOE	Volvo Olympian	Alexander RH	B47/29F	1997	London United, 2003
31808	HX	R936YOV	Volvo Olympian	Alexander RH	B47/29F	1998	London United, 2003

31820-31830

			Volvo Olympian	Northern Counties Palatine	B47/27D	1997	London General, 2005
31820	CE	P920RYO	**31826**	CE	P926RYO	**31828**	CE	P908RYO	**31830**	CE	P930RYO
31821	CE	P921RYO								

31836	CE	R336LGH	Volvo Olympian	Northern Counties Palatine	B47/27D	1998	London General, 2005
31841	CE	R241LGH	Volvo Olympian	Northern Counties Palatine	BC47/31F	1998	Ensign, Purfleet, 2005
31846	CE	R246LGH	Volvo Olympian	Northern Counties Palatine	BC47/31F	1998	London General, 2005
31877	CE	R277LGH	Volvo Olympian	Northern Counties Palatine	B47/27D	1998	London General, 2005
31878	CE	R278LGH	Volvo Olympian	Northern Counties Palatine	B47/27D	1998	London General, 2005
31925	TEs	P425PVW	Dennis Arrow	East Lancs Pyoneer	B49/33F	1997	
31929	TE	R429ULE	Dennis Arrow	East Lancs Pyoneer	B49/30F	1998	
31943	OMtu	R443ULE	Dennis Arrow	East Lancs Pyoneer	B49/30F	1998	

32001-32024

Volvo B7TL — Alexander ALX400 — N49/29F 2000

32001	WS	W801PAE	32007	MS	W807PAE	32014	LH	W814PAE	32019	LH	W819PAE
32002	LH	W802PAE	32008	LH	W808PAE	32015	LH	W815PAE	32021	LH	W821PAE
32003	LH	W803PAE	32009	LH	W809PAE	32016	LH	W816PAE	32022	LH	W822PAE
32004	LH	W804PAE	32011	LH	W811PAE	32017	LH	W817PAE	32023	LH	W823PAE
32005	LH	W805PAE	32012	LH	W812PAE	32018	LH	W818PAE	32024	LH	W824PAE
32006	MS	W806PAE	32013	LH	W813PAE						

32027	MS	V124LGC	Volvo B7TL	Alexander ALX400	N43/29F	2000	*On loan from Volvo Bus*

32031-32046

Volvo B7TL — Alexander ALX400 — N49/29F 2000

32031	SO	W801EOW	32035	SO	W805EOW	32039	SO	W809EOW	32044	SO	W814EOW
32032	SO	W802EOW	32036	SO	W806EOW	32041	SO	W811EOW	32045	SO	W815EOW
32033	SO	W803EOW	32037	PT	W807EOW	32042	SO	W812EOW	32046	SO	W816EOW
32034	SO	W804EOW	32038	SO	W808EOW	32043	SO	W813EOW			

32052	LFs	X578RJW	Volvo B7TL 10.2m	East Lancs Vyking	Classroom 2000		

32053-32065   Volvo B7TL   Alexander ALX400   N49/29F   2000

32053	NE	W213XBD	32056	LE	W216XBD	32059	LE	W219XBD	32063	YAu	W223XBD
32054	NE	W214XBD	32057	LE	W217XBD	32061	LE	W221XBD	32064	LE	W224XBD
32055	LE	W215XBD	32058	LE	W218XBD	32062	YAu	W422SRP	32065	LE	W425SRP

32066-32099   Volvo B7TL   Alexander ALX400   N49/29F   2002

32066	LE	KP51VZO	32075	LE	KP51WAO	32084	LE	KP51WBU	32092	LE	KP51WCN
32067	LE	KP51VZR	32076	LE	KP51WAU	32085	LE	KP51WBV	32093	LE	KP51WCO
32068	LE	KP51VZS	32077	LE	KP51WBD	32086	LE	KP51WBY	32094	LE	KP51WCR
32069	LE	KP51VZT	32078	LE	KP51WBG	32087	LE	KP51WBZ	32095	LE	KP51WCW
32070	LE	KP51VZW	32079	LE	KP51WBJ	32088	LE	KP51WCA	32096	LE	KP51WCX
32071	LE	KP51VZX	32080	LE	KP51WBK	32089	LE	KP51WCF	32097	LE	KP51WCY
32072	LE	KP51VZY	32081	LE	KP51WBL	32090	LE	KP51WCG	32098	LE	KP51WDD
32073	LE	KP51VZZ	32082	LE	KP51WBO	32091	LE	KP51WCJ	32099	LE	KP51WDE
32074	LE	KP51WAJ	32083	LE	KP51WBT						

32100-32112   Volvo B7TL 10m   Plaxton President 4.4m   N39/24F   2002

32100	VN	LT02ZCJ	32104	VN	LT02ZCO	32107	VN	LT02ZCY	32110	OG	LT02ZDJ
32101	VN	LT02ZCK	32105	VN	LT02ZCU	32108	OG	LT02ZCZ	32111	OG	LT02ZDK
32102	VN	LT02ZCL	32106	VN	LT02ZCV	32109	OG	LT02ZDH	32112	VN	LT02ZDL
32103	VN	LT02ZCN									

32200-32228   Volvo B7TL 10.6m   Plaxton President 4.4m   N42/27F   2002

32200	YA	LT52WTE	32208	YA	LT52WTO	32215	OG	LT52WTY	32222	MU	LT52WUG
32201	YA	LT52WTF	32209	YA	LT52WTP	32216	OG	LT52WTZ	32223	MU	LT52WUH
32202	YA	LT52WTG	32210	YA	LT52WTR	32217	OG	LT52WUA	32224	MU	LT52WUJ
32203	VN	LT52WTJ	32211	VN	LT52WTU	32218	OG	LT52WUB	32225	LV	LT52WUK
32204	YA	LT52WTK	32212	YA	LT52WTV	32219	OG	LT52WUC	32226	LV	LT52WUL
32205	YA	LT52WTL	32213	YA	LT52WTW	32220	OG	LT52WUD	32227	LV	LT52XAL
32206	YA	LT52WTM	32214	YA	LT52WTX	32221	LV	LT52WUE	32228	LV	LT52XAM
32207	YA	LT52WTN									

32249-32276   Volvo B7TL 10.6m   Alexander ALX400 4.4m   N45/24F   2003

32249	DN	LT52WVM	32256	SO	LT52WWB	32263	DN	LT52WWJ	32270	DN	LT52WWR
32250	DN	LT52WVN	32257	SO	LT52WWC	32264	DN	LT52WWK	32271	DN	LT52WWS
32251	LH	LT52WVO	32258	SO	LT52WWD	32265	DN	LT52WWL	32272	DN	LT52WWU
32252	LH	LT52WVP	32259	SO	LT52WWE	32266	DN	LT52WWM	32273	DN	LT52WXC
32253	LH	LT52WVY	32260	DN	LT52WWF	32267	DN	LT52WWN	32274	DN	LT52WXD
32254	SO	LT52WVZ	32261	DN	LT52WWG	32268	DN	LT52WWO	32275	DN	KDZ5104
32255	SO	LT52WWA	32262	DN	LT52WWH	32269	DN	LT52WWP	32276	DN	LT52WXF

32277	LE	KP51WDF	Volvo B7TL	Alexander ALX400 4.4m	N49/27F	2002
32278	MS	YU52VYM	Volvo B7TL	Alexander ALX400 4.4m	N49/27F	2003

32279-32292   Volvo B7TL 11.2m   TransBus ALX400 4.4m   N49/27F   2003

32279	HG	WR03YZL	32283	BA	WR03YZS	32287	LH	WR03YZW	32290	LH	WX53UKL
32280	LH	WR03YZM	32284	BA	WR03YZT	32288	LH	WR03YZX	32291	MS	WR03ZBC
32281	BA	WR03YZN	32285	BA	WR03YZU	32289	LH	WX53UKK	32292	LH	WR03ZBD
32282	BA	WR03YZP	32286	LH	WR03YZV						

32294-32312   Volvo B7TL 10.6m   TransBus President 4.4m   N44/23F   2003

32294	LV	LK03NGJ	32299	LV	LK03NGY	32303	SN	LK03NHC	32309	OG	LK03NHJ
32295	LV	LK03NGN	32300	LV	LK03NGZ	32304	SN	LK03NHD	32310	OG	LK03NHL
32296	LV	LK03NGU	32301	SN	LK03NHA	32305	SN	LK03NHE	32311	OG	LK03NHM
32297	LV	LK03NGV	32302	SN	LK03NHB	32308	OG	LK03NHH	32312	OG	LK03NHN
32298	LV	LK03NGX									

32328-32348   Volvo B7TL 10.6m   Wrightbus Eclipse Gemini   N41/28F*   2003-04   *32348 is N41/25F

32328	HG	LK53LYH	32334	HG	LK53LYU	32339	HG	LK53LYZ	32344	HG	LK53LZE
32329	HG	LK53LYJ	32335	HG	LK53LYV	32340	HG	LK53LZA	32345	HG	LK53LZF
32330	HG	LK53LYO	32336	HG	LK53LYW	32341	HG	LK53LZB	32346	HG	LK53LZG
32331	HG	LK53LYP	32337	HG	LK53LYX	32342	HG	LK53LZC	32347	HG	LK53LZH
32332	HG	LK53LYR	32338	HG	LK53LYY	32343	HG	LK53LZD	32348	BL	LK53LZL
32333	HG	LK53LYT									

32349-32360   Volvo B7TL 10.1m   Wrightbus Eclipse Gemini   N38/24F   2004

32349	BA	LK53LZM	32352	BA	LK53LZP	32355	LH	LK53LZU	32358	LH	LK53LZX
32350	BA	LK53LZN	32353	BA	LK53LZR	32356	LH	LK53LZV	32359	LH	LK53MBF
32351	BA	LK53LZO	32354	BA	LK53LZT	32357	LH	LK53LZW	32360	LH	LK04HYP

32431-32473 — Volvo B7TL 10.1m — Wrightbus Eclipse Gemini — N45/29F — 2004

32431	BM	YW04VAU	32440	BM	YJ04FYL	32449	BM	YJ04FYW	32465	BM	YJ04FZP
32432	BM	YJ04FYB	32441	BM	YJ04FYM	32450	BM	YJ04FYX	32466	BM	YJ04FZR
32433	BM	YJ04FYC	32442	BM	YJ04FYN	32451	BM	YJ04FYY	32467	BM	YJ04FZS
32434	BM	YJ04FYD	32443	BM	YJ04FYP	32452	BM	YJ04FYZ	32468	BM	YJ04FZT
32435	BM	YJ04FYE	32444	BM	YJ04FYR	32460	HXu	YJ04FZH	32469	BM	YJ04FZU
32436	BM	YJ04FYF	32445	BM	YJ04FYS	32461	BM	YJ04FZK	32470	BM	YJ04FZV
32437	BM	YJ04FYG	32446	BM	YJ04FYT	32462	BM	YJ04FZL	32471	BM	YJ04FZX
32438	BM	YJ04FYH	32447	BM	YJ04FYU	32463	BM	YJ04FZM	32472	BM	YJ04FZY
32439	BM	YJ04FYK	32448	BM	YJ04FYV	32464	BM	YJ04FZN	32473	BM	YJ04FZZ

32475-32494 — Volvo B7TL 10.7m — TransBus ALX400 4.3m — N49/29F — 2003

32475	CO	AU53HJJ	32480	CO	AU53HJX	32485	CO	AU53HKC	32490	IP	AU53HKH
32476	CO	AU53HJK	32481	CO	AU53HJY	32486	IP	AU53HKD	32491	IP	AU53HKJ
32477	CO	AU53HJN	32482	CO	AU53HJZ	32487	IP	AU53HKE	32492	IP	AU53HKK
32478	CO	AU53HJO	32483	CO	AU53HKA	32488	IP	AU53HKF	32493	IP	AU53HKL
32479	IP	AU53HJV	32484	CO	AU53HKB	32489	IP	AU53HKG	32494	IP	AU53HKM

32503-32542 — Volvo B7TL 10.7m — Wrightbus Eclipse Gemini — N45/29F — 2004-05

32503	HU	YJ54XTO	32513	HU	YJ54XUB	32523	HX	YJ54XUO	32533	BD	YJ54XVA
32504	HU	YJ54XTP	32514	HU	YJ54XUC	32524	HX	YJ54XUP	32534	BD	YJ54XVB
32505	HU	YJ54XTR	32515	HU	YJ54XUD	32525	HX	YJ54XUR	32535	BD	YJ54XVC
32506	HU	YJ54XTT	32516	HU	YJ54XUE	32526	HX	YJ54XUT	32536	BD	YJ54XVD
32507	HU	YJ54XTU	32517	HU	YJ54XUF	32527	HX	YJ54XUU	32537	BD	YJ05VUX
32508	HU	YJ54XTV	32518	HU	YJ54XUG	32528	BD	YJ54XUV	32538	BD	YJ05VUW
32509	HU	YJ54XTW	32519	HU	YJ54XUH	32529	BD	YJ54XUW	32539	HX	YJ05VWG
32510	HU	YJ54XTX	32520	HX	YJ54XUK	32530	BD	YJ54XUX	32540	HX	YJ05VWE
32511	HU	YJ54XTZ	32521	HX	YJ54XUM	32531	BD	YJ54XUY	32541	HX	YJ05VWF
32512	HU	YJ54XUA	32522	HX	YJ54XUN	32532	BD	YJ05VUY	32542	HX	YJ05VWH

32543-32626 — Volvo B7TL 10.7m — Wrightbus Eclipse Gemini — N45/29F — 2004-05

32543	LF	SF54OSD	32564	LF	SF54OTE	32585	PH	SF54OUE	32606	B	SF54TKJ
32544	LF	SF54OSE	32565	LF	SF54OTG	32586	SN	SF54OUG	32607	B	SF54TKK
32545	SN	SF54OSG	32566	PH	SF54OTH	32587	PH	SF54OUH	32608	B	SF54TKO
32546	LF	SF54OSJ	32567	PH	SF54OTJ	32588	SN	SF54OUJ	32609	B	SF54TKN
32547	LF	SF54OSK	32568	PH	SF54OTK	32589	PH	SF54OUK	32610	B	SF54TKT
32548	SN	SF54OSL	32569	LF	SF54OTL	32590	SN	SF54OUL	32611	LF	SF54TKU
32549	LF	SF54OSM	32570	SN	SF54OTM	32591	SN	SF54OUM	32612	LF	SF54TKV
32550	SN	SF54OSN	32571	LF	SF54OTN	32592	SN	SF54OUN	32613	PH	SF54TKX
32551	LF	SF54OSO	32572	LF	SF54OTP	32593	SN	SF54THV	32614	LF	SF54TKY
32552	SN	SF54OSP	32573	PH	SF54OTR	32594	SN	SF54THX	32615	PH	SF54TKZ
32553	SN	SF54OSR	32574	LF	SF54OTT	32595	SN	SF54THZ	32616	PH	SF54TLJ
32554	SN	SF54OSU	32575	SN	SF54OTU	32596	SN	SF54TJO	32617	PH	SF54TLK
32555	SN	SF54OSV	32576	SN	SF54OTV	32597	SN	SF54TJU	32618	PH	SF54TLN
32556	PH	SF54OSW	32577	PH	SF54OTW	32598	LF	SF54TJV	32619	PH	SF54TLO
32557	PH	SF54OSX	32578	PH	SF54OTX	32599	LF	SF54TJX	32620	PH	SF54TLU
32558	PH	SF54OSY	32579	PH	SF54OTY	32600	LF	SF54TJY	32621	PH	SF54TLX
32559	PH	SF54OSZ	32580	PH	SF54OTZ	32601	LF	SF54TJZ	32622	LF	SF54TLY
32560	PH	SF54OTA	32581	PH	SF54OUA	32602	LF	SF54TKA	32623	LF	SF54TLZ
32561	LF	SF54OTB	32582	SN	SF54OUB	32603	LF	SF54TKC	32624	LF	SF54TMO
32562	LF	SF54OTC	32583	LF	SF54OUC	32604	B	SF54TKD	32625	LF	SF54TMU
32563	LFu	SF54OTD	32584	PH	SF54OUD	32605	B	SF54TKE	32626	LF	SF54TMV

32627-32650 — Volvo B7TL 10.7m — Wrightbus Eclipse Gemini — N45/29F — 2005

32627	NE	KP54KAO	32633	NE	KP54LAE	32639	NE	KP54AZA	32645	LE	KP54AZJ
32628	BS	KP54KAU	32634	NE	KP54LAO	32640	BS	KP54AZB	32646	LE	KP54AZL
32629	LE	KP54KAX	32635	NE	KX05MGV	32641	BS	KP54AZC	32647	LE	KP54AZN
32630	LE	KP54KBE	32636	HG	WX05UAF	32642	BS	KP54AZD	32648	LE	KP54KBK
32631	BS	KP54KBF	32637	HG	WX05UAG	32643	LE	KP54AZF	32649	LE	KP54KBN
32632	NE	KP54KBJ	32638	HG	WX05UAH	32644	LE	KP54AZG	32650	LE	KP54KBO

32651-32656 — Volvo B7TL 10.7m — ADL ALX400 — N49/27F — 2005

32651	CO	AU05MUO	32653	IP	AU05MUV	32655	IP	AU05MUY	32656	IP	AU05MVA
32652	CO	AU05MUP	32654	CO	AU05MUW						

32657	LF	LK55ACO	Volvo B7TL 10.7m	Wrightbus Eclipse Gemini	N41/25F	2005

High-back seating is provided for the Tamar link with Plymouth as illustrated by East Lancs-bodied Trident 32760, WA54OLR, one of thirteen supplied to Devon in 2005. *Mark Bailey*

32669-32683

Volvo B7TL 10.7m — Wrightbus Eclipse Gemini — N45/29F — 2005

32669	GS	SN55HDZ	32673	LV	SN55HFA	32677	LV	SN55HFE	32681	LV	SN55HFJ
32670	GS	SN55HEJ	32674	LV	SN55HFB	32678	LV	SN55HFF	32682	LV	SN55HFK
32671	GS	SN55HEU	32675	LV	SN55HFC	32679	LV	SN55HFG	32683	LV	SN55HFL
32672	GS	SN55HEV	32676	LV	SN55HFD	32680	LV	SN55HFH			

32684-32691

Volvo B7TL 10.7m — Wrightbus Eclipse Gemini — N45/27F — 2006

32684	MS	WX56HJZ	32686	MS	WX56HKB	32688	MS	WX56HKD	32690	MS	WX56HKF
32685	MS	WX56HKA	32687	MS	WX56HKC	32689	MS	WX56HKE	32691	MS	WX56HKG

32692-32697

Volvo B7TL 10.7m — Wrightbus Eclipse Gemini — N45/29F — 2006

32692	HX	YJ06XLK	32694	HX	YJ06XLM	32696	HX	YJ06XLO	32697	HP	YJ06XLP
32693	HX	YJ06XLL	32695	HX	YJ06XLN						

32701-32717

Dennis Trident — East Lancs Lolyne — N49/30F — 2000

32701	WH	V701FFB	32705	SO	W705PHT	32709	PL	W709RHT	32714	PL	W714RHT
32702	WH	W702PHT	32706	SO	W706PHT	32711	PL	W711RHT	32715	PL	W715RHT
32703	WH	W703PHT	32707	WH	W707PHT	32712	PL	W712RHT	32716	PL	W716RHT
32704	SO	W704PHT	32708	WH	W708PHT	32713	PL	W713RHT	32717	PL	W717RHT

32751-32754

Dennis Trident — East Lancs Lolyne — N49/30F — 2000

32751	PL	X501BFJ	32752	PL	X502BFJ	32753	PL	X503BFJ	32754	PL	X504BFJ

32755	PL	WK52SYE	TransBus Trident	East Lancs Myllennium Lolyne N49/30F	2002

32756-32768

ADL Trident 9.9m — East Lancs Myllennium Lolyne NC49/31F — 2005

32756	PL	WA54OLO	32760	PL	WA54OLR	32763	WH	WJ55CSF	32766	WH	WJ55CSV
32757	PL	WA54OLP	32761	PL	WJ55CRX	32764	SO	WJ55CSO	32767	SO	WJ55CTE
32758	PL	WA54OLT	32762	PL	WJ55CRZ	32765	WH	WJ55CSU	32768	SO	WJ55CTF
32759	PL	WA54OLN									

Heading for Dartmouth on route 81 is Plaxton President 32873, HIG1523, now converted to single door. This view illustrates the staircase position and the distance the foot of their stairs are from the entrance. *Steve Rice*

32801-32821   Dennis Trident 9.9m   Plaxton President 4.4m   N39/24F   1999

32801	BS	T801LLC	32806	CMt	T806LLC	32811	LV	T811LLC	32817	CE	T817LLC
32802	CE	T802LLC	32807	BSt	T807LLC	32813	LV	T813LLC	32818	BS	T818LLC
32803	CE	T803LLC	32808	CE	T808LLC	32814	LV	T814LLC	32819	CE	T819LLC
32804	BS	T804LLC	32809	HH	T809LLC	32815	PHu	T815LLC	32820	PHu	T820LLC
32805	PHu	T805LLC	32810	CN	T810LLC	32816	CDu	T816LLC	32821	LV	T821LLC

32823-32853   Dennis Trident 9.9m   Plaxton President 4.4m   N39/27F   1999

32823	LT	T823LLC	32831	LT	T831LLC	32839	CDu	T839LLC	32847	BS	T847LLC
32824	LFu	T824LLC	32832	PHu	T832LLC	32840	CDu	T840LLC	32848	CDu	T848LLC
32825	LFu	T825LLC	32833	PHu	T833LLC	32841	LT	T841LLC	32849	BS	T849LLC
32826	LFu	T826LLC	32834	LT	T834LLC	32842	LT	T842LLC	32850	HH	T850LLC
32827	LFu	T827LLC	32835	PHu	T835LLC	32843	PHu	T843LLC	32851	PL	HIG1519
32828	LFu	T828LLC	32836	PHu	T836LLC	32844	CDu	T844LLC	32852	WR	T852LLC
32829	LFu	T829LLC	32837	LV	T837LLC	32845	AB	T845LLC	32853	CE	HIG1512
32830	LT	T830LLC	32838	LV	T838LLC	32846	CE	T846LLC			

32854-32887   Dennis Trident 9.9m   Plaxton President 4.4m   N39/24F   1999

32854	WR	T854KLF	32864	BS	T864KLF	32870	LV	T870KLF	32876	CE	HIG1527
32855	BS	V855HBY	32865	CDu	T865KLF	32871	CDu	T871KLF	32878	CE	HIG1531
32856	CN	V856HBY	32866	PHu	T866KLF	32872	BW	HIG1521	32879	CE	HIG1533
32858	CE	HIG1528	32867	OX	V867HBY	32873	BW	HIG1523	32880	CE	HIG1538
32859	BS	V859HBY	32868	CDu	T868KLF	32874	BW	HIG1524	32883	BS	T883LLC
32861	CE	HIG1540	32869	BN	V869HBY	32875	CE	HIG1526	32887	BS	V887HBY
32863	BS	V863HBY									

32888-32930   Dennis Trident 9.9m   Plaxton President 4.4m   N43/27F   2000

32888	Bu	V988HLH	32900	u	V990HLH	32911	BN	W896VLN	32921	LT	W921VLN
32889	LT	V889HLH	32901	u	W901VLN	32912	BN	W912VLN	32922	LT	W922VLN
32890	Bu	V890HLH	32902	u	W902VLN	32913	BN	W913VLN	32923	AB	W923VLN
32891	CDu	V891HLH	32903	u	W903VLN	32914	LT	W914VLN	32924	LT	W924VLN
32892	LT	V892HLH	32904	LT	W904VLN	32915	BN	W915VLN	32925	SN	W898VLN
32893	LT	V893HLH	32905	BS	W905VLN	32916	BN	W916VLN	32926	BN	W926VLN
32895	LT	V895HLH	32906	BN	W906VLN	32917	LV	W917VLN	32927	AB	W927VLN
32896	LT	V896HLH	32907	LT	W907VLN	32918	AB	W918VLN	32928	ABu	W928VLN
32897	AB	V897HLH	32908	BN	W908VLN	32919	LT	W919VLN	32929	u	W929VLN
32898	AB	V898HLH	32909	LT	W909VLN	32920	LFu	W897VLN	32930	SNu	W899VLN
32899	BN	V899HLH	32910	LT	W895VLN						

East Lothian names are carried by Dennis Trident 33138, LT02ZFK, seen in Edinburgh at the start of its journey to East Berwick. *Mark Doggett*

32931-32952

Dennis Trident 9.9m   Alexander ALX400 4.4m   N45/27F   2000

32931	PH	W931ULL	32937	PH	W937ULL	32942	PH	W942ULL	32949	LT	W949ULL
32934	LV	W934ULL	32939	PH	W939ULL	32946	PH	W946ULL	32950	PH	W132VLO
32935	PH	W935ULL	32940	PH	W840VLO	32947	PH	W947ULL	32951	LV	W951ULL
32936	PH	W936ULL	32941	PH	W941ULL	32948	LV	W948ULL	32952	PHu	W952ULL

32954-32983

Dennis Trident 9.9m   Plaxton President 4.4m   N39/23F   2001

32954	PL	X954HLT	32962	AB	X962HLT	32970	ABu	X613HLT	32977	B	X977HLT
32955	OG	X611HLT	32963	u	X963HLT	32971	LFu	X971HLT	32978	PH	X978HLT
32956	SN	X956HLT	32964	PH	X964HLT	32972	BN	X972HLT	32979	SN	Y224NLF
32957	OG	X957HLT	32965	CDu	X965HLT	32973	AB	X973HLT	32980	PH	X614HLT
32958	CDu	X958HLT	32967	LV	X967HLT	32974	AB	X974HLT	32981	SN	X981HLT
32959	OX	X959HLT	32968	LT	X968HLT	32975	AB	X975HLT	32982	B	Y346NLF
32960	B	X612HLT	32969	SN	X969HLT	32976	AB	Y223NLF	32983	B	Y344NLF
32961	LF	X961HLT									

32984-33000

Dennis Trident 9.9m   Plaxton President 4.4m   N39/20F   2001

32984	B	Y984NLP	32989	B	Y989NLP	32993	SN	Y993NLP	32997	B	Y997NLP
32985	SN	Y985NLP	32990	B	Y932NLP	32994	AB	Y994NLP	32998	PH	Y998NLP
32986	SN	Y986NLP	32991	B	Y991NLP	32995	LT	Y995NLP	32999	B	Y933NLP
32987	B	Y987NLP	32992	B	Y992NLP	32996	PH	Y996NLP	33000	LF	Y934NLP
32988	B	Y988NLP									

33001-33035

Dennis Trident 10.5m   Plaxton President 4.4m   N42/25F   2001

33001	HH	LK51UZO	33012	LF	LK51UZL	33020	PH	LK51UYX	33028	PH	LK51UYJ
33002	HH	LK51UZP	33013	LF	LK51UZM	33021	PH	LK51UYY	33029	OG	LK51UYL
33003	VN	LK51UZS	33014	LF	LK51UZN	33022	PH	LK51UYZ	33030	OG	LK51UYM
33004	VN	LK51UZT	33015	LF	LK51UYS	33023	PH	LK51UZA	33031	OG	LK51UYN
33007	VN	LK51UZE	33016	LF	LK51UYT	33024	PH	LK51UZB	33032	OG	LK51UYO
33008	LF	LK51UZF	33017	LF	LK51UYU	33025	PH	LK51UYF	33033	PH	LK51UYP
33009	LF	LK51UZG	33018	LF	LK51UYV	33026	PH	LK51UYG	33034	PH	LK51UYR
33010	LF	LK51UZH	33019	LF	LK51UYW	33027	PH	LK51UYH	33035	PH	LK51UYD
33011	LF	LK51UZJ									

33037-33071 — Dennis Trident 9.9m — Plaxton President 4.4m — N39/20F — 2001

33037	MU	LN51DWA	33046	LF	LN51DVL	33057	VN	LN51GJJ	33065	OG	LN51GKZ
33039	WR	LN51DWD	33047	BS	LN51DVM	33058	VN	LN51GJK	33066	OG	LN51GLF
33040	LF	LN51DWE	33050	MU	LN51GKF	33059	MU	LN51GJO	33067	OG	LN51GLJ
33041	OG	LN51DWF	33052	OG	LN51GKJ	33060	VN	LN51GJU	33068	OG	LN51GLK
33042	HD	LN51DWG	33053	LF	LN51GKK	33061	OG	LN51GKU	33069	OG	LN51GLV
33043	HD	LN51DVG	33054	LF	LN51GKL	33062	OG	LN51GKV	33070	OG	LN51GLY
33044	BR	LN51DVH	33055	VN	LN51GKO	33063	OG	LN51GKX	33071	OG	LN51GKA
33045	BRu	LN51DVK	33056	VN	LN51GKP	33064	OG	LN51GKY			

33072-33099 — Dennis Trident 10.5m — Plaxton President 4.4m — N44/25F — 2002

33072	HH	LN51GOC	33081	HH	LN51GNU	33088	BR	LN51GMU	33094	LF	LN51NRK
33073	HH	LN51GOE	33082	OG	LN51GNV	33089	LF	LN51GMV	33095	HH	LN51NRL
33074	HH	LN51GOH	33083	OG	LN51GNX	33090	HH	LN51GMX	33096	LF	LN51GNY
33077	BS	LN51GNF	33084	OG	LN51GME	33091	LF	LN51GMY	33097	LF	LN51GNZ
33078	BR	LN51GNJ	33086	BR	LN51GMG	33092	LF	LN51GMZ	33098	HH	LN51GOA
33079	OG	LN51GNK	33087	BR	LN51GMO	33093	MU	LN51NRJ	33099	OG	LN51GLZ
33080	BR	LN51GNP									

33113-33129 — Dennis Trident 9.9m — Plaxton President 4.4m — N39/23F — 2002

33113	VN	LT02NVX	33118	LF	LT02NWA	33122	LF	LT02NVL	33126	OG	LT02NVO
33114	LF	LT02NVW	33119	LF	LT02NWB	33123	OGu	LT02NVK	33127	OG	LT02NVP
33115	LF	LT02NVV	33120	LF	LT02NWC	33124	OG	LT02NVM	33128	OG	LT02NVR
33116	LF	LT02NVU	33121	LF	LT02NWD	33125	OG	LT02NVN	33129	OG	LT02NVS
33117	LF	LT02NVZ									

33131-33140 — Dennis Trident 10.5m — Plaxton President 4.4m — N42/26F — 2002

33131	MU	LT02ZBX	33134	HH	LT02ZCA	33137	MU	LT02ZFJ	33139	MU	LT02ZFL
33132	HH	LT02ZBY	33135	MU	LT02ZCE	33138	MU	LT02ZFK	33140	MU	LT02ZFM
33133	HH	LT02ZBZ	33136	HH	LT02ZCF						

33141-33154 — Dennis Trident 9.9m — Plaxton President 4.4m — N39/23F — 2002

33141	BL	LR02LWW	33145	BL	LR02LXA	33149	VN	LR02LXH	33152	VN	LR02LXL
33142	BL	LR02LWX	33146	VN	LR02LXB	33150	VN	LR02LXJ	33153	BL	LR02LXM
33143	BL	LR02LWY	33147	BL	LR02LXC	33151	VN	LR02LXK	33154	VN	LR02LXN
33144	BL	LR02LWZ	33148	BL	LR02LXG						

33155-33196 — Dennis Trident 9.9m — Plaxton President 4.4m — N39/23F — 2002

33155	VN	LR02LXO	33165	VN	LR02LYC	33175	PL	LR02LYU	33186	BR	LT52WVB
33156	VN	LR02LXP	33166	VN	LR02LYD	33176	PL	LR02LYV	33188	BS	LT52WVD
33157	VN	LR02LXS	33167	VN	LR02LYF	33177	PL	LR02LYW	33189	u	LT52WVE
33158	VN	LR02LXT	33168	VN	LR02LYG	33178	BS	LR02LYX	33190	BR	LT52XAA
33159	VN	LR02LXU	33169	VN	LR02LYJ	33179	BL	LR02LYY	33191	u	LT52XAB
33160	VN	LR02LXV	33170	VN	LR02LYK	33180	BL	LR02LYZ	33192	BS	LT52XAC
33161	VN	LR02LXW	33171	VN	LR02LYO	33181	BL	LR02LZA	33194	BS	LT52XAE
33162	VN	LR02LXX	33172	PL	LR02LYP	33182	BL	LR02LZB	33195	BR	LT52XAF
33163	VN	LR02LXZ	33173	PL	LR02LYS	33183	BL	LR02LZC	33196	BR	LT52XAG
33164	VN	LR02LYA	33174	PL	LR02LYT	33184	BR	LR02LZD			

33229-33248 — Dennis Trident 9.9m — Plaxton President 4.4m — N39/23F — 2002-03

33229	HH	LT52WXG	33235	VN	LT52WWY	33239	VN	LT52WVH	33245	VN	LT52WUW
33230	OG	LT52WXH	33236	VN	LT52WWZ	33240	VN	LT52WVJ	33246	VN	LT52WUX
33232	HH	LT52WXK	33237	VN	LT52WVF	33242	VN	LT52WVL	33247	VN	LT52WUY
33233	VN	LT52WWV	33238	VN	LT52WVG	33244	VN	LT52WUV	33248	VN	LT52WVA
33234	VN	LT52WWX									

33343-33386 — TransBus Trident 10.5m — TransBus ALX400 4.4m — N42/24F — 2003

33343	PH	LK53EZV	33354	PH	LK53FDA	33365	PH	LK53EYF	33376	HH	LK53EYV
33344	PH	LK53EZW	33355	PH	LK53EXT	33366	PH	LK53EYG	33377	TN	LK53EYW
33345	PH	LK53EZX	33356	PH	LK53EXU	33367	PH	LK53EYH	33378	TN	LK53EYX
33346	PH	LK53EZZ	33357	PH	LK53EXV	33368	PH	LK53EYJ	33379	TN	LK53EYY
33347	PH	LK53FCF	33358	PH	LK53EXW	33369	PH	LK53EYL	33380	TN	LK53EYZ
33348	PH	LK53FCG	33359	PH	LK53EXX	33370	PH	LK53EYM	33381	TN	LK53EZA
33349	PH	LK53FCJ	33360	PH	LK53EXZ	33371	PH	LK53EYO	33382	TN	LK53EZB
33350	PH	LK53FCL	33361	PH	LK53EYA	33372	PH	LK53EYP	33383	PH	LK53EZC
33351	PH	LK53FCX	33362	PH	LK53EYB	33373	HH	LK53EYR	33384	HH	LK53EZD
33352	PH	LK53FCY	33363	PH	LK53EYC	33374	PH	LK53EYT	33385	HH	LK53EZE
33353	PH	LK53FCZ	33364	PH	LK53EYD	33375	PH	LK53EYU	33386	PH	LK53EZF

Illustrating the colours applied to Enviro 400s operating the express link between Bristol and Weston-super-Mare is 33411, WA56FUB, one of a batch of nine supplied in 2006. *Dave Heath*

33401-33405

			TransBus Trident 10.7m			TransBus ALX400 4.4m			N47/27F	2004	
33401	WR	VX54MTV	**33403**	WR	VX54MTZ	**33404**	WR	VX54MUA	**33405**	WR	VX54MUB
33402	WR	VX54MTY									

33411-33419

			ADL Trident 2 11m			ADL Enviro 400			NC39/32F	2006	
33411	WS	WA56FUB	**33414**	WS	WA56FTK	**33416**	WS	WA56FTO	**33418**	WS	WA56FTT
33412	WS	WA56FUD	**33415**	WS	WA56FTN	**33417**	WS	WA56FTP	**33419**	WS	WA56FTU
33413	WS	WA56FUE									

33420	PL	WA08MVE	ADL Trident 2 11m	ADL Enviro 400	NC41/27F	2008	
33421	PL	WA08MVF	ADL Trident 2 11m	ADL Enviro 400	NC41/27F	2008	
33422	PL	WA08MVG	ADL Trident 2 11m	ADL Enviro 400	NC41/27F	2008	
33423	YA	SN60CAA	ADL Trident 2 11m	ADL Enviro 400	NC41/27F	2010	Connex, Jersey, 2013
33424	BS	VT59JPT	ADL Trident 2 11m	ADL Enviro 400	N41/27F	2010	JPT, Middleton, 2013
33425	BS	SN59AWV	ADL Trident 2 11m	ADL Enviro 400	NC41/26F	2010	Ensign Bus, 2013

33504-33508

			ADL Trident 2 11m			ADL Enviro 400			N41/30F	2008	
33504	LE	LK08FLX	**33506**	LE	LK08FKY	**33507**	LE	LK08FKZ	**33508**	LE	LK08FLA

33544-33553

			ADL Trident 2 11m			ADL Enviro 400			N41/30F	2008	
33544	LE	SN58CFK	**33547**	LE	SN58CFO	**33550**	LE	SN58CFV	**33552**	LE	SN58CFY
33545	LE	SN58CFL	**33548**	LE	SN58CFP	**33551**	LE	SN58CFX	**33553**	LE	SN58CFZ
33546	LE	SN58CFM	**33549**	LE	SN58CFU						

33554-33574

			ADL Trident 2 10.8m			ADL Enviro 400			N41/30F	2008	
33554	LE	SN58CGE	**33560**	LE	SN58CGV	**33565**	LE	SN58CHD	**33570**	LE	SN58CHK
33555	LE	SN58CGF	**33561**	LE	SN58CGX	**33566**	LE	SN58CHF	**33571**	LE	SN58CHL
33556	LE	SN58CGG	**33562**	LE	SN58CGY	**33567**	LE	SN58CHG	**33572**	LE	SN58CHO
33557	LE	SN58CGK	**33563**	LE	SN58CGZ	**33568**	LE	SN58CHH	**33573**	LE	SN58ENR
33558	LE	SN58CGO	**33564**	LE	SN58CHC	**33569**	LE	SN58CHJ	**33574**	LE	SN58ENT
33559	LE	SN58CGU									

Manchester fleet names have been applied to 33724, SN12AKV, from the Bolton allocation. It is seen passing through Salford while operating the principal bus link between Bolton and Manchester started back in the 1920s as a joint service between Bolton and Salford Corporations and Lancashire United Transport. *Richard Godfrey*

33656-33755   ADL E40D   ADL Enviro 400   N45/29F   2012

33656	OM	SN12ADU	33681	OM	SN12AFF	33706	OM	SN12AHP	33731	BN	SN12AMO
33657	BN	SN12ADV	33682	OM	SN12AFJ	33707	BN	SN12AHU	33732	BN	SN12AMU
33658	PL	SN12ADX	33683	OM	SN12AFK	33708	OM	SN12AHV	33733	BN	SN12AMV
33659	PL	SN12ADZ	33684	OM	SN12AFO	33709	BN	SN12AHX	33734	BN	SN12AMX
33660	PL	SN12AEA	33685	OM	SN12AFU	33710	BN	SN12AHY	33735	BN	SN12ANF
33661	PL	SN12AEB	33686	OM	SN12AFV	33711	BN	SN12AHZ	33736	BN	SN12ANP
33662	PL	SN12AED	33687	OM	SN12AFX	33712	BN	SN12AJO	33737	BN	SN12ANR
33663	OM	SN12AEE	33688	OM	SN12AFY	33713	BN	SN12AJU	33738	OM	SN12ANU
33664	PL	SN12AEF	33689	OM	SN12AFZ	33714	BN	SN12AJV	33739	BN	SN12ANV
33665	PL	SN12AEG	33690	OM	SN12AGO	33715	BN	SN12AJX	33740	BN	SN12ANX
33666	PL	SN12AEJ	33691	BN	SN12AGU	33716	BN	SN12AJY	33741	OM	SN12AOA
33667	PL	SN12AEK	33692	OM	SN12AGV	33717	BN	SN12AKF	33742	BN	SN12AOB
33668	OM	SN12AEL	33693	BN	SN12AGX	33718	BN	SN12AKG	33743	BN	SN12AOC
33669	OM	SN12AEM	33694	OM	SN12AGY	33719	BN	SN12AKJ	33744	OM	SN12AOD
33670	OM	SN12AEO	33695	BN	SN12AGZ	33720	BN	SN12AKK	33745	OM	SN12AOE
33671	OM	SN12AEP	33696	BN	SN12AHA	33721	BN	SN12AKO	33746	OM	SN12AOF
33672	OM	SN12AET	33697	BN	SN12AHC	33722	BN	SN12AKP	33747	OM	SN12AOG
33673	BN	SN12AEU	33698	OM	SN12AHD	33723	OM	SN12AKU	33748	OM	SN12AOH
33674	OM	SN12AEV	33699	BN	SN12AHE	33724	BN	SN12AKV	33749	BN	SN12AOJ
33675	OM	SN12AEW	33700	BN	SN12AHF	33725	BN	SN12AKX	33750	OM	SN12AOK
33676	OM	SN12AEX	33701	OM	SN12AHG	33726	BN	SN12AKY	33751	OM	SN12AOL
33677	BN	SN12AEY	33702	OM	SN12AHJ	33727	BN	SN12AKZ	33752	OM	SN12AOM
33678	OM	SN12AEZ	33703	OM	SN12AHK	33728	BN	SN12ALO	33753	BN	SN12AOO
33679	OM	SN12AFA	33704	BN	SN12AHL	33729	BN	SN12ALU	33754	OM	SN12AOP
33680	OM	SN12AFE	33705	BN	SN12AHO	33730	BN	SN12AMK	33755	OM	SN12AOR

33788	OM	SN13CHZ	ADL E40D Euro 6	ADL Enviro 400	NC41/29F	2013	On loan from ADL

Another X1 livery, this time applied to the service connecting Lowestoft with King's Lynn and Peterborough. One of twenty-two recently added to the fleet, 33815, YX63LKD, is shown. These are the only model now allocated to the King's Lynn depot. *Mark Doggett*

33803-33824

		ADL E40D				ADL Enviro 400			NC41/26F	2013	
33803	KL	YX63LJF	**33809**	KL	YX63LJU	**33815**	KL	YX63LKD	**33820**	KL	YX63LKK
33804	KL	YX63LJJ	**33810**	KL	YX63LJV	**33816**	KL	YX63LKE	**33821**	KL	YX63LKL
33805	KL	YX63LJK	**33811**	KL	YX63LJY	**33817**	KL	YX63LKF	**33822**	KL	YX63LKM
33806	KL	YX63LJL	**33812**	KL	YX63LJZ	**33818**	KL	YX63LKG	**33823**	KL	YX63LKN
33807	KL	YX63LJN	**33813**	KL	YX63LKA	**33819**	KL	YX63LKJ	**33824**	KL	YX63LKO
33808	KL	YX63LJO	**33814**	KL	YX63LKC						

33825-33830

		ADL E40D				ADL Enviro 400			N45/29F	2013	
33825	WS	SN63MYH	**33827**	WS	SN63MYK	**33829**	WS	SN63MYM	**33830**	WS	SN63MYO
33826	WS	SN63MYJ	**33828**	WS	SN63MYL						

33831-33872

		ADL E40D				ADL Enviro 400			N45/29F	2014	
33831	OX	-	**33842**	OX	-	**33853**	OX	-	**33863**	OG	-
33832	OX	-	**33843**	OX	-	**33854**	OX	-	**33864**	OG	-
33833	OX	-	**33844**	OX	-	**33855**	OX	-	**33865**	OG	-
33834	OX	-	**33845**	OX	-	**33856**	OX	-	**33866**	OG	-
33835	OX	-	**33846**	OX	-	**33857**	OX	-	**33867**	OG	-
33836	OX	-	**33847**	OX	-	**33858**	OG	-	**33868**	OG	-
33837	OX	-	**33848**	OX	-	**33859**	OG	-	**33869**	OG	-
33838	OX	-	**33849**	OX	-	**33860**	OG	-	**33870**	OG	-
33839	OX	-	**33850**	OX	-	**33861**	OG	-	**33871**	OG	-
33840	OX	-	**33851**	OX	-	**33862**	OG	-	**33872**	OG	-
33841	OX	-	**33852**	OX	-						

33873-33890

		ADL E40D				ADL Enviro 400			NC45/29F	2014	
33873	BM	-	**33878**	BM	-	**33883**	BM	-	**33887**	BM	-
33874	BM	-	**33879**	BM	-	**33884**	BM	-	**33888**	BM	-
33875	BM	-	**33880**	BM	-	**33885**	BM	-	**33889**	BM	-
33876	BM	-	**33881**	BM	-	**33886**	BM	-	**33890**	BM	-
33877	BM	-	**33882**	BM	-						

More Enviro 400s have been ordered for delivery during 2014, a model now assembled at both the Falkirk and Scarborough facilities of Alexander Dennis. Free WiFi is being supplied on all the First buses currently on order. Seen at Clydebank is 33918, SN61BEU, which is one of the low-height models currently wearing a silver-based livery. *Richard Godfrey*

33901-33923

ADL Trident 2 11m   ADL Enviro 400 low-height   N47/29F   2011

33901	SN	SN11FOJ	33907	LF	SN11FOV	33913	LF	SN61BDX	33919	LF	SN61BEY
33902	SN	SN11FOK	33908	LF	SN11FPA	33914	LF	SN61BDY	33920	LF	SN61BFA
33903	SN	SN11FOM	33909	LF	SN11FPC	33915	LF	SN61BDZ	33921	LF	SN61BFE
33904	LF	SN11FOP	33910	LF	SN11FPD	33916	LF	SN61BEJ	33922	LF	SN61BFF
33905	LF	SN11FOT	33911	LF	SN61BDU	33917	LF	SN61BEO	33923	LF	SN61BFJ
33906	LF	SN11FOU	33912	LF	SN61BDV	33918	LF	SN61BEU			

34003	PL	K803ORL	Volvo Olympian		Northern Counties Palatine	BC39/30F	1993		

34014-34022

Volvo Olympian   Northern Counties Palatine   B49/33F*   1996   Stagecoach, 2003
*34022 is B47/27D

34014	CO	P554EFL	34016	HO	P536EFL	34017	HO	P540EFL	34022	HOu	P542HMP
34015	BK	P535EFL									

34041-34052

Volvo Olympian   Northern Counties Palatine II   B43/27F   1996

34041	CE	P241UCW	34044	WH	P244UCW	34049	CE	P249UCW	34051	CE	P251UCW
34043	w	P243UCW	34048	GS	P248UCW	34050	CE	P250UCW	34052	CE	P252UCW

34059-34079

Volvo Olympian   Northern Counties Palatine   B49/33F   1996   Stagecoach, 2003

34059	HO	P559EFL	34066	BK	P566EFL	34068	PL	P568EFL	34076	BK	P576EFL
34064	TN	P564EFL	34067	BK	P567EFL	34075	BK	P575EFL	34079	SO	P579EFL

34088-34107

Volvo Olympian   Northern Counties Palatine   B47/31F   1999

34088	TE	T988KLF	34093	OM	T893KLF	34097	OM	T897KLF	34102	OM	T902KLF
34089	TE	T889KLF	34094	OM	T894KLF	34098	OM	T898KLF	34104	BN	T904KLF
34090	OGu	T890KLF	34095	OMu	T895KLF	34099	OGu	T899KLF	34105	BN	T905KLF
34091	OM	T891KLF	34096	OM	T896KLF	34100	OM	T990KLF	34107	HX	T907KLF
34092	OM	T892KLF									

34108-34114

Volvo Olympian   Alexander Royale   BC43/29F   2000   Blazefield, 2005-06

34108	YA	W435CWX	34110	YAu	W437CWX	34112	YAu	W432CWX	34114	YAu	W434CWX
34109	YA	W436CWX	34111	YAu	W431CWX	34113	YAu	W433CWX			

34116	CE	L816CFJ	Volvo Olympian	Northern Counties Palatine	B47/29F	1993	
34129	SO	P829FEF	Volvo Olympian	Northern Counties Palatine	B49/33F	1996	Stagecoach, 2003
34137	CEu	L637SEU	Volvo Olympian	Northern Counties Palatine II	O47/29F	1993	
34138	CE	L638SEU	Volvo Olympian	Northern Counties Palatine II	B47/29F	1993	

Many Olympians were taken from service during 2013, as new vehicles were delivered. Illustrating the Northern Counties Palatine II style as it leaves Weston-super-Mare is 34170, S670AAE. *Richard Godfrey*

34155-34164

			Volvo Olympian			Northern Counties Palatine II	B47/29F*	1997	*34161-4 are B43/29F

34155	LOu	P655UFB	34158	NE	P658UFB	34162	PT	R662NHY	34164	PT	R664NHY
34156	LOu	P656UFB	34161	PTu	R661NHY	34163	PT	R663NHY			

34165-34187

Volvo Olympian · Northern Counties Palatine II · B43/29F · 1998

34165	WH	S665AAE	34172	CE	S672AAE	34177	CE	S677AAE	34183	CE	S683AAE
34167	WH	S667AAE	34173	CE	S673AAE	34178	BW	S678AAE	34184	CE	S684AAE
34168	WH	S668AAE	34174	TN	S674AAE	34179	BW	S679AAE	34185	CE	S685AAE
34170	HO	S670AAE	34175	WH	S675AAE	34181	CE	S681AAE	34186	YA	S686AAE
34171	BW	S671AAE	34176	TN	S676AAE	34182	CE	S682AAE	34187	YA	S687AAE

34188-34191

Volvo Olympian · Northern Counties Palatine II · BC47/29F · 1998

34188	BW	S688AAE	34189	BW	S689AAE	34190	BW	S690AAE	34191	CE	S691AAE

34192-34200

Volvo Olympian · Alexander Royale · BC43/22F · 1995 · National Express, 2004

34192	CE	530OHU	34195	CEu	TJI4838	34197	CE	HVJ716	34199	CE	NER621
34193	CE	VJT738	34196	CE	OWB243	34198	CE	UKT552	34200	CE	VOO273
34194	CE	481FPO									

34206-34219

Volvo Olympian · Northern Counties Palatine · B47/31F* · 1998 · *34215/6/8 are B47/27D

34206	QSu	S206LLO	34211	HX	S211LLO	34215	BLs	S215LLO	34218	BLs	S218LLO
34209	QSu	S209LLO	34214	HX	S214LLO	34216	BLs	S216LLO	34219	BN	S219LLO
34210	BNu	S210LLO									

34259	CE	N533LHG	Volvo Olympian	Northern Counties Palatine	B47/30F	1995	Go-Ahead London, 2004
34261	CE	N542LHG	Volvo Olympian	Northern Counties Palatine	B47/30F	1995	Go-Ahead London, 2005

34285-34290

Volvo Olympian · Alexander RL · B47/32F · 1996

34285	NEu	P185TGD	34286	NE	P186TGD	34288	NEu	P188TGD	34290	BK	P191TGD

34295	HO	P295KPX	Volvo Olympian	Northern Counties Palatine	B47/30F	1996	
34305	CM	L305PWR	Volvo Olympian	Northern Counties Palatine	B47/29F	1994	
34311	NE	L311PWR	Volvo Olympian	Northern Counties Palatine	B47/29F	1994	

34615	CE	K615LAE	Leyland Olympian ON2R56C16Z4	Northern Counties Palatine	B47/30F	1993
34626	CEu	K626LAE	Leyland Olympian ON2R56C16Z4	Northern Counties Palatine	O47/32F	1993
34629	CE	K629LAE	Leyland Olympian ON2R56C16Z4	Northern Counties Palatine	B47/30F	1993

36001-36006
Scania N94UD — East Lancs OmniDekka — NC43/26F — 2004-05

| 36001 | BP | YN04GNV | 36003 | WH | YN04GNY | 36005 | WH | YN04GLV | 36006 | WH | YN05HGA |
| 36002 | BP | YN04GNX | 36004 | WH | YN04GNZ | | | | | | |

36007-36030
Scania N94UD — East Lancs OmniDekka — N47/33F — 2005

36007	MU	SN05HWW	36013	BK	SN05HWL	36019	LV	SN05HWH	36025	MU	SN05HWS
36008	MU	SN05HWX	36014	LV	SN05HWK	36020	LV	SN05HWF	36026	BK	SN05HWU
36009	LV	SN05HWY	36015	LV	SN05HWO	36021	BK	SN05HWP	36027	LV	SN05HWV
36010	MU	SN05HWZ	36016	LV	SN05HWM	36022	BF	SN05HWE	36028	BK	SN05HWT
36011	MU	SN05HXA	36017	LV	SN05HWJ	36023	MU	SN05HWD	36029	BK	SN55KKE
36012	LV	SN05HXB	36018	LV	SN05HWG	36024	LV	SN05HWR	36030	MU	SN55KKF

36166-36180
Volvo B9TL — Wrightbus Eclipse Gemini 2 — N45/29F — 2011

36166	VN	BD11CFK	36170	VN	BD11CFP	36174	VN	BD11CFY	36178	VN	BD11CDX
36167	VN	BD11CFM	36171	VN	BD11CFU	36175	VN	BD11CFZ	36179	VN	BD11CDY
36168	VN	BD11CFN	36172	VN	BD11CFV	36176	VN	BD11CGE	36180	VN	BD11CDZ
36169	VN	BD11CFO	36173	VN	BD11CFX	36177	VN	BD11CGF			

36181-36280
Volvo B9TL — Wrightbus Eclipse Gemini 2 — N45/27F — 2012

36181	HP	BN12KXU	36206	HP	BN12WOM	36231	HP	BD12TBZ	36256	HP	BG12YJN
36182	HP	BN12KXV	36207	HP	BJ12VWO	36232	HP	BD12TCV	36257	HP	BG12YJO
36183	HP	BN12JYF	36208	HP	BJ12VWP	36233	HP	BD12TCU	36258	HP	BG12YJP
36184	HP	BN12JYG	36209	HP	BJ12VWR	36234	HP	BD12TCY	36259	HP	BG12YJR
36185	HP	BN12JYH	36210	HP	BJ12VWS	36235	HP	BD12TCX	36260	HP	BG12YJS
36186	HP	BN12JYJ	36211	HP	BJ12VWT	36236	HP	BN12WOR	36261	HP	BG12YJT
36187	HP	BN12JYK	36212	HP	BJ12VWU	36237	HP	BN12WOU	36262	HP	BG12YJU
36188	HP	BN12JYL	36213	HP	BJ12VWV	36238	HP	BN12WOV	36263	HP	BG12YJV
36189	HP	BN12JYO	36214	HP	BJ12VWW	36239	HP	BN12WOX	36264	HP	BG12YJW
36190	HP	BN12JYP	36215	HP	BJ12VWX	36240	HP	BN12WOY	36265	HP	BG12YJX
36191	HP	BN12JYR	36216	HP	BJ12VWY	36241	HP	BN12WPA	36266	HP	BG12YJY
36192	HP	BN12JYS	36217	HP	BJ12VXA	36242	HP	BN12WPD	36267	HP	BG12YJZ
36193	HP	BN12JYT	36218	HP	BJ12VXB	36243	HP	BN12WPE	36268	HP	BG12YKA
36194	HP	BN12JYU	36219	HP	BJ12VXC	36244	HP	BN12WPF	36269	HP	BG12YKB
36195	HP	BN12JYV	36220	HP	BJ12VXD	36245	HP	BN12WPJ	36270	HP	BG12YKC
36196	HP	BN12JYW	36221	HP	BJ12VXE	36246	HP	BJ12VNR	36271	HP	BG12YKD
36197	HP	BN12WNX	36222	HP	BD12SZY	36247	HP	BJ12PNS	36272	HP	BG12YKE
36198	HP	BN12WNY	36223	HP	BD12SZZ	36248	HP	BG12UKM	36273	HP	BG12YKF
36199	HP	BN12WNZ	36224	HP	BD12TAO	36249	HP	BF12KWU	36274	HP	BD12TDV
36200	HP	BN12WOA	36225	HP	BD12TAV	36250	HP	BG12YJF	36275	HP	BD12TCO
36201	HP	BN12WOB	36226	HP	BD12TBO	36251	HP	BG12YJH	36276	HP	BD12TCK
36202	HP	BN12WOC	36227	HP	BD12TBU	36252	HP	BG12YJJ	36277	HP	BD12TDO
36203	HP	BN12WOD	36228	HP	BD12TBV	36253	HP	BG12YJK	36278	HP	BD12TCZ
36204	HP	BN12WOH	36229	HP	BD12TBX	36254	HP	BG12YJL	36279	OM	BD12TDU
36205	HP	BN12WOJ	36230	HP	BD12TBY	36255	HP	BG12YJM	36280	OM	BD12TCJ

37001-37020
Volvo B7TL — Wrightbus Eclipse Gemini — N45/29F — 2005

37001	HG	WX55VHK	37006	LH	WX55VHP	37011	LH	WX55VHW	37016	HG	WX55VJD
37002	HG	WX55VHL	37007	LH	WX55VHR	37012	LH	WX55VHY	37017	HG	WX55VJE
37003	LH	WX55VHM	37008	HG	WX55VHT	37013	LH	WX55VHZ	37018	HG	WX55VJF
37004	LH	WX55VHN	37009	HG	WX55VHU	37014	LH	WX55VJA	37019	HG	WX55VJG
37005	LH	WX55VHO	37010	HG	WX55VHV	37015	HG	WX55VJC	37020	HG	WX55VJJ

37021-37062
Volvo B7TL — Wrightbus Eclipse Gemini — N45/29F — 2006

37021	OG	YJ06XKK	37032	OG	YJ06XKX	37043	HP	YJ06XLT	37053	HX	YJ06XMD
37022	OG	YJ06XKL	37033	OG	YJ06XKY	37044	HP	YJ06XLU	37054	HX	YJ06XME
37023	OG	YJ06XKM	37034	OG	YJ06XKZ	37045	YK	YJ06XLV	37055	BD	YJ06XMF
37024	OG	YJ06XKN	37035	OG	YJ06XLA	37046	HX	YJ06XLW	37056	BD	YJ06XMG
37025	OG	YJ06XKO	37036	HP	YJ06XLB	37047	HX	YJ06XLX	37057	BD	YJ06XMH
37026	OG	YJ06XKP	37037	HP	YJ06XLC	37048	HX	YJ06XLY	37058	BD	YJ06XMK
37027	OG	YJ06XKS	37038	HP	YJ06XLD	37049	HX	YJ06XLZ	37059	BD	YJ06XML
37028	OG	YJ06XKT	37039	HP	YJ06XLE	37050	HX	YJ06XMA	37060	HP	YJ06XMM
37029	OG	YJ06XKU	37040	HP	YJ06XLF	37051	HX	YJ06XMB	37061	HP	YJ06XMO
37030	OG	YJ06XKV	37041	HP	YJ06XLG	37052	HX	YJ06XMC	37062	HP	YJ06XMP
37031	OG	YJ06XKW	37042	HP	YJ06XLH						

The 2005 delivery of Volvo B7TLs for the Bristol area continue to be divided between Laurence Hill and Hengrove depots. Seen heading back to the latter is 37010, WX55VHV, which carries West of England lettering. *Mark Doggett*

37063-37132

Volvo B9TL — Wrightbus Eclipse Gemini — N45/29F — 2007-08

37063	BM	YK57EZS	37081	BD	YJ08GVT	37099	BD	YJ08GWP	37116	OG	YK07AYP
37064	BM	YK57EZT	37082	BD	YJ08GVU	37100	BD	YJ08GWU	37117	OG	YK07AYS
37065	BD	YK57EZU	37083	BD	YJ08GVV	37101	BD	YJ08GWV	37118	OG	YK07AYT
37066	BD	YK57EZV	37084	BD	YJ08GVW	37102	BD	YJ08GWW	37119	OG	YK07AYU
37067	BD	YK57EZW	37085	BD	YJ08GVX	37103	OG	YK07AYA	37120	OG	YK07AYV
37068	BD	YK57EZX	37086	BD	YJ08GVY	37104	OG	YK07AYB	37121	OG	YK07AYW
37069	BD	YK57EZZ	37087	BD	YJ08GVZ	37105	OG	YK07AYC	37122	OG	YK07AYX
37070	BD	YK57FAA	37088	BD	YJ08GWA	37106	OG	YK07AYD	37123	HP	YK07AYY
37071	BD	YJ08GVE	37089	BD	YJ08GWC	37107	OG	YK07AYE	37124	HP	YK07AYZ
37072	BD	YJ08GVF	37090	BD	YJ08GWD	37108	OG	YK07AYF	37125	HP	YK57CJF
37073	BD	YJ08GVG	37091	BD	YJ08GWE	37109	OG	YK07AYG	37126	HP	YK57CJJ
37074	BD	YJ08GVK	37092	BD	YJ08GWF	37110	OG	YK07AYH	37127	HP	YK57CJO
37075	BD	YJ08GVL	37093	BD	YJ08GWG	37111	OG	YK07AYJ	37128	HP	YK57CJU
37076	BD	YJ08GVM	37094	BD	YJ08GWK	37112	OG	YK07AYL	37129	HP	YK57CJV
37077	BD	YJ08GVN	37095	BD	YJ08GWL	37113	OG	YK07AYM	37130	HP	YK57CJX
37078	BD	YJ08GVO	37096	BD	YJ08GWM	37114	OG	YK07AYN	37131	HP	YK57CJY
37079	BD	YJ08GVP	37097	BD	YJ08GWN	37115	OG	YK07AYO	37132	HP	YK57CJZ
37080	BD	YJ08GVR	37098	BD	YJ08GWO						

37133-37145

Volvo B9TL — Wrightbus Eclipse Gemini — N45/29F — 2007

37133	GS	SN57HDH	37137	LV	SN57HCV	37140	LV	SN57HCZ	37143	LV	SN57HDD
37134	GS	SN57HDJ	37138	LV	SN57HCX	37141	LV	SN57HDA	37144	LV	SN57HDE
37135	LV	SN57HCP	37139	LV	SN57HCY	37142	LV	SN57HDC	37145	LV	SN57HDF
37136	LV	SN57HCU									

37146-37155

Volvo B7TL — Wrightbus Eclipse Gemini — N45/29F — 2006

37146	LE	YN06UPZ	37149	PH	YN06URC	37152	PH	YN06URF	37154	PH	YN06URH
37147	PH	YN06URA	37150	PH	YN06URD	37153	PH	YN06URG	37155	PH	YN06URJ
37148	PH	YN06URB	37151	PH	YN06URE						

37156-37165

Volvo B7TL — Wrightbus Eclipse Gemini — N45/29F — 2007

37156	NE	AU07DXS	37159	NE	AU07DXW	37162	SO	HY07FSV	37164	SO	HY07FSU
37157	NE	AU07DXT	37160	NE	AU07DXX	37163	SO	HY07FSZ	37165	SO	HY07FSX
37158	NE	AU07DXV	37161	SO	HY07FTA						

Salford commemorative livery has been applied to 37290, MX07BTF, seen here on one of the principal routes through the city linking Manchester with Cadishead. The vehicle is allocated to Queen's Road depot, as no depots now remain in Salford. *Richard Godfrey*

37166-37185

Volvo B7TL · Wrightbus Eclipse Gemini · N45/29F · 2007

37166	LF	SF07FCP	37171	LF	SF07FDA	37176	LF	SF07FDJ	37181	B	SF07FDO
37167	LF	SF07FCV	37172	LF	SF07FDC	37177	LF	SF07FDK	37182	B	SF07FDP
37168	LF	SF07FCX	37173	LF	SF07FDD	37178	LF	SF07FDL	37183	B	SF07FDU
37169	LF	SF07FCY	37174	LF	SF07FDE	37179	LF	SF07FDM	37184	B	SF07FDV
37170	LF	SF07FCZ	37175	LF	SF07FDG	37180	B	SF07FDN	37185	B	SF07FDX

37186-37227

Volvo B9TL · Wrightbus Eclipse Gemini · N45/29F · 2007

37186	LF	SF07FDY	37197	LF	SF07FEM	37208	LF	SF57MKG	37218	LF	SF57MKX
37187	LF	SF07FDZ	37198	LF	SF07FEO	37209	LF	SF57MKJ	37219	LF	SF57MKZ
37188	LF	SF07FCC	37199	LF	SF07FCL	37210	LF	SF57MKK	37220	LF	SF57MLE
37189	LF	SF07FCD	37200	LF	SF07FEP	37211	LF	SF57MKL	37221	LF	SF57MLJ
37190	LF	SF07FCE	37201	LF	SF07FCM	37212	LF	SF57MKM	37222	LF	SF57MLK
37191	LF	SF07FCG	37202	LF	SF07FCO	37213	LF	SF57MKN	37223	LF	SF57MLL
37192	LF	SF07FCJ	37203	LF	SF07FET	37214	LF	SF57MKO	37224	LF	SF57MLN
37193	LF	SF07FEG	37204	LF	SF07FEU	37215	LF	SF57MKP	37225	LF	SF57MLO
37194	LF	SF07FEH	37205	LF	SF57MKA	37216	LF	SF57MKU	37226	LF	SF57MLU
37195	LF	SF07FEJ	37206	LF	SF57MKC	37217	LF	SF57MKV	37227	LF	SF57MLV
37196	LF	SF07FEK	37207	LF	SF57MKD						

37228-37265

Volvo B9TL · Wrightbus Eclipse Gemini · N45/29F · 2007-08

37228	DN	YN57RJU	37238	B	YN08LCT	37247	YK	YN07MKE	37256	YK	YN07MKV
37229	OG	3910WE	37239	B	YN08LCU	37248	YK	YN07MKF	37257	DN	YN07MKX
37230	DN	YN08LCK	37240	B	YN08LCV	37249	YK	YN07MKG	37258	RO	YN07MKZ
37231	RO	YN08LCL	37241	B	YN08LCW	37250	YK	YN07MKJ	37259	RO	YN07MLE
37232	DN	YN57RJZ	37242	B	YN08LCY	37251	YK	YN07MKK	37261	RO	YN07MLJ
37233	DN	YN57RKA	37243	B	YN08LCZ	37252	YK	YN07MKL	37262	RO	YN07MLK
37234	DN	YN08LCM	37244	B	YN08LDA	37253	YK	YN07MKM	37263	RO	YN07MLL
37235	DN	YN08LCO	37245	B	YN08LDC	37254	YK	YN07MKO	37264	RO	YN07MLO
37236	DN	YN57RKJ	37246	YK	YN07MKD	37255	YK	YN07MKP	37265	RO	YN07MLU
37237	DN	YN08LCP									

Another former municipal operation that became part of the SELNEC operation was Bury Corporation and that fleet, too, has been commemorated by a Volvo B9TL, in this case 37297, MX07BUE. It is seen about to leave that town for Bolton on service 471 that links Rochdale with Bolton along the route of the one-time TransLancs Express. *Dave Heath*

37266-37278

Volvo B9TL Wrightbus Eclipse Gemini N45/29F 2008 *37274-6 are NC39/26F

37266	LV	SN57HDG	37269	LV	SN57JBE	37272	LV	SN57JBV	37275	BL	LK58EDJ
37267	LV	SN57JAO	37270	LV	SN57JBO	37273	LV	SN57JBX	37276	BL	LK58EDL
37268	LV	SN57JAU	37271	LV	SN57JBU	37274	BL	LK58EDF	37278	B	YN08LDD

37279-37304

Volvo B9TL Wrightbus Eclipse Gemini N45/29F 2007

37279	QS	MX07BPY	37286	QS	MX07BSV	37293	BY	MX07BTV	37299	BY	MX07BUH
37280	QS	MX07BPZ	37287	QS	MX07BSY	37294	BY	MX07BTY	37300	BY	MX07BUJ
37281	QS	MX07BRF	37288	QS	MX07BSZ	37295	BY	MX07BTZ	37301	QS	MX57HDZ
37282	QS	MX07BRV	37289	QS	MX07BTE	37296	BY	MX07BUA	37302	BY	MX57HEJ
37283	QS	MX07BRZ	37290	QS	MX07BTF	37297	BY	MX07BUE	37303	QS	MX07BUU
37284	QS	MX07BSO	37291	BY	MX07BTO	37298	BY	MX07BUF	37304	QS	MX07BUV
37285	QS	MX07BSU	37292	BY	MX07BTU						

37315-37359

Volvo B9TL Wrightbus Eclipse Gemini N45/29F 2007

37315	HG	WX57HJO	37327	LH	WX57HKH	37338	LH	WX57HKW	37349	LH	WX57HLK
37316	HG	WX57HJU	37328	LH	WX57HKJ	37339	LH	WX57HKY	37350	LH	WX57HLM
37317	HG	WX57HJV	37329	LH	WX57HKK	37340	LH	WX57HKZ	37351	HG	WX57HLN
37318	HG	WX57HJY	37330	LH	WX57HKL	37341	LH	WX57HLA	37352	LH	WX57HLO
37319	LH	WX57HJZ	37331	LH	WX57HKM	37342	LH	WX57HLC	37353	LH	WX57HLP
37320	LH	WX57HKA	37332	LH	WX57HKN	37343	LH	WX57HLD	37354	LH	WX57HLR
37321	LH	WX57HKB	37333	LH	WX57HKO	37344	LH	WX57HLE	37355	LH	WX57HLU
37322	LH	WX57HKC	37334	LH	WX57HKP	37345	LH	WX57HLF	37356	LH	WX57HLV
37323	LH	WX57HKD	37335	LH	WX57HKT	37346	LH	WX57HLG	37357	LH	WX57HLW
37324	LH	WX57HKE	37336	LH	WX57HKU	37347	LH	WX57HLH	37358	BA	WX57HLY
37325	LH	WX57HKF	37337	LH	WX57HKV	37348	LH	WX57HLJ	37359	BA	WX57HLZ
37326	LH	WX57HKG									

37360-37440 — Volvo B9TL — Wrightbus Eclipse Gemini — N45/29F — 2008-09

No		Reg	No		Reg	No		Reg	No		Reg
37360	BD	YJ58GNP	37381	QS	MX58DWM	37401	BY	MX58DXM	37421	BY	MX58DYP
37361	BD	YJ58GMO	37382	QS	MX58DWN	37402	BN	MX58DXO	37422	BY	MX58DYS
37362	BD	YJ58GNU	37383	TE	MX58DWO	37403	BY	MX58DXP	37423	BY	MX58DYT
37363	BD	YJ58GMU	37384	QS	MX58DWP	37404	BY	MX58DXR	37424	BY	MX58DYU
37364	BD	YJ58GNV	37385	QS	MX58DWU	37405	BN	MX58DXS	37425	BY	MX58DYV
37365	BD	YJ58GMW	37386	TE	MX58DWV	37406	BY	MX58DXT	37426	BY	MX58DYW
37366	BD	YJ58GNX	37387	TE	MX58DWW	37407	BN	MX58DXU	37427	BY	MX58DYY
37367	QS	MX58DVU	37388	TE	MX58DWY	37408	BN	MX58DXV	37428	BY	MX58DZA
37368	QS	MX58DVV	37389	QS	MX58DWZ	37409	BN	MX58DXW	37429	BY	MX58DZB
37369	QS	MX58DVW	37390	QS	MX58DXA	37410	BN	MX58DXZ	37430	BN	MX58DZC
37370	QS	MX58DVY	37391	BY	MX58DXB	37411	QS	MX58DYA	37431	BY	MX58DZD
37371	QS	MX58DVZ	37392	BY	MX58DXC	37412	TE	MX58DYC	37432	OM	MX58DZE
37372	QS	MX58DWA	37393	BY	MX58DXD	37413	TE	MX58DYD	37433	TE	MX58DZF
37373	QS	MX58DWC	37394	QS	MX58DXE	37414	TE	MX58DYF	37434	TE	MX58DZG
37374	QS	MX58DWD	37395	QS	MX58DXF	37415	BN	MX58DYG	37435	TE	MX58DZH
37375	QS	MX58DWE	37396	QS	MX58DXG	37416	BN	MX58DYH	37436	TE	MX58DZJ
37376	QS	MX58DWF	37397	BN	MX58DXH	37417	BY	MX58DYJ	37437	TE	MX58DZK
37377	QS	MX58DWG	37398	BY	MX58DXJ	37418	BY	MX58DYM	37438	TE	MX58DZL
37378	QS	MX58DWJ	37399	BY	MX58DXK	37419	BY	MX58DYN	37439	OM	MX58DZN
37379	QS	MX58DWK	37400	BY	MX58DXL	37420	BY	MX58DYO	37440	QS	MX58DZO
37380	QS	MX58DWL									

37441-37471 — Volvo B9TL — Wrightbus Eclipse Gemini — N45/29F — 2008-09

No		Reg	No		Reg	No		Reg	No		Reg
37441	OM	MX58DZP	37449	OM	MX58DZZ	37457	OM	MX58EAO	37465	TE	MX58EBK
37442	QS	MX58DZR	37450	OM	MX58EAA	37458	OM	MX58EAP	37466	TE	MX58EBL
37443	OM	MX58DZS	37451	OM	MX58EAC	37459	OM	MX58EAY	37467	OM	MX58EBM
37444	OM	MX58DZT	37452	QS	MX58EAF	37460	OM	MX58EBA	37468	OM	MX58EBN
37445	OM	MX58DZU	37453	OM	MX58EAG	37461	OM	MX58EBC	37469	OM	MX09GXY
37446	OM	MX58DZV	37454	OM	MX58EAJ	37462	OM	MX58EBD	37470	OM	MX09GXZ
37447	OM	MX58DZW	37455	OM	MX58EAK	37463	OM	MX58EBF	37471	BY	MX09GYG
37448	OM	MX58DZY	37456	QS	MX58EAM	37464	TE	MX58EBG			

37472-37529 — Volvo B9TL — Wrightbus Eclipse Gemini — N45/29F — 2008

No		Reg	No		Reg	No		Reg	No		Reg
37472	OG	YN08NLL	37487	RO	YN08NMK	37502	DN	YN08PMV	37516	OG	YN58ETA
37473	OG	YN08NLM	37488	RO	YN08NMM	37503	DN	YN08PMX	37517	OG	YN58ETD
37474	OG	YN08NLO	37489	RO	YN08NMU	37504	DN	YN08PMY	37518	OG	YN58ETE
37475	OG	YN08NLP	37490	RO	YN08NMV	37505	DN	YN08PNE	37519	OG	YN58ETF
37476	OG	YN08NLR	37491	RO	YN08NMX	37506	DN	YN08PNF	37520	OG	YN58ETJ
37477	OG	YN08NLT	37492	RO	YN08NMY	37507	DN	YN08PNJ	37521	OG	YN58ETK
37478	OG	YN08NLU	37493	RO	YN08PLF	37508	DN	YN08PNK	37522	OG	YN58ETL
37479	OG	YN08NLV	37494	RO	YN58ERX	37509	RO	YN58ERZ	37523	OG	YN58ETO
37480	OG	YN08NLX	37495	RO	YN08PLO	37510	RO	YN58ESF	37524	OG	YN58ETR
37481	OG	YN08NLY	37496	RO	YN08PLU	37511	OG	YN58ESG	37525	DN	YN58ETT
37482	OG	YN08NLZ	37497	RO	YN58ERY	37512	OG	YN58ESO	37526	OG	YN58ETU
37483	OG	YN08NMA	37498	RO	YN08PLX	37513	OG	YN58ESU	37527	OG	YN58ETV
37484	OG	YN08NME	37499	RO	YN08PLZ	37514	OG	YN58ESV	37528	OG	YN58ETX
37485	OG	YN08NMF	37500	DN	YN08PMO	37515	OG	YN58ESY	37529	OG	YN58ETY
37486	OG	YN08NMJ	37501	DN	YN08PMU						

37530-37544 — Volvo B9TL — Wrightbus Eclipse Gemini — N45/29F — 2008

No		Reg	No		Reg	No		Reg	No		Reg
37530	LF	SF08SMU	37534	LF	SF08SNK	37538	LF	SF08SNX	37542	LF	SF58ATZ
37531	LF	SF08SMV	37535	LF	SF08SNN	37539	LF	SF08SNY	37543	LF	SF58AUA
37532	LF	SF08SMX	37536	LF	SF08SNU	37540	LF	SF08SNZ	37544	LF	SF58AUC
37533	LF	SF08SNJ	37537	LF	SF08SNV	37541	LF	SF58ATY			

37545-37561 — Volvo B9TL — Wrightbus Eclipse Gemini — N45/29F — 2009

No		Reg	No		Reg	No		Reg	No		Reg
37545	OM	MX09GYE	37550	OM	MX09GYD	37554	BY	MX09GYH	37558	OM	MX09HUU
37546	OM	MX09GYJ	37551	BY	MX09HUK	37555	OM	MX09LMK	37559	OM	MX09HUP
37547	OM	MX09GYK	37552	OM	MX09GYB	37556	OM	MX09LML	37560	OM	MX09LMF
37548	OM	MX09GYC	37553	OM	MX09GYF	37557	OM	MX09HUO	37561	OM	MX09LMJ
37549	OM	MX09GYA									

37562	YA	FJ08FYN	Volvo B9TL	Wrightbus Eclipse Gemini	N45/29F	2008	Beestons, Hadleigh, 2013

Also part of the Greater Manchester commemorative fleet is 37451, MX58EAC, which carries the colours of the one-time Lancashire town of Rochdale. Allocated to Oldham, it is seen on the main service 24 that connects Rochdale with Manchester via Royton and Chadderton. *Richard Godfrey*

37563-37579

							Volvo B9TL			Wrightbus Eclipse Gemini		NC45/26F	2008	
37563	LO	AU58ECA	37568	LO	AU58ECJ	37572	YA	AU58ECW	37576	YA	AU58EDC
37564	LO	AU58ECC	37569	LO	AU58ECN	37573	YA	AU58ECX	37577	YA	AU58EDF
37565	LO	AU58ECD	37570	LO	AU58ECT	37574	YA	AU58ECY	37578	YA	AU58EDJ
37566	LO	AU58ECE	37571	LO	AU58ECV	37575	YA	AU58ECZ	37579	YA	AU58EDK
37567	LO	AU58ECF									

37580-37586

							Volvo B9TL			Wrightbus Eclipse Gemini		NC43/27F	2008	
37580	BP	HX08DHL	37582	WH	HX08DHK	37584	WH	HX08DHG	37586	WH	HX08DHJ
37581	WH	HX08DHF	37583	WH	HX08DHE	37585	WH	HX08DHY			

37587-37632

							Volvo B9TL			Wrightbus Eclipse Gemini		N45/29F	2008	
37587	HG	WX58JWU	37599	HG	WX58JXV	37611	HG	WX58JXV	37622	LH	WX58JYH
37588	HG	WX58JWV	37600	HG	WX58JXJ	37612	HG	WX58JXW	37623	LH	WX58JYJ
37589	HG	WX58JWW	37601	HG	WX58JXK	37613	LH	WX58JXY	37624	LH	WX58JYK
37590	HG	WX58JWY	37602	HG	WX58JXL	37614	LH	WX58JXZ	37625	LH	WX58JYL
37591	HG	WX58JWZ	37603	HG	WX58JXM	37615	LH	WX58JYA	37626	LH	WX58JYN
37592	HG	WX58JXA	37604	HG	WX58JXN	37616	LH	WX58JYB	37627	LH	WX58JYO
37593	HG	WX58JXB	37605	HG	WX58JXO	37617	LH	WX58JYC	37628	LH	WX58JYP
37594	HG	WX58JXC	37606	HG	WX58JXP	37618	LH	WX58JYD	37629	LH	WX58JYR
37595	HG	WX58JXD	37607	LH	WX58JXR	37619	LH	WX58JYE	37630	LH	WX58JYS
37596	HG	WX58JXE	37608	HG	WX58JXS	37620	LH	WX58JYF	37631	LH	WX58JYT
37597	HG	WX58JXF	37609	HG	WX58JXT	37621	LH	WX58JYG	37632	LH	WX58JYU
37598	HG	WX58JXG	37610	HG	WX58JXU						

37633-37644

							Volvo B9TL			Wrightbus Eclipse Gemini		N45/29F	2008	
37633	AB	SV08FXP	37636	AB	SV08FXT	37639	AB	SV08FXW	37642	AB	SV08FYA
37634	AB	SV08FXR	37637	AB	SV08FXU	37640	AB	SV08FXY	37643	AB	SV08FYB
37635	AB	SV08FXS	37638	AB	SV08FXW	37641	AB	SV08FXZ	37644	AB	SV08FYC

37645-37685 — Volvo B9TL — Wrightbus Eclipse Gemini — NC45/29F — 2009

No	Code	Reg	No	Code	Reg	No	Code	Reg	No	Code	Reg
37645	BM	YJ58RNN	37656	BM	YJ58RPV	37666	BM	YJ58RSO	37676	HP	YJ09FVG
37646	BM	YJ58RNO	37657	BM	YJ58RPX	37667	HP	YJ58RSU	37677	HP	YJ09FVH
37647	BM	YJ58RNU	37658	BM	YJ58RPY	37668	HP	YJ58RSV	37678	HP	YJ09FVK
37648	BM	YJ58RNV	37659	BM	YJ58RPZ	37669	HP	YJ58RSX	37679	HP	YJ09FVL
37649	BM	YJ58RNX	37660	BM	YJ58RRO	37670	HP	YJ58RSY	37680	BM	YJ09FVM
37650	BM	YJ58RNZ	37661	BM	YJ58RRU	37671	HP	YJ58RSZ	37681	HP	YJ09FVN
37651	BM	YJ58ROH	37662	BM	YJ58RRV	37672	HP	YJ58RTO	37682	HP	YJ09FVO
37652	BM	YJ58ROH	37663	BM	YJ58RRX	37673	HP	YJ58RTU	37683	HP	YJ09FVP
37653	BM	YJ58ROU	37664	BM	YJ58RRY	37674	HP	YJ58RTV	37684	HP	YJ09FVE
37654	BM	YJ58RPO	37665	BM	YJ58RRZ	37675	HP	YJ58RTX	37685	HP	YJ09FVF
37655	BM	YJ58RPU									

37686-37772 — Volvo B9TL — Wrightbus Eclipse Gemini — N45/29F — 2009

No	Code	Reg	No	Code	Reg	No	Code	Reg	No	Code	Reg
37686	HP	YJ09NZY	37708	BM	YJ09OBC	37730	BM	YJ09OCB	37752	BM	YJ59KSO
37687	BM	YJ09OAA	37709	BM	YJ09OBD	37731	BM	YJ09OCC	37753	BM	YJ59KSU
37688	BM	YJ09OAB	37710	BM	YJ09OBE	37732	BD	YJ09OCD	37754	BM	YJ59KSV
37689	BM	YJ09OAC	37711	BM	YJ09OBF	37733	BD	YJ09OCE	37755	BM	YJ59KSY
37690	HP	YJ09OAD	37712	BM	YJ09OBG	37734	BD	YJ09OCF	37756	BM	YJ59KSZ
37691	HP	YJ09OAE	37713	BM	YJ09OBH	37735	BD	YJ09OCG	37757	LH	WX09KBK
37692	HP	YJ09OAG	37714	BM	YJ09OBK	37736	LF	SF09LDD	37758	LH	WX09KBN
37693	HP	YJ09OAH	37715	BM	YJ09OBL	37737	LF	SF09LDE	37759	LH	WX09KBO
37694	HP	YJ09OAL	37716	BM	YJ09OBM	37738	LF	SF09LDJ	37760	LH	WX09KBP
37695	HP	YJ09OAM	37717	BM	YJ09OBN	37739	LF	SF09LDK	37761	LH	WX09KBU
37696	HP	YJ09OAN	37718	BM	YJ09OBO	37740	LF	SF09LDL	37762	LH	WX09KBV
37697	HP	YJ09OAO	37719	BM	YJ09OBP	37741	LF	SF09LDN	37763	LH	WX09KBY
37698	HP	YJ09OAP	37720	BM	YJ09OBR	37742	LF	SF09LDO	37764	LH	WX09KBZ
37699	HP	YJ09OAS	37721	BM	YJ09OBS	37743	LF	SF09LDU	37765	LH	WX09KCA
37700	HP	YJ09OAU	37722	BM	YJ09OBT	37744	LF	SF09LDV	37766	LH	WX09KCC
37701	HP	YJ09OAV	37723	BM	YJ09OBU	37745	LF	SF09LDX	37767	LH	WX09KCE
37702	HP	YJ09OAW	37724	BM	YJ09OBV	37746	LF	SF09LDY	37768	LH	WX09KCF
37703	HP	YJ09OAX	37725	BM	YJ09OBW	37747	LF	SF09LDZ	37769	LH	WX09KCG
37704	HP	YJ09OAY	37726	BM	YJ09OBX	37748	LF	SF09LEJ	37770	LH	WX09KCJ
37705	HP	YJ09OAZ	37727	BM	YJ09OBY	37749	LF	SF09LEU	37771	LH	WX09KCK
37706	BM	YJ09OBA	37728	BM	YJ09OBZ	37750	LF	SF09LFA	37772	LH	WX09KCN
37707	BM	YJ09OBB	37729	BM	YJ09OCA	37751	LF	SF09LFB			

No	Code	Reg	Chassis	Body	Type	Year
37985	BL	BJ11XGY	Volvo B9TL	Wrightbus Eclipse Gemini 2	NC39/26F	2011
37986	BL	BJ11ECY	Volvo B9TL	Wrightbus Eclipse Gemini 2	NC39/26F	2011
37987	BL	BJ11ECX	Volvo B9TL	Wrightbus Eclipse Gemini 2	NC39/26F	2011
37997	BL	BF63HDV	Volvo B9TL	Wrightbus Eclipse Gemini 2	NC39/26F	2013
37998	BL	BF63HDX	Volvo B9TL	Wrightbus Eclipse Gemini 2	NC39/26F	2013
37999	BL	BF63HDY	Volvo B9TL	Wrightbus Eclipse Gemini 2	NC39/26F	2013

38000-38006 — Volvo Citybus B10M-50 — Alexander RV — O47/35F — 1987

No	Code	Reg	No	Code	Reg	No	Code	Reg	No	Code	Reg
38000	CEu	D700GHY	38002	CEu	D702GHY	38005	CEu	D705GHY	38006	CEu	D706GHY
38001	CEu	D701GHY	38004	CEu	D704GHY						

No	Code	Reg	Chassis	Body	Type	Year
38125	NE	K125URP	Volvo Citybus B10M-50	Alexander RV	BC47/35F	1992

38201-38225 — ADL Trident 2 3-axle — ADL Enviro 500 — N53/29F — 2009

No	Code	Reg	No	Code	Reg	No	Code	Reg	No	Code	Reg
38201	LF	SN09CAU	38208	LF	SN09CBX	38214	LF	SN09CCJ	38220	LF	SN09CCY
38202	LF	SN09CAV	38209	LF	SN09CBY	38215	LF	SN09CCK	38221	LF	SN09CCZ
38203	LF	SN09CAX	38210	LF	SN09CCA	38216	LF	SN09CCO	38222	LF	SN09CDE
38204	LF	SN09CBF	38211	LF	SN09CCD	38217	LF	SN09CCU	38223	LF	SN09CDF
38205	LF	SN09CBO	38212	LF	SN09CCE	38218	LF	SN09CCV	38224	LF	SN09CDK
38206	LF	SN09CBU	38213	LF	SN09CCF	38219	LF	SN09CCX	38225	LF	SN09CDO
38207	LF	SN09CBV									

39001-39005 — VDL Bus Hybrid HEV — Wrightbus Gemini 2 — N41/27F — 2008

No	Code	Reg	No	Code	Reg	No	Code	Reg	No	Code	Reg
39001	YK	LK58ECV	39003	YK	LK58ECX	39004	YK	LK58ECY	39005	YK	LK58ECZ
39002	YK	LK58ECW									

39101-39110 — ADL E400H — ADL Enviro 400 — NC45/30F — 2011

No	Code	Reg	No	Code	Reg	No	Code	Reg	No	Code	Reg
39101	SN	SN61BFK	39104	SN	SN61BFO	39107	SN	SN61BFV	39109	SN	SN61BFY
39102	SN	SN61BFL	39105	SN	SN61BFP	39108	SN	SN61BFX	39110	SN	SN61BFZ
39103	SN	SN61BFM	39106	SN	SN61BFU						

Double-deck deliveries in 2011 and subsequently have included the Alexander Dennis Enviro 400. Ten of the hybrid model are allocated to Scotstoun and eight to Bath for its park and ride service. Pictured at work as it leaves Bath city centre is 39137, SN62AWO. *Dave Heath*

39133-39141   ADL E40H   ADL Enviro 400   N45/29F   2012

| 39133 | BA | SN62AWA | 39135 | BA | SN62AWG | 39138 | BA | SN62AWR | 39140 | BA | SN62AXB |
| 39134 | BA | SN62AWF | 39137 | BA | SN62AWO | 39139 | BA | SN62AWY | 39141 | BA | SN62AXC |

39201-39206   Volvo B5LH   Wrightbus Gemini 2   N41/23F   2011

| 39201 | HP | BJ60BZA | 39203 | HP | BJ60BZC | 39205 | HP | BJ60BZE | 39206 | HP | BJ60BZF |
| 39202 | HP | BJ60BZB | 39204 | HP | BJ60BZD | | | | | | |

39207-39220   Volvo B5LH   Wrightbus Gemini 2   NC41/23F   2011

39207	QS	BN61MWE	39211	QS	BN61MWK	39215	QS	BN61MWP	39218	QS	BN61MWW
39208	QS	BN61MWF	39212	QS	BN61MWL	39216	QS	BN61MWU	39219	QS	BN61MWX
39209	QS	BN61MWG	39213	QS	BN61MWM	39217	QS	BN61MWV	39220	QS	BN61MWY
39210	QS	BN61MWJ	39214	QS	BN61MWO						

39221-39236   Volvo B5LH   Wrightbus Gemini 2   N41/23F   2011

39221	HP	BP11JWA	39225	HP	BP11JWF	39229	HP	BP11JWN	39233	HP	BP11JWU
39222	HP	BP11JWD	39226	HP	BP11JWG	39230	HP	BP11JWJ	39234	HP	BP11JWV
39223	HP	BP11JWC	39227	HP	BP11JWL	39231	HP	BP11JWK	39235	HP	BP11JWX
39224	HP	BP11JWE	39228	HP	BP11JWM	39232	HP	BP11JWO	39236	HP	BP11JWW

39480	YAs	JJD480D	AEC Routemaster R2RH1	Park Royal	B40/32R	1966	
39623	YAs	NML623E	AEC Routemaster R2RH1	Park Royal	B40/32R	1967	
39735	BLs	SMK735F	AEC Routemaster R2RH1	Park Royal	B40/32R	1967	
39810	BLs	510CLT	AEC Routemaster R2RH	Park Royal	O32/25R	1962	London Buses, 2004
39920	WHu	L650SEU	Volvo Olympian	Northern Counties Palatine II	O47/29F	1993	
39971	RAu	MOD571P	Bristol VRT/SL3/6LXB	Eastern Coach Works	O43/31F	1976	

| 40002 | PL | S764RNE | Dennis Dart SLF 8.8m | Plaxton Pointer MPD | N28F | 1999 | Springfield Cs, Wigan, 2001 |
| 40003 | AG | S766RNE | Dennis Dart SLF 8.8m | Plaxton Pointer MPD | N28F | 1999 | Springfield Cs, Wigan, 2001 |

40006-40012 — Optare Solo M850 — Optare — N27F — 1999

| 40006 | WH | T159BBF | 40008 | BR | T161BBF | 40010 | NE | T163BBF | 40012 | WH | T165BBF |
| 40007 | NE | T160BBF | 40009 | AG | T162BBF | 40011 | NE | T164BBF | | | |

40015-40019 — Optare Solo M850 — Optare — N27F — 2000

| 40015 | NE | W474SVT | 40017 | NE | W476SVT | 40018 | NE | W477SVT | 40019 | NE | W478SVT |
| 40016 | NE | W475SVT | | | | | | | | | |

40020-40029 — Optare Solo M850 — Optare — N27F — 2000

40020	NE	X289FFA	40023	AG	X293FFA	40026	AG	X296FFA	40028	AG	X298FFA
40021	AG	X291FFA	40024	AG	X294FFA	40027	AG	X297FFA	40029	AG	X299FFA
40022	AG	X292FFA	40025	AG	X295FFA						

| 40030 | AG | T371NUA | Dennis Dart SLF | Alexander ALX200 | N37F | 1999 |

40033-40039 — Dennis Dart SLF 10.2m — Plaxton Pointer 2 — N41F — 1998-99 — New World First Bus, 2001

| 40033 | PLu | S343SUX | 40035 | PL | S375SUX | 40037 | PL | S377SUX | 40039 | PL | S389SUX |
| 40034 | PL | S374SUX | 40036 | PL | S376SUX | 40038 | PLu | S378SUX | | | |

40137	NE	R979NVT	Dennis Dart SLF	Plaxton Pointer 2	N37F	1998
40140	NE	T982LBF	Dennis Dart SLF	Alexander ALX200	N37F	1999
40147	NE	V989GBF	Dennis Dart SLF	Alexander ALX200	N37F	1999

40150-40155 — Dennis Dart SLF — Alexander ALX200 — N37F — 1999-2000

| 40150 | NE | X993FFA | 40153 | NE | T364NUA | 40154 | AG | T365NUA | 40155 | AG | T372NUA |
| 40151 | NE | X994FFA | | | | | | | | | |

40161	PTu	P117NLW	Dennis Dart SLF	Marshall Capital	N31F	1997
40173	AG	P126NLW	Dennis Dart SLF	Marshall Capital	N29F	1997
40175	AG	S247CSF	Dennis Dart SLF	Plaxton Pointer 2	N31F	1998
40179	AGu	R330HYG	Dennis Dart SLF	Plaxton Pointer 2	N31F	1998
40180	NE	V41DTE	Optare Solo M850	Optare	N24F	1999
40181	OM	V42DTE	Optare Solo M850	Optare	N24F	1999
40304	NE	V71GEH	Optare Solo M850	Optare	N24F	1999

40308-40317 — Optare Solo M850 — Optare — N28F — 2000

| 40308 | OM | X611OBN | 40313 | OM | X616OBN | 40315 | OM | X618OBN | 40317 | OM | X627OBN |
| 40312 | TEu | X615OBN | 40314 | OM | X617OBN | 40316 | OM | X619OBN | | | |

40318-40322 — Optare Solo M920 — Optare — N28F — 2001

| 40318 | OM | Y901KNB | 40320 | OM | Y903KNB | 40321 | OM | Y904KNB | 40322 | OM | Y905KNB |
| 40319 | OM | Y902KNB | | | | | | | | | |

40323-40326 — Optare Solo M850 — Optare — N24F — 2001

| 40323 | OM | MA51AET | 40324 | TE | MA51AEU | 40325 | TE | MA51AEV | 40326 | TE | MA51AEW |

40327-40336 — Optare Solo M920 — Optare — N28F — 2002

40327	TE	ML02OFW	40330	OM	ML02OFZ	40333	OM	ML02OGC	40335	OM	ML02OGE
40328	OM	ML02OFX	40331	OM	ML02OGA	40334	OM	ML02OGD	40336	OM	ML02OGF
40329	OM	ML02OFY	40332	OM	ML02OGB						

40361-40406 — Dennis Dart SLF — Plaxton Pointer 2 — N37F — 1997

40361	OM	R235SBA	40369	OM	R243SBA	40376	AG	R250SBA	40403	TE	R277SBA
40364	OM	R238SBA	40373	AG	R247SBA	40378	AG	R252SBA	40406	OM	R280SBA
40367	AG	R241SBA	40375	AG	R249SBA	40383	AG	R257SBA			

| 40416 | OM | P510LND | Dennis Dart SLF | Wright Crusader 2 | N41F | 1996 |

40437-40444 — Volvo B6BLE — Wright Crusader 2 — N36F — 1999

| 40437 | QS | T701PND | 40439 | QS | T703PND | 40441 | QS | T705PND | 40444 | QS | T708PND |
| 40438 | QS | T702PND | 40440 | QS | T704PND | 40443 | QS | T707PND | | | |

| 40502 | DN | T465JDT | Volvo B6BLE | Wright Crusader 2 | N36F | 1999 |

Almost all of the high-floor step-entrance Dennis Darts have now been withdrawn from the fleet, leaving the low-floor variant with Plaxton bodywork the most common model. Illustrating the type is 40823, R643DUS, an example new as MD102 in First Glasgow. It is seen in Portsmouth. *Dave Heath*

40517-40542

			Dennis Dart SLF 11.3m			Plaxton Pointer SPD		N40F	1998		
40517	WS	S512UAK	40529	BA	S524UAK	40535	BA	S530UAK	40542	BA	S537UAK
40525	BA	S520UAK	40534	BA	S529UAK	40541	BA	S536UAK			

40560-40566

			Volvo B6BLE			Wright Crusader 2		N36F	1999		
40560	PHu	T309VYG	40562	Bu	T311VYG	40565	BM	T314VYG	40566	BM	T315VYG

40570-40599

			Volvo B6BLE			Wrightbus Crusader 2		N38F	2001-02		
40570	PL	YJ51PZZ	40578	BM	YJ51RHU	40586	PL	YJ51RJX	40593	BA	YG02DHY
40571	YK	YJ51RKO	40579	BM	YJ51RHV	40587	BM	YJ51RFZ	40594	BA	YG02DLK
40572	YK	YJ51RKU	40580	PL	HIG8791	40588	BA	YJ51RGO	40595	DN	YG02DLF
40573	YK	YJ51RKV	40581	PL	XFF283	40589	BA	YJ51RGU	40596	DN	YG02DLE
40574	YK	YJ51RSV	40582	PL	UHW661	40590	BA	YJ51RGV	40597	DN	YG02DKY
40575	YK	YJ51RSX	40583	PL	260ERY	40591	BA	YJ51RGX	40598	DN	YG02DKX
40576	BM	YJ51RSY	40584	PL	HIG8790	40592	BA	YG02DHP	40599	DN	YG02DHX
40577	BM	YJ51RHO	40585	PL	YJ51RJV						

40683	OM	T167BBF	Optare Solo M850	Optare	N27F	1999
40703	GSu	R324HYG	Dennis Dart SLF	Plaxton Pointer 2	N35F	1998
40721	SH	T375NUA	Dennis Dart SLF 10.8m	Alexander ALX200	N37F	1999
40722	Ou	R308GHS	Dennis Dart SLF	Plaxton Pointer 2	N37F	1998

40786-40809

			Dennis Dart SLF			Plaxton Pointer 2		N37F	1997-98		
40786	TNu	R290GHS	40792	HOu	R296GHS	40795	RA	R299GHS	40805	HD	R312GHS
40788	TNu	R292GHS	40793	RA	R297GHS	40803	Ou	R310GHS	40809	O	R317GHS
40790	HI	R294GHS	40794	RA	R298GHS						

40819-40835

			Dennis Dart SLF			Plaxton Pointer 2		N37F	1997-98		
40819	O	R637DUS	40823	HI	R643DUS	40826	BLu	R646DUS	40830	SN	R667DUS
40820	O	R638DUS	40824	SOu	R644DUS	40827	HI	R647DUS	40835	BA	R672DUS
40822	SOu	R642DUS	40825	HI	R645DUS	40828	SN	R664DUS			

40891	LLu	R224GFS	Dennis Dart SLF		Plaxton Pointer 2	N37F	1997	
40892	LLu	S241CSF	Dennis Dart SLF		Plaxton Pointer 2	N37F	1999	
40899	GS	S251CSF	Dennis Dart SLF		Plaxton Pointer 2	N38F	1999	
40911	GS	P632CGM	Dennis Dart		Plaxton Pointer	B37F	1996	
40915	GS	P206NSC	Dennis Dart SLF		Plaxton Pointer	N35F	1997	
40935	PTw	R430PSH	Dennis Dart SLF		Plaxton Pointer 2	N37F	1998	
40938	BKu	S244CSF	Dennis Dart SLF		Plaxton Pointer 2	N38F	1999	
40946	BF	R233SBA	Dennis Dart SLF		Plaxton Pointer 2	N37F	1997	
40956	BL	S344SUX	Dennis Dart SLF 10.7m		Plaxton Pointer 2	N41F	1998	New World First Bus, 2001
40957	HI	S372SUX	Dennis Dart SLF 10.7m		Plaxton Pointer 2	N41F	1998	New World First Bus, 2001

40958-40961

Dennis Dart SLF 10.7m — Plaxton Pointer 2 — N36F — 1998 — New World First Bus, 2001

40958	PLu	S334TJX	40959	HI	S335TJX	40960	PL	S338TJX	40961	HOu	S474TJX

40965	SN	SJ03DNY	Optare Solo M920		Optare	N30F	2003	
40966	SN	SJ03DOA	Optare Solo M920		Optare	N30F	2003	

40973-40976

TransBus Dart SLF — Transbus Pointer — N37F — 2003

40973	DN	YV03UOY	40974	DN	YV03UOX	40975	DN	YV03UOW	40976	DN	YV03UOU

41011	HH	R711VLA	Dennis Dart SLF 10.3m		East Lancs Spryte	N34F	1998	
41070	AG	V370KLG	Dennis Dart SLF		Marshall Capital	N37F	1999	Chester Bus, 2007

41129-41156

Dennis Dart SLF — Marshall Capital — N31F — 1997

41129	TN	P129NLW	41143	CE	P143NLW	41147	HIu	P247OEW	41155	PT	P255RFL
41132	CE	P132NLW	41144	WS	P144NLW	41149	RA	P149NLW	41156	TN	P156NLW
41134	TN	P134NLW									

41162	BG	R162TLM	Dennis Dart SLF 9.3m		Marshall Capital	N31F	1998	

41165-41190

Dennis Dart SLF 10.2m — Marshall Capital — N35F* — 1997-98 — *seating varies

41165	HIu	R165TLM	41171	LLw	R171TLM	41185	PTw	R185TLM	41188	LL	R188TLM
41166	HIu	R166TLM	41174	PT	R174TLM	41186	LL	R186TLM	41190	PTu	R190TLM
41167	LL	R167TLM	41183	LLu	R183TLM						

41191-41200

Dennis Dart SLF 10.2m — Marshall Capital — N33F — 1998

41191	LL	R191VLD	41193	PTu	R193VLD	41197	LL	S197KLM	41200	PT	S220KLM
41192	LLu	R192VLD	41194	LLu	R194VLD	41198	LLu	S198KLM			

41216-41234

Dennis Dart SLF 9.3m — Marshall Capital — N23D — 1998

41216	B	R216TLM	41221	B	R221TLM	41230	BG	R230TLM	41234	PT	R234TLM
41217	B	R217TLM	41222	Bu	R322TLM	41233	LL	R233TLM			

41236-41246

Dennis Dart SLF 10.2m — Marshall Capital — N33D — 1998

41236	Bu	S236KLM	41240	BS	S240KLM	41243	LFu	S243KLM	41245	LFu	S245KLM
41238	BS	S238KLM	41241	BS	S241KLM	41244	SN	S244KLM	41246	B	S246KLM
41239	BS	S239KLM	41242	B	S242KLM						

41265-41306

Dennis Dart SLF 9.3m — Marshall Capital — N22D* — 1999 — seating varies

41265	BG	T265JLD	41282	HX	T282JLD	41295	PLu	T295JLD	41303	SN	T303JLD
41278	SN	T278JLD	41283	HX	T283JLD	41301	SN	T301JLD	41304	SN	T304JLD
41279	SN	T279JLD	41288	SN	T288JLD	41302	SN	T302JLD	41306	B	T306JLD
41281	HX	T281JLD	41291	PL	T291JLD						

41307-41317

Dennis Dart SLF 10.2m — Marshall Capital — N28D* — 1999 — *41315-7 are N31F

41307	B	V307GBY	41310	B	V310GBY	41313	SN	V313GBY	41316	HX	V316GBY
41308	Ou	V308GBY	41311	SN	V311GBY	41314	B	V314GBY	41317	HX	V317GBY
41309	Ou	V309GBY	41312	SN	V312GBY	41315	HX	V315GBY			

41330-41335

Dennis Dart SLF 8.9m — Marshall Capital — N25F — 1999

41330	LL	V330GBY	41332	WS	V332GBY	41334	WS	V334GBY	41335	WS	V335GBY
41331	LL	V331GBY	41333	WS	V433HBY						

41336	SH	T336ALR	Dennis Dart SLF 10.2m		Marshall Capital	N35F	1999	

41337-41348

Dennis Dart SLF 8.9m — Marshall Capital — N25F — 1999

41337	LT	T337ALR	41341	LLu	T341ALR	41345	LLu	V345DLH	41347	PT	V347DLH
41338	PT	T338ALR	41343	PT	T343ALR	41346	HI	V346DLH	41348	HI	V348DLH
41340	LL	T340ALR	41344	PT	T344ALR						

First was involved with specification of Marshall Capital-bodied Darts, and thus operates the largest fleet of the model many of which originally operated on London duties. Now refurbished and allocated to Llanelli is 41331, V331GBY, one of the 8.9 metre examples. It was pictured while based at Weston-super-Mare. *Richard Godfrey*

41381-41400

Dennis Dart SLF 10.2m   Marshall Capital   N31F   2000

41381	PT	X381HLR	41386	PT	X386HLR	41391	PT	X391HLR	41397	PTu	X397HLR
41382	PT	X382HLR	41387	HI	X387HLR	41392	RA	X392HLR	41398	PT	X398HLR
41383	PT	X383HLR	41388	PT	X388HLR	41393	PT	X393HLR	41399	PT	X399HLR
41384	RA	X384HLR	41389	PT	X389HLR	41394	PT	X394HLR	41400	PT	X79HLR
41385	PT	X385HLR	41390	RA	X78HLR	41395	PT	X395HLR			

41403-41426

Dennis Dart SLF 10.2m   Marshall Capital   N28D   2001

41403	SHt	RG51FWX	41408	SN	RG51FXE	41416	PH	LN51DWZ	41421	HGt	LN51DXE
41404	HGt	RG51FXA	41409	SN	RG51FXF	41417	PH	LN51DXA	41422	O	LN51DXF
41405	PH	RG51FXB	41410	B	RG51FXH	41418	PH	LN51DXB	41423	HGt	LN51DXG
41406	PH	RG51FXC	41414	PH	LK51JYO	41419	u	LN51DXC	41426	B	LN51DWK
41407	SN	RG51FXD	41415	PH	LN51DWY	41420	HGt	LN51DXD			

41435-41449

Dennis Dart SLF 9.3m   Marshall Capital   N24D   2001

41435	u	LN51DVW	41441	u	LN51DVR	41447	O	LN51DUU	41449	O	LN51DUY
41437	u	LN51DVY	41446	O	LN51DUJ	41448	O	LN51DUV			

41487-41491

TransBus Dart 8.9m   Marshall Capital   N25F   2002

41487	BK	LT02ZDY	41489	PT	LT02ZFA	41490	PT	LT02ZFB	41491	RA	LT02ZFC
41488	LT	LT02ZDZ									

41492-41514

TransBus Dart 10.5m   Caetano Nimbus   N29D*   2003   *41513 is B29F

41492	AG	LK03LMJ	41496	AG	LK03LMF	41500	AG	LK03LNW	41512	AG	LK03NGE
41493	AG	LK03LLX	41497	AG	LK03LNU	41501	AG	LK03LNX	41513	BS	LK03NGF
41494	AG	LK03LLZ	41498	AG	LK03NLN	41502	AG	LK03NLD	41514	AG	LK03NGG
41495	AG	LK03LME	41499	AG	LK03LNV						

41515-41519

Dennis Dart SLF 10.7m   Plaxton Pointer 2   N37F   1998

41515	HOu	R415WPX	41517	SOu	R417WPX	41518	LL	R418WPX	41519	LL	R419WPX
41516	SOu	R416WPX									

41520-41544 TransBus Dart 10.5m — Caetano Nimbus — N28D — 2003

41520	AG	LK03UEX	41524	BS	LK03UFB	41539	BS	LK53FDY	41542	BS	LK53FEG
41521	AG	LK03UEY	41525	BS	LK03UFC	41540	AG	LK53FDZ	41543	BS	LK53FEH
41522	AG	LK03UEZ	41527	BS	LK53FDD	41541	BS	LK53FEF	41544	BS	LK53FEJ
41523	BS	LK03UFA	41538	BS	LK53FDX						

41633-41646 Dennis Dart SLF 10.2m — Marshall Capital — N37F — 1997-98

41633	HI	R633VLX	41636	HIu	R636VLX	41643	HI	R643TLM	41646	HIu	R646TLM
41634	HIu	R634VLX									

41681-41687 Dennis Dart SLF 9.3m — Marshall Capital — N24D — 2000

41681	LFu	W681ULL	41683	B	W683ULL	41685	SN	W685ULL	41687	WS	W687ULL
41682	LFu	W682ULL	41684	SN	W684ULL	41686	WS	W686ULL			

41718-41738 Dennis Dart SLF 10.2m — Marshall Capital — N28D* — 2000 — 41718-29 are N31F

41718	PT	W718ULL	41726	PT	W726ULL	41730	HH	X503JLO	41736	HH	X736HLF
41719	PT	W719ULL	41727	PT	W727ULL	41732	HH	X732HLF	41737	HH	X737HLF
41720	PT	W133VLO	41728	PTu	W728VLO	41735	HH	X735HLF	41738	u	X738HLF
41721	PT	W721ULL	41729	PT	X729HLF						

41751-41771 Dennis Dart SLF 10.2m — Marshall Capital — N28D — 2000-01

41751	GS	X751JLO	41754	BF	X754HLR	41756	GS	X756HLR	41762	HH	X762HLR
41752	GS	X752HLR	41755	BF	X506HLR	41761	HH	X761HLR	41771	t	X771HLR
41753	GS	X753HLR									

41773-41788 Dennis Dart SLF 9.3m — Marshall Capital — N24D — 2001

41773	B	X773HLR	41778	B	X778HLR	41782	OM	X782HLR	41786	TE	X514HLR
41775	B	X511HLR	41779	B	X779HLR	41783	TE	X783HLR	41787	TE	X787HLR
41776	B	X776HLR	41780	TE	X513HLR	41784	TE	X784HLR	41788	OM	X788HLR
41777	B	X512HLR	41781	TE	X781HLR	41785	TE	X785HLR			

41795	PLu	LN51GOU	Dennis Dart SLF 9.3m	Marshall Capital	N24D	2001

42109-42123 Dennis Dart SLF 10.7m — Plaxton Pointer 2 — N37F — 1998

42109	HO	R609YCR	42114	BL	R614YCR	42118	HOu	R618YCR	42121	HOu	R621YCR
42111	HOu	R611YCR	42115	BL	R615YCR	42119	HOu	R619YCR	42122	HOu	R622YCR
42112	HOu	R612YCR	42116	HO	R616YCR	42120	HO	R620YCR	42123	HOu	R623YCR
42113	BL	R613YCR	42117	HO	R617YCR						

42124-42134 Dennis Dart SLF 10.7m — Plaxton Pointer 2 — N37F — 1998-99

42124	HO	S624KTP	42127	HO	S627KTP	42130	HO	S630KTP	42133	HO	S633KTP
42125	HO	S625KTP	42128	HO	S628KTP	42131	HO	S631KTP	42134	HO	S634KTP
42126	HO	S626KTP	42129	HO	S629KTP	42132	HO	S632KTP			

42136-42142 Dennis Dart SLF 10.7m — Plaxton Pointer 2 — N37F — 1999

42136	HO	S636XCR	42138	HO	S638XCR	42140	HO	S640XCR	42142	HO	S642XCR
42137	HO	S637XCR	42139	HO	S639XCR	42141	HO	S641XCR			

42207-42221 Dennis Dart SLF 10.7m — Plaxton Pointer 2 — N37F — 1998

42207	CE	R207MSA	42212	RA	R212MSA	42214	RA	R214MSA	42218	PTu	R218MSA
42208	RA	R208MSA	42213	RA	R213MSA	42216	RA	R216MSA	42221	WHu	R221MSA
42211	RA	R211MSA									

42232	HO	T32JCV	Dennis Dart SLF	Plaxton Pointer 2	N34F	1999	Truronian, 2008
42234	HO	T34JCV	Dennis Dart SLF	Plaxton Pointer 2	N34F	1999	Truronian, 2008
42235	CE	T35JCV	Dennis Dart SLF	Plaxton Pointer 2	N34F	1999	Truronian, 2008
42252	CEt	P452SCV	Dennis Dart SLF	Plaxton Pointer	N34F	1997	Truronian, 2008
42255	CE	P455SCV	Dennis Dart SLF	Plaxton Pointer	N34F	1997	Truronian, 2008

42322-42337 Dennis Dart SLF 10.8m — Alexander ALX200 — N37F — 1999

42322	BG	T622SEJ	42327	PT	T627SEJ	42331	BG	T631SEJ	42335	PT	T635SEJ
42323	PT	T623SEJ	42328	PT	T628SEJ	42332	PT	T632SEJ	42336	BGu	T636SEJ
42325	PT	T625SEJ	42329	PT	T629SEJ	42333	PT	T633SEJ	42337	PT	T637SEJ
42326	PT	T626SEJ	42330	PT	T630SEJ	42334	PT	T634SEJ			

42338-42347 Dennis Dart SLF 10.8m — Alexander ALX200 — N37F — 2000

42338	SH	X238AMO	42341	SH	X241AMO	42344	SH	X244AMO	42347	SH	X247AMO
42339	SH	X239AMO	42343	SH	X243AMO	42346	SH	X246AMO			

42350	WH	W809VMA	Dennis Dart SLF	Caetano Nimbus	N40F	2000	Caetano demo, 2002

Carrying *Millbrook Flyer* lettering, Southampton's 42524, R424WPX, is one of the most common lengths of Pointer in the fleet at 10.7 metres. It was pictured on a cold day in February 2013. *Dave Heath*

42351-42356

Dennis Dart SLF 10.2m   Caetano Nimbus   N34F   2001

| 42351 | HD | Y351AUY | 42353 | HD | Y353AUY | 42354 | HD | Y354AUY | 42356 | HD | Y356AUY |
| 42352 | HD | Y352AUY | | | | | | | | | |

42358	YA	EY05FYP	Dennis Dart SLF			Caetano Nimbus	N40F	2005	Connex, Jersey, 2013
42376	O	V676FPO	Dennis Dart SLF 10.7m			UVG UrbanStar	N40F	1999	Clarkson, S Emsall, 2003
42412	RA	N212WRD	Dennis Dart SLF 10.7m			Plaxton Pointer	N32F	1996	
42430	CE	P430ORL	Dennis Dart SLF 10.7m			Plaxton Pointer	NC35F	1996	
42439	HH	P439ORL	Dennis Dart SLF 10.7m			Plaxton Pointer	NC35F	1996	

42447-42463

Dennis Dart SLF 10.7m   Plaxton Pointer 2   N35F   1997-98

| 42447 | BR | R447CCV | 42453 | PT | R453CCV | 42456 | LLu | R456CCV | 42462 | PTu | R462CCV |
| 42449 | LLw | R449CCV | 42454 | SOu | R454CCV | 42459 | PL | R459CCV | 42463 | PL | R463CCV |

42469-42478

Dennis Dart SLF 10.7m   Alexander ALX200   N37F   1999-2000

42469	CE	T469JCV	42472	CE	T472YTT	42475	CE	X475SCY	42477	CE	X477SCY
42470	CE	T470JCV	42473	CE	T473YTT	42476	CE	X476SCY	42478	PT	X478SCY
42471	CE	T471JCV	42474	CE	X474SCY						

42482-42489

TransBus Dart 10.8m   TransBus Pointer   N37F   2003-04

| 42482 | BR | SN03WLD | 42484 | BR | SN03WLW | 42486 | BR | SN03WMX | 42488 | BR | SN53KJX |
| 42483 | BRu | SN03WLK | 42485 | BR | SN03WMM | 42487 | BR | SN03WME | 42489 | BR | SN53KJY |

42504-42507

Dennis Dart SLF 10.7m   Plaxton Pointer   N37F   1996

| 42504 | SO | P404KOW | 42505 | SO | P405KOW | 42506 | SO | P406KOW | 42507 | HI | P407KOW |

42508-42514

Dennis Dart SLF 10.7m   Plaxton Pointer 2   N37F   1998

| 42508 | BL | R408WPX | 42510 | SOu | R410WPX | 42512 | SOu | R412WPX | 42514 | SOu | R414WPX |
| 42509 | SO | R409WPX | 42511 | SO | R411WPX | 42513 | SO | R413WPX | | | |

| 42519 | BS | LK03NKN | TransBus Dart 10.5m | | | Caetano Nimbus | N29D | 2003 | |

42520-42527

Dennis Dart SLF 10.7m   Plaxton Pointer 2   N37F   1998

| 42520 | LL | R420WPX | 42522 | SO | R422WPX | 42524 | SO | R424WPX | 42526 | SO | R426WPX |
| 42521 | SO | R421WPX | 42523 | SO | R423WPX | 42525 | SO | R425WPX | 42527 | SO | R427WPX |

| 42551 | BS | S551WAT | Dennis Dart SLF 8.8m | | | Plaxton Pointer MPD | N29F | 1999 | |

42552-42563 · ADL Dart 9.4m · ADL Pointer · N31F · 2005

42552	BA	WX05UAJ	42555	BA	WX05UAM	42558	CE	SN05DZU
42553	BA	WX05UAK	42556	BA	WX05UAN	42559	CE	SN05DZV
42554	BA	WX05UAL	42557	BA	WX05UAO	42560	CE	SN05DZW

42561	BA	SN05DZX
42562	PL	SN05DZY
42563	PL	SN05DZZ

42569-42575 · Dennis Dart SLF 9m · Plaxton Pointer · N31F · 1996

42569	PT	P569BTH	42573	PT	P573BTH	42574	PT	P574BTH	42575	PT	P575BTH

42581-42599 · Dennis Dart SLF 9m · Plaxton Pointer 2 · N29F · 1998

42581	RA	R581SWN	42586	RA	R586SWN	42591	RA	R591SWN	42596	RAu	R596SWN
42582	RA	R582SWN	42587	RA	R587SWN	42592	RA	R592SWN	42597	RA	R597SWN
42583	RA	R583SWN	42588	RA	R588SWN	42593	RA	R593SWN	42598	RA	R598SWN
42585	RA	R585SWN	42589	RA	R589SWN	42595	RA	R595SWN	42599	LLu	R599SWN

42600-42614 · ADL Dart 9.4m · ADL Pointer · N31F · 2005

42600	RA	CU54HYK	42604	RA	CU54HYO	42608	RA	CU54HYV	42612	RA	CU54HYZ
42601	RA	CU54HYL	42605	RA	CU54HYP	42609	RA	CU54HYW	42613	LL	CU54HZA
42602	RA	CU54HYM	42606	RA	CU54HYR	42610	RA	CU54HYX	42614	RA	CU54HZB
42603	RA	CU54HYN	42607	RA	CU54HYT	42611	RA	CU54HYY			

Fleet	Op	Reg	Chassis	Body	Seats	Year	Previous owner
42620	BG	R120FUP	Dennis Dart SLF 10.2m	Plaxton Pointer 2	N35F	1997	York Pullman, 2000
42621	RA	R121FUP	Dennis Dart SLF 10.2m	Plaxton Pointer 2	N35F	1997	York Pullman, 2000
42622	RA	R122FUP	Dennis Dart SLF 10.2m	Plaxton Pointer 2	N35F	1997	York Pullman, 2000
42631	PT	R131FUP	Dennis Dart SLF 10.2m	Plaxton Pointer 2	N29F	1997	York Pullman, 2000
42634	TN	P834YUM	Dennis Dart SLF	Plaxton Pointer	N37F	1997	
42642	LL	S342EWU	Dennis Dart SLF	Plaxton Pointer 2	N37F	1998	
42643	BA	S343EWU	Dennis Dart SLF	Plaxton Pointer 2	N37F	1998	
42654	SH	V154LUA	Dennis Dart SLF	Alexander ALX200	N37F	1999	
42656	SH	T356VWU	Dennis Dart SLF 10.8m	Alexander ALX200	N37F	1999	
42659	SH	T359VWU	Dennis Dart SLF 10.8m	Alexander ALX200	N37F	1999	
42673	SH	T373NUA	Dennis Dart SLF 10.8m	Alexander ALX200	N37F	1999	

42674-42692 · TransBus Dart 10.2m · TransBus Pointer · N31F* · 2003 · *42679-84 are N37F

42674	LL	CU53APO	42679	RA	CU53ARX	42684	LL	CU53AUP	42689	BG	CU53AVW
42675	RA	CU53APV	42680	LL	CU53ARO	42685	BG	CU53AUO	42690	BG	CU53AUX
42676	LL	CU53APX	42681	LL	CU53ARF	42686	PT	CU53AUT	42691	PT	CU53AUY
42677	LL	CU53ASO	42682	LL	CU53APZ	42687	BG	CU53AUV	42692	BG	CU53AVB
42678	LL	CU53ARZ	42683	LL	CU53APY	42688	BG	CU53AUW			

42693	LL	CU03BHV	TransBus Dart 10.2m	TransBus Pointer	N29F	2003
42694	LL	CU03BHW	TransBus Dart 10.2m	TransBus Pointer	N29F	2003

42701-42718 · Dennis Dart SLF 9.3m · Plaxton Pointer 2 · N29F · 1997

42701	BA	R701BAE	42706	LH	R706BAE	42711	HG	R711BAE	42715	BG	R715BAE
42702	MSw	R702BAE	42707	WS	R707BAE	42712	HG	R712BAE	42716	RA	R716BAE
42703	LH	R703BAE	42708	HG	R708BAE	42713	BG	R713BAE	42717	WHu	R717BAE
42704	BA	R704BAE	42709	HG	R709BAE	42714	RA	R714BAE	42718	HG	R718BAE
42705	LH	R705BAE	42710	HG	R710BAE						

42719	CE	R719RAD	Dennis Dart SLF 9.3m	Plaxton Pointer 2	N29F	1998

42720-42725 · Dennis Dart SLF 10.2m · Plaxton Pointer 2 · N35F · 1998-99

42720	CE	S720AFB	42722	BG	S722AFB	42724	PLu	S724AFB	42725	CE	S725AFB
42721	BG	S721AFB	42723	HG	S723AFB						

42726	AG	T726REU	Dennis Dart SLF 10.2m	Plaxton Pointer 2	N35F	1999
42727	AG	T727REU	Dennis Dart SLF 10.2m	Plaxton Pointer 2	N35F	1999
42728	HI	T728REU	Dennis Dart SLF 10.2m	Plaxton Pointer 2	N35F	1999
42730	WS	T730REU	Dennis Dart SLF 10.2m	Alexander ALX200	N37F	1999
42731	WS	T731REU	Dennis Dart SLF 10.2m	Alexander ALX200	N37F	1999

42732-42738 · Dennis Dart SLF 10.7m · Alexander ALX200 · N35F · 2000

42732	HG	V732FAE	42734	HG	V734FAE	42736	HG	V736FAE	42738	WS	V738FAE
42733	HG	V733FAE	42735	HG	V735FAE	42737	HG	V737FAE			

42752-42784 · Dennis Dart SLF 10.7m · Plaxton Pointer 2 · N36F · 1998-99 · New World First Bus, 2001

42752	PL	S652SNG	42758	PL	S658SNG	42773	HO	S673SNG	42779	PL	S679SNG
42753	PLu	S753SNG	42759	HO	S659SNG	42777	PL	S677SNG	42783	HIu	S683SNG
42754	HO	S653SNG	42764	PL	S664SNG	42778	HI	S678SNG	42784	PL	S684SNG
42757	HO	S657SNG									

TransBus was formed on 1st January 2001 by the merger of Mayflower Corporation-owned Dennis with facilities in Guildford and Alexander (Falkirk), and Henlys-owned Plaxton (Scarborough and Wigan) with the TransBus name being used on the vehicles as from late 2002. TransBus Pointer 42860, TT03TRU, carries a livery commemorating the 110th anniversary of the first Great Western Road Motors services.
Richard Godfrey

| 42801 | CE | Y1EDN | Dennis Dart SLF 10.7m | Plaxton Pointer 2 | N37F | 2001 | Truronian, 2008 |
| 42802 | CE | Y2EDN | Dennis Dart SLF 10.7m | Plaxton Pointer 2 | N37F | 2001 | Truronian, 2008 |

42817-42823
Dennis Dart SLF 10.7m — Plaxton Pointer 2 — N39F — 1998

| 42817 | BP | S817KPR | 42819 | WH | S819KPR | 42821 | WH | S821KPR | 42823 | WH | S823KPR |
| 42818 | WH | S818KPR | 42820 | WHu | S820KPR | 42822 | WH | S822KPR | | | |

42824	BA	S824WYD	Dennis Dart SLF		East Lancs Spryte	N35F	1999
42825	TN	S825WYD	Dennis Dart SLF		East Lancs Spryte	N35F	1999
42826	WH	T826AFX	Dennis Dart SLF 10.7m		Plaxton Pointer 2	N39F	1999
42827	WHu	T827AFX	Dennis Dart SLF 10.7m		Plaxton Pointer 2	N39F	1999
42828	WH	T828AFX	Dennis Dart SLF 10.7m		Plaxton Pointer 2	N39F	1999
42829	WH	T829AFX	Dennis Dart SLF 10.7m		Plaxton Pointer 2	N39F	1999

42830-42835
Dennis Dart SLF 10.7m — East Lancs Spryte — N37F — 1999

| 42830 | TN | T830RYC | 42832 | TN | V832DYD | 42834 | TN | V834DYD | 42835 | TN | V835DYD |
| 42831 | TNu | T831RYC | 42833 | TN | V833DYD | | | | | | |

42841-42845
Dennis Dart SLF 10.7m — Alexander ALX200 — N37F — 1999

| 42841 | TN | T366NUA | 42843 | TN | T368NUA | 42844 | TN | T369NUA | 42845 | PT | T370NUA |
| 42842 | TN | T367NUA | | | | | | | | | |

| 42860 | CE | TT03TRU | TransBus Dart 10.2m | TransBus Pointer | N37F | 2003 | Truronian, 2008 |

42861-42870
TransBus Dart 10.7m — TransBus Pointer — N37F — 2003

42861	HV	CU53AVJ	42864	LL	CU53AVM	42867	RA	CU53AVR	42869	HV	CU53AVV
42862	HV	CU53AVK	42865	RA	CU53AVN	42868	RA	CU53AVP	42870	RA	CU53AVT
42863	LL	CU53AVL	42866	RA	CU53AVO						

42871-42876
TransBus Dart 10.7m — TransBus Pointer — N37F — 2003

| 42871 | CE | SN53KKA | 42873 | CE | SN53KKC | 42875 | CE | SN53KKE | 42876 | CE | SN53KJZ |
| 42872 | CE | SN53KKB | 42874 | CE | SN53KKD | | | | | | |

Caetano Nimbus bodywork is carried on Dart 43854, EG52FFZ, one of twenty joining the fleet in 2013 from the Connex fleet in Jersey. Allocated to Clacton, it operates local route 19 to St Osyth Beach.
Richard Godfrey

42877-42888   ADL Dart 10.7m   ADL Pointer   N37F   2005

42877	LL	SF05KWY	42880	HV	SF05KXB	42883	HV	SF05KXE	42886	PH	SF05KXK
42878	LL	SF05KWZ	42881	HV	SF05KXC	42884	HV	SF05KXH	42887	PH	SF05KXL
42879	HV	SF05KXA	42882	HV	SF05KXD	42885	PH	SF05KXJ	42888	PH	SF05KXM

42892	NE	VX54MUU	ADL Dart 10.7m	ADL Pointer	N37F	2004
42893	NE	VX54MUV	ADL Dart 10.7m	ADL Pointer	N37F	2004
42894	NE	VX05JWW	ADL Dart 10.7m	ADL Pointer	N37F	2005

42895-42916   ADL Dart 10.7m   ADL Pointer   N37F   2005

42895	LH	WX05RUW	42901	LH	WX05RVJ	42907	BA	WX05RVP	42912	LL	WX05RVW
42896	LH	WX05RUY	42902	BA	WX05RVK	42908	BA	WX05RVR	42913	LL	WX05RVX
42897	LH	WX05RVA	42903	BA	WX05RVL	42909	BA	WX05RVT	42914	BA	WX05RVZ
42898	LH	WX05RVC	42904	BA	WX05RVM	42910	BA	WX05RVU	42915	BA	WX05RWE
42899	LH	WX05RVE	42905	BA	WX05RVN	42911	BA	WX05RVV	42916	BA	WX05RWF
42900	LH	WX05RVF	42906	BA	WX05RVO						

42918-42939   ADL Dart 10.7m   ADL Pointer   N37F*   2005   *42918-23 are N34F

42918	CM	EU05AUK	42924	PL	SN05EAA	42930	CM	SN05EAM	42935	CM	SN05DZR
42919	YA	EU05AUL	42925	BA	SN05EAC	42931	CM	SN05EAO	42936	CM	SN05DZS
42920	YA	EU05AUM	42926	BA	SN05EAE	42932	CM	SN05EAP	42937	CN	SN05DZT
42921	YA	EU05AUN	42927	HH	SN05EAF	42933	CM	SN05DZO	42938	BA	WX05SVD
42922	HH	EU05AUO	42928	HH	SN05EAG	42934	CM	SN05DZP	42939	BA	WX05SVE
42923	HH	EU05AUP	42929	YA	SN05EAJ						

42940-42969   ADL Dart 10.7m   ADL Pointer   N37F   2006

42940	TE	MX56HXZ	42948	MS	WA56FTY	42956	MS	WX06OMO	42963	MS	WX06OMW
42941	TE	WA56OAO	42949	LH	WX06OMF	42957	LH	WX06OMP	42964	MS	WX06OMY
42942	CE	WA56OAP	42950	LH	WX06OMG	42958	LH	WX06OMR	42965	MS	WX06OMZ
42943	CE	WA56OAS	42951	MS	WX06OMH	42959	LH	WX06OMS	42966	MS	WX06ONA
42944	TE	WA56OAU	42952	MS	WX06OMJ	42960	MS	WX06OMT	42967	MS	WX06ONB
42945	TE	WA56OAV	42953	MS	WX06OMK	42961	LH	WX06OMV	42968	BA	WX06ONC
42946	PL	WA56FTV	42954	MS	WX06OML	42962	MS	WX06OMU	42969	MS	WA56FTZ
42947	MS	WA56FTX	42955	MS	WX06OMM						

43356-43360 Dennis Dart SLF 8.8m Plaxton Pointer MPD N29F 1999

43356	CM	V356DVG	**43357**	HH	V357DVG	**43359**	HH	V359DVG	**43360**	CM	V360DVG

43448	BR	P448NEX	Dennis Dart SLF 10.7m	Plaxton Pointer	N40F	1997
43466	LO	R466CAH	Dennis Dart SLF 10.7m	Plaxton Pointer 2	N37F	1998
43474	BR	R474CAH	Dennis Dart SLF 10.7m	Plaxton Pointer 2	N37F	1998

43480-43489 Dennis Dart SLF 10.7m Plaxton Pointer 2 N34F 1998

43480	BR	R680DPW	**43483**	BR	R683DPW	**43488**	lPu	R688DPW	**43489**	LO	R689DPW
43481	LO	R681DPW	**43485**	BR	R685DPW						

43584	RA	R584SWN	Dennis Dart SLF 9m	Plaxton Pointer 2	N29F	1998	
43677	LLu	R677MEW	Dennis Dart SLF 9.3m	Marshall Capital	N31F	1998	
43679	BR	R679MEW	Dennis Dart SLF 9.3m	Marshall Capital	N31F	1998	
43680	LL	R680MEW	Dennis Dart SLF 9.3m	Marshall Capital	N31F	1998	
43681	YA	EG52FJG	Dennis Dart SLF 9m	Caetano Nimbus	N29F	2002	Connex Jersey, 2013

43712-43721 Dennis Dart SLF 10.7m Plaxton Pointer 2 N37F 1998

43712	HH	R712DJN	**43714**	HH	R714DJN	**43717**	HH	R717DJN	**43720**	HH	R720DJN
43713	CN	R713DJN	**43715**	HH	R715DJN	**43719**	HH	R719DJN	**43721**	HH	R721DJN

43729-43738 Dennis Dart SLF 10.7m Plaxton Pointer 2 N37F 1998

43729	HH	S729TWC	**43732**	HH	S732TWC	**43734**	HH	S734TWC	**43736**	HH	S737TWC
43731	HH	S731TWC	**43733**	HH	S733TWC	**43735**	HH	S735TWC	**43738**	HH	S738TWC

43741	CN	V741GPU	Dennis Dart SLF 10.7m	Alexander ALX200	N37F	1999	
43742	CN	V742GPU	Dennis Dart SLF 10.7m	Alexander ALX200	N37F	1999	
43743	CNw	V743GPU	Dennis Dart SLF 10.7m	Alexander ALX200	N37F	1999	
43801	CM	AO02ODM	Dennis Dart SLF 8.8m	Plaxton Pointer MPD	N29F	2002	
43802	CM	AO02ODN	Dennis Dart SLF 8.8m	Plaxton Pointer MPD	N29F	2002	
43809	PL	S549SCV	Dennis Dart SLF 8.8m	Plaxton Pointer MPD	N29F	1998	Truronian, 2008
43810	PL	KU52RXJ	TransBus Dart SLF 8.8m	TransBus Mini Pointer	N29F	2003	Truronian, 2008
43811	TN	WK52WTV	TransBus Dart SLF 8.8m	TransBus Mini Pointer	N29F	2003	
43812	CE	T12TRU	Dennis Dart SLF 8.8m	Plaxton Pointer MPD	N26F	1999	Truronian, 2008
43821	TN	X201HAE	Dennis Dart SLF 8.8m	Plaxton Pointer MPD	N29F	2000	
43822	TN	X202HAE	Dennis Dart SLF 8.8m	Plaxton Pointer MPD	N29F	2000	
43823	TN	X203HAE	Dennis Dart SLF 8.8m	Plaxton Pointer MPD	N29F	2000	
43833	LTu	W933JNF	Dennis Dart SLF 8.8m	Plaxton Pointer MPD	N26F	2000	
43834	LT	W934JNF	Dennis Dart SLF 8.8m	Plaxton Pointer MPD	N26F	2000	

43836-43841 TransBus Dart 8.8m TransBus Mini Pointer N26F 2003

43836	LL	SN53ESV	**43838**	LL	SN53ESY	**43840**	LL	SN53ETE	**43841**	LL	SN53ETF
43837	LL	SN53ESU	**43839**	LL	SN53ETD						

43842	LT	SN04EFX	TransBus Dart 8.8m	TransBus Mini Pointer	N29F	2004
43844	LT	SN04EFZ	TransBus Dart 8.8m	TransBus Mini Pointer	N29F	2004

43845-43849 ADL Dart 8.8m ADL Mini Pointer N29F 2005

43845	BS	SN55CXH	**43847**	BS	SN55CXJ	**43848**	BS	SN55CXE	**43849**	BA	SN05HEJ
43846	BS	SN55CXF									

43850-43853 ADL Dart 8.9m ADL Mini Pointer N29F 2006 Truronian, 2008

43850	PT	WK06AEE	**43851**	PT	WK06AEF	**43852**	PT	WK06AFU	**43853**	PT	WK06AFV

43854-43874 Dennis Dart 8.8m Caetano Nimbus N29F 2002 Connex, Jersey, 2013

43854	CN	EG52FFZ	**43860**	YA	EG52FGF	**43865**	LO	EG52FGU	**43870**	WR	EG52FFT
43855	CN	EG52FGC	**43861**	YA	EG52FGJ	**43866**	LO	EG52FGV	**43871**	WR	EG52FFV
43856	CN	EG52FGD	**43862**	YA	EG52FGK	**43867**	LO	EG52FHC	**43872**	WR	EG52FFU
43857	CN	EG52FGE	**43863**	YA	EG52FFK	**43868**	LO	EG52FGX	**43873**	WR	EG52FFJ
43859	YA	EG52FHD	**43864**	YA	EG52FGA	**43869**	WR	EG52FFL	**43874**	WR	EG52FFY

43875	NE	MX56MYO	ADL Dart 8.9m	ADL Pointer MPD	N29F	2006	Centrebus, 2013
43876	NE	MX56MYP	ADL Dart 8.8m	ADL Pointer MPD	N29F	2006	Centrebus, 2013
43877	NE	EU06KDK	ADL Dart 8.8m	Caetano Nimbus	N28F	2006	Poppletons, 2013
43901	LL	SN03LGG	TransBus Dart 11.3m	TransBus Super Pointer	N41F	2003	
43902	LL	SN03LGJ	TransBus Dart 11.3m	TransBus Super Pointer	N41F	2003	
43903	LL	SN03LGK	TransBus Dart 11.3m	TransBus Super Pointer	N41F	2003	

Allocated to Southampton, 44528, SN62AYZ, is an Alexander Dennis Enviro 200, and one of fourteen allocated to that city. *Mark Lyons*

44001-44006
ADL Dart 4 10.2m ADL Enviro 200 N32F 2008

44001	HH	LK57EJD	44003	HH	LK57EJF	44005	HH	LK57EJJ	44006	HH	LK57EJL
44002	HH	LK57EJE	44004	HH	LK57EJG						

44076-44081
ADL Dart 4 10.2m ADL Enviro 200 N32F 2009

44076	HH	YX58HVF	44078	HH	YX58HVH	44080	HH	YX58HVK	44081	HH	YX58HVL
44077	HH	YX58HVG	44079	HH	YX58HVJ						

44500	RA	WK56ABZ	ADL Dart 4 10.8m	ADL Enviro200	N38F	2006	Truronian, 2008

44501-44506
ADL Dart 4 10.8m ADL Enviro 200 N35F 2008

44501	RA	CU08ACY	44503	WH	CU08ADO	44505	WH	CU08ADX	44506	WH	CU08ADZ
44502	WH	CU08ACZ	44504	WH	CU08ADV						

44507-44510
ADL Dart 4 10.8m ADL Enviro 200 N36F 2009

44507	SO	YX58HWF	44508	SO	YX58HWG	44509	SO	YX58HWH	44510	SO	YX58HWJ

44511-44514
ADL Dart 4 10.8m ADL Enviro 200 N36F 2007 Lee, Holywell, 2012

44511	WR	DK57SPZ	44512	WR	DK57SXF	44513	LO	DK57SXG	44514	WR	MX07OZD

44515	WR	MX10DXU	ADL Dart 4 10.8m	ADL Enviro200	N36F	2010	Premiere, Nottingham, 2013

44516-44519
ADL Dart 4 10.8m ADL Enviro 200 N28F 2009

44516	CN	YX09ACV	44517	CN	YX09ACY	44518	CN	YX09ACZ	44519	CN	YX09ADO

44520-44526
ADL E20D 10.8m ADL Enviro 200 N33F 2012

44520	BA	YX62DVM	44522	BA	YX62DWM	44524	BA	YX62DXC	44526	BA	YX62DXH
44521	BA	YX62DWG	44523	BA	YX62DWO	44525	BA	YX62DXF			

44527-44536
ADL E20D 10.8m ADL Enviro 200 N39F 2012

44527	SO	SN62AYV	44530	SO	SN62AZB	44533	SO	SN62DBV	44535	SO	SN62DCY
44528	SO	SN62AYZ	44531	SO	SN62AZW	44534	SO	SN62DCX	44536	SO	SN62DCZ
44529	SO	SN62AZA	44532	SO	SN62DBO						

44537-44559
ADL E20D 10.8m ADL Enviro 200 N39F 2013 *42552-9 are N33F

44537	CM	YX13AEF	44543	CM	YX13AHZ	44549	CM	YX13AKO	44555	RA	YX13AEZ
44538	CM	YX13AHN	44544	CM	YX13AKF	44550	CM	YX13AKP	44556	RA	YX13AFA
44539	CM	YX13AHO	44545	CM	YX13AKG	44551	CM	YX13AKY	44557	RA	YX13AFE
44540	CM	YX13AHP	44546	CM	YX13AKJ	44552	RA	YX13AEV	44558	RA	YX13AKU
44541	CM	YX13AHU	44547	CM	YX13AKK	44553	RA	YX13AEW	44559	RA	YX13AKV
44542	CM	YX13AHV	44548	CM	YX13AKN	44554	RA	YX13AEY			

44560-44570 ADL E20D 10.8m ADL Enviro 200 N33F 2013

44560	SH	YX63LKV	44563	SH	YX63LLC	44566	SH	YX63LLF	44569	BG	YX63LKR
44561	SH	YX63LKY	44564	SH	YX63LLD	44567	SH	YX63LLG	44570	PT	YX63LKU
44562	SH	YX63LKZ	44565	SH	YX63LLE	44568	SH	YX63LLJ			

44573-44581 ADL E20D 9.6m ADL Enviro 200 N31F 2013

44573	RA	YX13BNA	44576	RA	YX13BNE	44578	RA	YX13BNJ	44580	RA	YX13BNL
44574	RA	YX13BNB	44577	RA	YX13BNF	44579	RA	YX13BNK	44581	RA	YX13BNN
44575	RA	YX13BND									

44582-44595 ADL E20D 10.8m ADL Enviro 200 N39F 2013-14

44582	PT	YX63ZUD	44585	PT	YX63ZVC	44588	PT	YX63ZVF	44591	BG	YX63LHK
44583	PT	YX63ZVA	44586	PT	YX63ZVD	44589	PT	YX63ZVG	44592	BG	YX63LHL
44584	PT	YX63ZVB	44587	PT	YX63ZVE	44590	BG	YX63ZVH	44593	BG	YX63LHM

44596	CN	EU60LFS	ADL Dart 4 10.8m	ADL Enviro200	N37F	2010	Connex, Jersey, 2013
44597	CN	FJ58YSL	ADL Dart 4 10.8m	ADL Enviro200	N36F	2008	Premiere, Nottingham, 2013
44598	CN	KX57BWF	ADL Dart 4 10.8m	ADL Enviro200	N37F	2008	Townlynx, Holywell, 2013
44599	CN	YX08HJF	ADL Dart 4 10.8m	ADL Enviro200	N37F	2008	Arriva Yorkshire, 2013

44600-44636 ADL E20D 10.8m ADL Enviro 200 N33F 2014

44600	RA	-	44610	RA	-	44619	RA	-	44628	RA	-
44601	RA	-	44611	RA	-	44620	RA	-	44629	RA	-
44602	RA	-	44612	RA	-	44621	RA	-	44630	RA	-
44603	RA	YX14RUO	44613	RA	-	44622	RA	-	44631	RA	-
44604	RA	-	44614	RA	-	44623	RA	-	44632	RA	-
44605	RA	YX14RUU	44615	RA	-	44624	RA	-	44633	RA	-
44606	RA	-	44616	RA	-	44625	RA	-	44634	RA	-
44607	RA	-	44617	RA	-	44626	RA	-	44635	RA	-
44608	RA	-	44618	RA	-	44627	RA	-	44636	RA	-
44609	RA	-									

44900	CM	AY08EKT	ADL Dart 4 10.8m	ADL Enviro200	N37F	2008	Carter, Chapel St Mary, 2013
44902	BA	WX08LNN	ADL Dart 4 8.9m	ADL Enviro 200	N29F	2008	*Operated for Wessex Water*
44903	BA	WX08LNO	ADL Dart 4 8.9m	ADL Enviro 200	N29F	2008	*Operated for Wessex Water*
44904	BA	WX08LNP	ADL Dart 4 8.9m	ADL Enviro 200	N29F	2008	*Operated for Wessex Water*

44905-44924 ADL Dart 4 8.9m ADL Enviro 200 N28F 2009

44905	WS	YX09AFN	44910	WS	YX09AFZ	44915	BA	YX09AHA	44920	BA	YX09AHG
44906	WS	YX09AFO	44911	WS	YX09AGO	44916	BA	YX09AHC	44921	BA	YX09ADU
44907	WS	YX09AFU	44912	WS	YX09AGU	44917	BA	YX09AHD	44922	TN	YX09ADV
44908	WS	YX09AFV	44913	BA	YX09AGV	44918	BA	YX09AHE	44923	TN	YX09ADZ
44909	WS	YX09AFY	44914	BA	YX09AGZ	44919	BA	YX09AHF	44924	TN	YX09AHK

44925	OG	YX11HNW	ADL Dart 4 8.9m	ADL Enviro 200	N29F	2011	
44926	OG	YX11HNY	ADL Dart 4 8.9m	ADL Enviro 200	N29F	2011	
44927	OG	YX11HNZ	ADL Dart 4 8.9m	ADL Enviro 200	N29F	2011	
44928	LO	EU08FHB	ADL Dart 4 8.9m	ADL Enviro 200	N28F	2008	Olympus, Harlow, 2012

45111-45115 ADL Dart 4 8.9m ADL Enviro 200 N28F 2008

45111	TN	YX58FRJ	45113	TN	YX58FRL	45114	TN	YX58FRN	45115	TN	YX58FRP
45112	TN	YX58FRK									

45116-45119 ADL Dart 4 8.9m ADL Enviro 200 N28F 2009 JP Travel, Middleton, 2012

45116	LO	VT09JPT	45117	LO	ST58JPT	45118	LO	ST09JPT	45119	LO	RT09JPT

46225	BAu	L225VHU	Dennis Dart 9.8m	Plaxton Pointer	B40F	1994
46235	CE	N235KAE	Dennis Dart 9.8m	Plaxton Pointer	B40F	1995
46239	BAu	N239KAE	Dennis Dart 9.8m	Plaxton Pointer	B40F	1995
46240	WSw	N240KAE	Dennis Dart 9.8m	Plaxton Pointer	B40F	1995
46244	MSw	N244LHT	Dennis Dart 9.8m	Plaxton Pointer	B40F	1995
46252	WSw	P252PAE	Dennis Dart 9.8m	Plaxton Pointer	B40F	1996
46259	BA	P259PAE	Dennis Dart SLF 10.2m	Plaxton Pointer	N39F	1996
46262	WS	P262PAE	Dennis Dart SLF 10.2m	Plaxton Pointer	N39F	1996
46264	MS	P264PAE	Dennis Dart SLF 10.2m	Plaxton Pointer	N39F	1996
46324	SO	N324ECR	Dennis Dart 9m	Plaxton Pointer	B35F	1995
46325	SO	N325ECR	Dennis Dart 9m	Plaxton Pointer	B35F	1995
46603	WS	L503VHU	Dennis Dart 9m	Plaxton Pointer	B35F	1993

46609-46647 Dennis Dart 9m — Plaxton Pointer — B35F — 1994-95

46609	WSw	M509DHU	**46620**	LHu	M520FFB	**46623**	MSw	M523FFB	**46647**	CE	N547HAE
46616	LHw	M516DHU					

46651	LHw	N551LHU	Dennis Dart 9m	Plaxton Pointer	B35F	1996
46653	LHw	N553LHU	Dennis Dart 9m	Plaxton Pointer	B35F	1996
46657	HGs	N557LHU	Dennis Dart 9m	Plaxton Pointer	B35F	1996
46727	WHu	P627CGM	Dennis Dart 9.8m	Plaxton Pointer	B37F	1996
46902	LHw	N802FLW	Dennis Dart 9m	Plaxton Pointer	B32F	1995
47015	HIw	N615DWY	Dennis Dart 10.7m	Plaxton Pointer	BC40F	1995

47405-47434 Wrightbus Streetlite DF — Wrightbus — N37F — 2013

47405	WH	SK63KLE	**47413**	HO	SK63KLU	**47421**	HI	SK63KMJ	**47428**	SO	SK63KMZ
47406	WH	SK63KLF	**47414**	HO	SK63KLV	**47422**	SO	SK63KMM	**47429**	SO	SK63KNA
47407	WH	SK63KLJ	**47415**	HO	SK63KLX	**47423**	SO	SK63KMO	**47430**	SO	SK63KNB
47408	WH	SK63KLL	**47416**	HO	SK63KLZ	**47424**	SO	SK63KMU	**47431**	HI	SK63KNC
47409	WH	SK63KLM	**47417**	HO	SK63KMA	**47425**	SO	SK63KMV	**47432**	HI	SK63KND
47410	WH	SK63KLO	**47418**	HO	SK63KME	**47426**	SO	SK63KMX	**47433**	HI	SK63KNE
47411	HO	SK63KLP	**47419**	HI	SK63KMF	**47427**	SO	SK63KMY	**47434**	HI	SK63KNF
47412	HO	SK63KLS	**47420**	HI	SK63KMG						

47435-47465 Wrightbus Streetlite DF — Wrightbus — N37F — 2013

47435	HG	SK63KNG	**47443**	HG	SK63KNR	**47451**	HG	SK63KKM	**47459**	HG	SK63KKW
47436	HG	SK63KNH	**47444**	HG	SK63KNS	**47452**	HG	SK63KKN	**47460**	HG	SK63KKX
47437	HG	SK63KNJ	**47445**	HG	SK63KNU	**47453**	HG	SK63KKO	**47461**	HG	SK63KKY
47438	HG	SK63KNL	**47446**	HG	SK63KNV	**47454**	HG	SK63KKP	**47462**	HG	SK63KKZ
47439	HG	SK63KNM	**47447**	HG	SK63KNX	**47455**	HG	SK63KKR	**47463**	HG	SK63KLA
47440	HG	SK63KNN	**47448**	HG	SK63KNY	**47456**	HG	SK63KKS	**47464**	HG	SK63KLC
47441	HG	SK63KNO	**47449**	HG	SK63KKJ	**47457**	HG	SK63KKU	**47465**	HG	SK63KLD
47442	HG	SK63KNP	**47450**	HG	SK63KKL	**47458**	HG	SK63KKV			

47466-47500 Wrightbus Streetlite DF — Wrightbus — N37F — 2014

47466	TE	-	**47475**	TE	-	**47484**	DN	-	**47493**	HU	-
47467	TE	-	**47476**	TE	-	**47485**	DN	-	**47494**	HU	-
47468	TE	-	**47477**	TE	-	**47486**	DN	-	**47495**	HU	-
47469	TE	-	**47478**	TE	-	**47487**	DN	-	**47496**	HU	-
47470	TE	-	**47479**	TE	-	**47488**	DN	-	**47497**	HU	-
47471	TE	-	**47480**	TE	-	**47489**	DN	-	**47498**	HU	-
47472	TE	-	**47481**	TE	-	**47490**	DN	-	**47499**	HU	-
47473	TE	-	**47482**	DN	-	**47491**	DN	-	**47500**	HU	-
47474	TE	-	**47483**	DN	-	**47492**	DN	-			

47501-47571 Wrightbus Streetlite DF — Wrightbus — N37F — 2014

47501	YA	-	**47517**	WR	-	**47533**	Scotland East		**47557**	BA	-
47502	YA	-	**47518**	WR	-	**47534**	Scotland East		**47558**	BA	-
47503	YA	-	**47519**	HH	-	**47544**	BA	-	**47559**	HG	-
47504	YA	-	**47520**	HH	-	**47545**	BA	-	**47560**	HG	-
47505	YA	-	**47521**	HH	-	**47546**	BA	-	**47561**	HG	-
47506	YA	-	**47522**	HH	-	**47547**	BA	-	**47562**	HG	-
47507	VN	-	**47523**	HH	-	**47548**	BA	-	**47563**	HG	-
47508	VN	-	**47524**	HH	-	**47549**	BA	-	**47564**	HG	-
47509	VN	-	**47525**	HH	-	**47550**	BA	-	**47565**	HG	-
47510	VN	-	**47526**	HH	-	**47551**	BA	-	**47566**	HG	-
47511	VN	-	**47527**	HH	-	**47552**	BA	-	**47567**	HG	-
47512	VN	-	**47528**	HH	-	**47553**	BA	-	**47568**	HG	-
47513	WR	-	**47529**	Scotland East		**47554**	BA	-	**47569**	HG	-
47514	WR	-	**47530**	Scotland East		**47555**	BA	-	**47570**	HG	-
47515	WR	-	**47531**	Scotland East		**47556**	BA	-	**47571**	HG	-
47516	WR	-	**47532**	Scotland East							

The Wrightbus Streetlite integral bus, a model launched in 2011, dominated the 2013 deliveries and feature strongly again in the 2014 order programme. First Hampshire & Dorset's 47427, SK63KMY, shows the styling as it heads for Southampton city centre. *Mark Lyons*

47573-47628

			Wrightbus Streetlite DF			Wrightbus			N37F	2014	
47573	HO	-	**47587**	HO	-	**47601**	SO	-	**47615**	Scotland East	
47574	HO	-	**47588**	HO	-	**47602**	SO	-	**47616**	Scotland East	
47575	HO	-	**47589**	HO	-	**47603**	SO	-	**47617**	Scotland East	
47576	HO	-	**47590**	HO	-	**47604**	SO	-	**47618**	PH	-
47577	HO	-	**47591**	HO	-	**47605**	SO	-	**47619**	PH	-
47578	HO	-	**47592**	HO	-	**47606**	SO	-	**47620**	PH	-
47579	HO	-	**47593**	HO	-	**47607**	SO	-	**47621**	PH	-
47580	HO	-	**47594**	HO	-	**47608**	SO	-	**47622**	PH	-
47581	HO	-	**47595**	SO	-	**47609**	SO	-	**47623**	PH	-
47582	HO	-	**47596**	SO	-	**47610**	SO	-	**47624**	PH	-
47583	HO	-	**47597**	SO	-	**47611**	SO	-	**47625**	PH	-
47584	HO	-	**47598**	SO	-	**47612**	SO	-	**47626**	PH	-
47585	HO	-	**47599**	SO	-	**47613**	Scotland East			**47627**	PH	-
47586	HO	-	**47600**	SO	-	**47614**	Scotland East			**47628**	PH	-

48045	LFs	N345CJA	Volvo B6 9.9m	Alexander Dash	B36F	1996
48201	PL	T801RHW	Volvo B6BLE	Wright Crusader 2	N36F	1999

48202-48210

			Volvo B6BLE			Wright Crusader 2			N36F	1999	
48202	WH	V802EFB	**48205**	WH	V805EFB	**48208**	WH	V808EFB	**48210**	HG	V810EFB
48204	WH	V804EFB	**48207**	WH	V807EFB	**48209**	WH	V809EFB			

48211-48234

			Volvo B6BLE			Wright Crusader 2			N36F	2000	
48211	HG	W811PFB	**48217**	HG	W817PFB	**48224**	HG	W824PFB	**48229**	PL	W829PFB
48212	HG	W812PFB	**48218**	HG	W818PFB	**48225**	PL	W825PFB	**48231**	PL	W831PFB
48213	HG	W813PFB	**48219**	HG	W819PFB	**48226**	PL	W826PFB	**48232**	PL	W832PFB
48214	HG	W814PFB	**48221**	HG	W821PFB	**48227**	PL	W827PFB	**48233**	PL	W833PFB
48215	HG	W815PFB	**48222**	HG	W822PFB	**48228**	PL	W828PFB	**48234**	PL	W834PFB
48216	HG	W816PFB	**48223**	HG	W823PFB						

48261-48269

			Volvo B6BLE			Wright Crusader 2			N37F	2000	
48261	PL	W601PAF	**48263**	PL	W603PAF	**48265**	PL	W605PAF	**48267**	PL	W607PAF
48262	PL	W602PAF	**48264**	PL	W604PAF	**48266**	PL	W606PAF	**48269**	PL	W609PAF

While thirty-seven Optare Versa hybrid buses are operated for Transport for Greater Manchester (TfGM) a few standard buses are operated in South Wales. Seen in Cardiff while heading for Porthcawl is one of Optare's vehicles on extended loan to First and YJ62FLD has been numbered 49300. Since the picture was taken the bus has moved on to Bath for further evaluation. *Dave Heath*

48270-48273

			Volvo B6BLE			Wrightbus Crusader 2		N38F	2002		
48270	WH	WK02TYD	48271	PL	WK02TYF	48272	WH	WK02TYH	48273	WH	YG02DLV

49002-49010

			Optare Versa V1080			Optare		N36F	2013		
49002	BG	YJ13HMD	49005	BG	YJ13HMG	49007	BG	YJ13HMK	49009	BG	YJ13HMV
49003	BG	YJ13HME	49006	BG	YJ13HMH	49008	BG	YJ13HMU	49010	BG	YJ13HMX
49004	BG	YJ13HMF									

49101-49119

			Optare Versa V1100 Hybrid			Optare		N27F	2010-12	*Operated for TfGM*	
49101	QS	YJ60KCU	49106	QS	YJ60KDF	49111	QS	YJ60KDV	49116	BN	YJ61JHU
49102	QS	YJ60KCV	49107	QS	YJ60KDK	49112	QS	YJ60KDX	49117	BN	YJ61JFU
49103	QS	YJ60KCX	49108	QS	YJ60KDN	49113	TE	YJ61JHK	49118	QS	YJ61JFV
49104	QS	YJ60KCY	49109	QS	YJ60KDO	49114	TE	YJ61JHL	49119	QS	YJ61JFX
49105	QS	YJ60KCZ	49110	QS	YJ60KDU	49115	TE	YJ61JHO			

49202-49222

			Optare Versa V1200 Hybrid			Optare		S57F	2012	*Operated for TfGM*	
49202	OM	YJ12MYF	49208	QS	YJ12MYN	49213	QS	YJ12MYT	49217	BN	YJ12MYX
49203	OM	YJ12MYG	49209	OM	YJ12MYO	49214	BN	YJ12MYU	49218	QS	YJ12MYY
49204	QS	YJ12MYH	49210	OM	YJ12MYP	49215	OM	YJ12MYV	49220	QS	YJ12MZD
49205	OM	YJ12MYK	49211	BN	YJ12MYR	49216	OM	YJ12MYW	49222	OM	YJ12MZF
49206	OM	YJ12MYL	49212	OM	YJ12MYS						

49227	BN	YJ12GXZ	Optare Versa V1200 Hybrid	Optare		S57F	2012	Maytree, Bolton, 2013
49228	BN	YJ12GXY	Optare Versa V1200 Hybrid	Optare		S57F	2012	Maytree, Bolton, 2013
49300	BA	YJ62FLD	Optare Versa V1170	Optare		NC43F	2013	*On loan from Optare*

49301-49309

			Optare Versa V1170			Optare		NC40F	2013		
49301	PT	YJ13HLR	49304	PT	YJ13HLW	49306	PT	YJ13HLY	49308	PT	YJ13HMA
49302	PT	YJ13HLU	49305	PT	YJ13HLX	49307	PT	YJ13HLZ	49309	PT	YJ13HMC
49303	PT	YJ13HLV									

49901-49912

			Optare Versa V1100 EV			Optare		NC36F	2014		
49901	YK	-	49904	YK	-	49907	YK	-	49910	YK	-
49902	YK	-	49905	YK	-	49908	YK	-	49911	YK	-
49903	YK	-	49906	YK	-	49909	YK	-	49912	YK	-

The 2014 First Bus Handbook

50019 AGsuV117DLH Iveco TurboDaily 40.10 Whittaker Suzzara M13 1999

50232-50239 Optare Solo M850 Optare N26F 2001-02

50232	DN	Y251HHL	**50234**	DN	Y253HHL	**50236**	DN	Y256HHL	**50238**	DN	YT51EZX
50233	DN	Y252HHL	**50235**	DN	Y254HHL	**50237**	DN	YT51EZW	**50239**	DN	YR02UVU

50270 WH S301EWU Optare Solo M850 Optare N27F 1998
50272 WH S303EWU Optare Solo M850 Optare N27F 1998
50275 GS S306EWU Optare Solo M850 Optare N27F 1998

50276-50296 Optare Solo M850 Optare N27F 2000

50276	CE	W307DWX	**50282**	HD	W313DWX	**50286**	BD	W317DWX	**50293**	WH	W324DWX
50277	HI	W308DWX	**50283**	LT	W314DWX	**50290**	BD	W331DWX	**50294**	BDw	W335DWX
50278	HI	W309DWX	**50284**	CE	W315DWX	**50291**	BD	W322DWX	**50295**	BD	W326DWX
50279	RA	W329DWX	**50285**	CE	W336DWX	**50292**	BD	W337DWX	**50296**	HD	W327DWX
50281	HD	W312DWX									

50318 BA YN53ELO Optare Solo M850 Optare N27F 2003
50319 HX YN53ELJ Optare Solo M850 Optare N27F 2003
50407 HX YN03ZVX Optare Solo M850 Optare N27F 2003

50460-50468 Optare Solo M850 Optare N27F 2003

50460	LT	SJ03DOH	**50463**	SN	SJ03DPN	**50465**	SN	SJ03DPV	**50467**	BW	SJ03DPY
50461	SN	SJ03DPE	**50464**	SN	SJ03DPU	**50466**	BW	SJ03DPX	**50468**	LT	SJ03DPZ
50462	SN	SJ03DPF									

51590 BWu N890HWS Mercedes-Benz 709D Plaxton Beaver B22F 1995
51685 BWu N583WND Mercedes-Benz 709D Plaxton Beaver B27F 1995 Epsom Coaches, 1998

52513-52560 Mercedes-Benz Vario O814 Plaxton Beaver 2 B22F 1998

52513	HI	S513RWP	**52533**	HI	S533RWP	**52554**	CE	S554RWP	**52559**	HIw	S559RWP
52517	HIw	S517RWP	**52540**	WH	S540RWP	**52558**	HI	S558RWP	**52560**	HI	S560RWP
52526	CE	S526RWP									

53001-53015 Optare Solo M850 Optare N27F 1999-2000

53001	BW	V801KAF	**53006**	HIw	W806PAF	**53009**	BW	W809PAF	**53013**	BW	W813PAF
53002	WH	V802KAF	**53007**	CE	W807PAF	**53011**	PL	W811PAF	**53014**	BW	W814PAF
53003	RA	V803KAF	**53008**	HO	W808PAF	**53012**	WH	W812PAF	**53015**	CE	W815PAF
53005	RA	W805PAF									

53028 WH W338DWX Optare Solo M850 Optare N27F 2000
53034 DN Y546XNW Optare Solo M850 Optare N29F 2001 Clarkson, S Emsall, 2003
53035 DN Y547XNW Optare Solo M850 Optare N29F 2001 Clarkson, S Emsall, 2003

53040-53051 Optare Solo M850 Optare N22F 2002-03

53040	HD	VU02PKX	**53043**	WR	VU03YJV	**53046**	WR	VU03YJY	**53049**	WR	VU03YKC
53041	HD	VU02PKY	**53044**	WR	VU03YJW	**53047**	WR	VU03YJZ	**53050**	WR	VU03YKD
53042	HD	VU03YJT	**53045**	WR	VU03YJX	**53048**	WR	VU03YKB	**53051**	WR	VU03YKE

53052-53057 Optare Solo M850 Optare N22F 2004

53052	SH	LK53MBX	**53055**	SH	LK53MDF	**53056**	SH	LK53MDJ	**53057**	SH	LK53PNO
53054	SH	LK53MDE									

53058-53064 Optare Solo M850 Optare N22F 2004

53058	HD	VX53OEV	**53060**	WR	VX53OEO	**53062**	WR	VX53OER	**53064**	HD	VX53OEU
53059	HD	VX53OEN	**53061**	WR	VX53OEP	**53063**	WR	VX53OET			

53065 BL YJ58CEV Optare Solo M850 Optare N28F 2008

53101-53111 Optare Solo M850 Optare N26F 2002

53101	BD	EO02FLA	**53104**	BD	EO02FLD	**53108**	CE	EO02FLH	**53110**	PL	EO02FLK
53102	BA	EO02FLB	**53107**	CE	EO02FLG	**53109**	PL	EO02FLJ	**53111**	PL	EO02FKZ
53103	BA	EO02FLC									

The Optare Solo currently dominates First's minibus fleet and is typified by 53207, CN07KZK, one of three Slimline M950s acquired from Veolia Transportation in 2012 and now allocated to the Potteries.
John Birtwistle

53112-53137

							Optare Solo M920			Optare		N30F	2002	
53112	CM	EO02NDX	53119	VN	EO02NEY	53126	CM	EO02NFH	53132	CM	EO02NFP
53113	CM	EO02NDY	53120	VN	EO02NFA	53127	CM	EO02NFJ	53133	CM	EO02NFR
53114	CM	EO02NDZ	53121	CM	EO02NFC	53128	CM	EO02NFK	53134	CM	EO02NFT
53115	CM	EO02NEF	53122	VN	EO02NFD	53129	CM	EO02NFL	53135	CM	EO02NFU
53116	CM	EO02NEJ	53123	VN	EO02NFE	53130	CM	EO02NFM	53136	CM	EO02NFV
53117	CM	EO02NEN	53124	VN	EO02NFF	53131	CM	EO02NFN	53137	CM	EO02NFX
53118	VN	EO02NEU	53125	CM	EO02NFG						

53138	CM	EU54BNK	Optare Solo M920	Optare	N33F	2004	
53139	CM	EU54BNJ	Optare Solo M920	Optare	N33F	2004	
53140	HI	YJ05XOP	Optare Solo M920	Optare	N33F	2005	

53143-53150

							Optare Solo M920			Optare		N30F	2004	
53143	TE	MX54GZA	53145	TE	MX54GZC	53147	TE	MX54GZE	53149	TE	MX54GZG
53144	TE	MX54GZB	53146	TE	MX54GZD	53148	TE	MX54GZF	53150	TE	MX54GZH

53151	HI	YN03ZVW	Optare Solo M850	Optare	N27F	2003	
53154	PL	HIG8433	Optare Solo M920	Optare	N29F	2005	Truronian, 2008
53155	AG	CN06BXH	Optare Solo M920	Optare	N31F	2006	Veolia, 2012
53201	SN	YJ54BSV	Optare Solo M950	Optare	N30F	2004	
53202	SN	SF05KUJ	Optare Solo M950	Optare	N28F	2005	
53203	SN	SF05KUK	Optare Solo M950	Optare	N28F	2005	
53204	BA	TU04TRU	Optare Solo M950	Optare	N33F	2004	Truronian, 2008
53205	PL	HIG8434	Optare Solo M950	Optare	N33F	2005	Truronian, 2008
53206	HI	T77TRU	Optare Solo M950	Optare	N33F	2004	Truronian, 2008
53207	AG	CN07KZK	Optare Solo M950 SL	Optare	N29F	2007	Veolia, 2012
53208	AG	CN07KZL	Optare Solo M950 SL	Optare	N29F	2007	Veolia, 2012
53209	AG	CN07KZM	Optare Solo M950 SL	Optare	N29F	2007	Veolia, 2012
53301	HX	YJ54BVA	Optare Solo M1020	Optare	N34F	2004	Addison, Steeton, 2013
53302	HX	YJ54BVB	Optare Solo M1020	Optare	N34F	2004	Addison, Steeton, 2013
53303	HX	YJ54BVC	Optare Solo M1020	Optare	N34F	2004	Addison, Steeton, 2013

53401-53404

							Optare Solo M880			Optare		N29F	2004	53403/4 operated for Cornwall
53401	WS	TO54TRU	53402	CE	T20TVL	53403	CE	TL54TVL	53404	CE	TT54TVL

53405	AG	VX57CYO	Optare Solo M880 SL	Optare	N28F	2007	Veolia, 2012

53501-53515

							Optare Solo M880 SR			Optare		N28F	2014	
53501	HO	-	53505	HO	-	53509	HO	-	53513	WH	-
53502	HO	-	53506	HO	-	53510	WH	-	53514	WH	-
53503	HO	-	53507	WH	-	53511	WH	-	53515	WH	-
53504	HO	-	53508	HO	-	53512	WH	-			

East Scotland's 53706, LK05DXU, is one of the shorter 7.8 metre variants of the Optare Solo which seats just twenty-one passengers. Seen just south of Loch Lomond, it is heading from Balfron to Balloch during March 2013. *Bill Potter*

53701-53706

		Optare Solo M780 SL				Optare		N21F	2005	
53701	CM	LK05DYO	53703	LT	LK05DXR	53705	BF	LK05DXT	53706	LT	LK05DXU
53702	LT	LK05DXP	53704	BF	LK05DXS					

53707	LL	MX58KZA	Optare Solo M780 SL	Optare	N23F	2008	*Operated for Carmarthenshire CC*
53708	LL	MX58KZB	Optare Solo M780 SL	Optare	N23F	2008	*Operated for Carmarthenshire CC*
53801	CE	YK04KWR	Optare Solo M850 SL	Optare	N22F	2004	

53802-53820

		Optare Solo M850 SL				Optare		N26F	2005
53802	LL	WX05RRV	53807	BA	WX05RSV	53812	BA	WX05RTV	53817	BA	WX05RUO
53803	CE	WX05RRY	53808	BA	WX05RSY	53813	BA	WX05RTZ	53818	BA	WX05RUR
53804	RA	WX05RRZ	53809	BA	WX05RSZ	53814	BA	WX05RUA	53819	BA	WX05RUU
53805	BA	WX05RSO	53810	BA	WX05RTO	53815	BA	WX05RUC	53820	BA	WX05RUV
53806	BA	WX05RSU	53811	BA	WX05RTU	53816	BA	WX05RUJ			

53826	CE	YK05CDN	Optare Solo M780 SL	Optare	N24F	2005	Truronian, 2008
53827	PL	YK05CDO	Optare Solo M780 SL	Optare	N26F	2005	Truronian, 2008
53828	AG	MX56NLJ	Optare Solo M850 SL	Optare	N28F	2006	Veolia, 2012
53829	AG	MX56NLK	Optare Solo M850 SL	Optare	N28F	2006	Veolia, 2012
53830	AG	CN06BXF	Optare Solo M850 SL	Optare	N27F	2006	Veolia, 2012

53904-53912

		Optare Solo M920 SL				Optare		N32F	2005-08	*Operated for Metro, WYPTE*
53904	HP	YJ55ENR	53906	HP	YJ55ENN	53909	HP	YJ07EHR	53911	BD	YJ58CDX
53905	HP	YJ55ENM	53907	HP	YJ07EHO	53910	BD	YJ58CDV	53912	BD	YJ58CDY

54302	B	YX10AXP	Volkswagen Transporter	Bluebird Tucana	N14F	2010	*Operated for Strathclyde PT*
54304	B	YX10AYL	Volkswagen Transporter	Bluebird Tucana	N14F	2010	*Operated for Strathclyde PT*
54307	B	YX10AXT	Volkswagen Transporter	Bluebird Tucana	N14F	2010	*Operated for Strathclyde PT*
54401	O	YX12CHK	Fiat Ducato	Bluebird Orion	N14F	2012	*Operated for Strathclyde PT*
54402	O	YX12CHL	Fiat Ducato	Bluebird Orion	N16F	2012	*Operated for Strathclyde PT*
54403	B	YX12CHO	Fiat Ducato	Bluebird Orion	N16F	2012	*Operated for Strathclyde PT*
54404	LF	YX12CJF	Fiat Ducato	Bluebird Orion	N16F	2012	*Operated for Strathclyde PT*
54405	LF	YX12CJJ	Fiat Ducato	Bluebird Orion	N16F	2012	*Operated for Strathclyde PT*
54406	LF	YX12CJO	Fiat Ducato	Bluebird Orion	N16F	2012	*Operated for Strathclyde PT*
54407	LF	YX12CJU	Fiat Ducato	Bluebird Orion	N16F	2012	*Operated for Strathclyde PT*
54601	HGs	RA04YGX	Ford Transit	Ford	M16	2004	Truronian, 2008
54602	CE	RA04YHS	Ford Transit	Ford	M16	2004	Truronian, 2008

Queen's Road depot in Cheetham Hill operates the free shuttle Transport for Greater Manchester service in the city centre that links Piccadilly and Victoria rail stations. Seen on the route is 59008, YJ60KCO, a hybrid Optare M820 SR. *Richard Godfrey*

56000	CE	W4TRU	Mercedes-Benz Vario O814	Plaxton Cheetah	C27F	2000	Truronian, 2008	
56001	AB	YN53VBT	Mercedes-Benz Vario O814	Plaxton Cheetah	C29F	2003		
56002	MU	YN53VBU	Mercedes-Benz Vario O814	Plaxton Cheetah	C29F	2003		
56003	GS	YN53VBV	Mercedes-Benz Vario O814	Plaxton Cheetah	C29F	2003		
56004	MU	EY54BPX	Mercedes-Benz Vario O814	Plaxton Cheetah	C29F	2004		
56005	AB	EY54BPZ	Mercedes-Benz Vario O814	Plaxton Cheetah	C29F	2004		
56006	AB	EY54BRF	Mercedes-Benz Vario O814	Plaxton Cheetah	C29F	2004		
56007	AB	EY54BRV	Mercedes-Benz Vario O814	Plaxton Cheetah	C29F	2004		
56008	AB	EY54BRX	Mercedes-Benz Vario O814	Plaxton Cheetah	C29F	2004		
56009	AB	EY54BRZ	Mercedes-Benz Vario O814	Plaxton Cheetah	C29F	2004		
56501	AB	YX05AVV	Mercedes-Benz Atego O1120L	Optare/Ferqui Solera	C28F	2005		
57000	BA	MX06AEB	Enterprise Plasma EB01	Plaxton Primo	N28F	2006	Truronian, 2008	
57001	LT	YN56NHE	Enterprise Plasma EB01	Plaxton Primo	N28F	2006		
57002	LT	YN56NHF	Enterprise Plasma EB01	Plaxton Primo	N28F	2006		

59001-59008			Optare Solo M820 SR Hybrid	Optare		N23F	2010	*Operated for TfGM*	
59001	QS	YJ60KCA	**59003**	QS	YJ60KCE	**59005**	QS	YJ60KCG	**59007** QS YJ60KCN
59002	QS	YJ60KCC	**59004**	QS	YJ60KCF	**59006**	QS	YJ60KCK	**59008** QS YJ60KCO

59009-59016			Optare Solo M820 SR Hybrid	Optare		N28F	2012	*Operated for TfGM*	
59009	TE	YJ61JDO	**59011**	TE	YJ61JDX	**59013**	QS	YJ61JEO	**59015** TE YJ61JFA
59010	TE	YJ61JDU	**59012**	QS	YJ61JDZ	**59014**	TE	YJ61JEU	**59016** TE YJ61JFE

59100	WSu	YJ62FAM	Optare Solo M950 SR	Optare	N29F	2013	*On loan from Optare*

60004-60012			Scania L113CRL	Wright Axcess-ultralow	N40F	1998		
60004	AG	S356MFP	**60006**	AG	S350MFP	**60011**	AG	R346SUT	**60012** AG S348MFP

60013	NE	S103TNB	Scania L94UB	Wright Axcess Floline	N40F	1998
60015	NE	S106TNB	Scania L94UB	Wright Axcess Floline	N40F	1998

The 2014 First Bus Handbook

Seen leaving Hanley on a short working of route 20 to Alsager is Scania L94UB 60193, V141DND. The Wrightbus Axcess Floline was the low-floor single-deck body built on this chassis between 1998 and 2001, being superseded by the similar looking Axcess-ultralow that was built on Scania's L113CRL chassis. *Mark Bailey*

60057-60063

		Scania L113CRL			Wright Axcess-ultralow		N40F	1998	
60057	AG	S815AEH	60059	AG	S817AEH	60061	AG	S819AEH	60063	AG	S821AEH
60058	AG	S816AEH	60060	AG	S818AEH	60062	AG	S820AEH			

60065-60074

		Scania L94UB			Wright Axcess Floline		N43F*	1999	*60065/6 are N37F
60065	BM	T823SFS	60067	HP	T825SFS	60069	NE	T827SFS	60073	AG	V831GBF
60066	BM	T824SFS	60068	NE	T826SFS	60072	NE	V830GBF	60074	NE	V832GBF

60075-60079

		Scania L113CRL			Wright Axcess-ultralow		N49F	1998	
60075	AG	R438ALS	60076	BNu	R439ALS	60078	AG	R441ALS	60079	AG	R442ALS

60081	NE	S101TNB	Scania L94UB	Wright Axcess Floline	N40F	1998
60083	AG	S353MFP	Scania L113CRL	Wright Axcess-ultralow	N40F	1998
60112	BNu	R878ERE	Scania L113CRL	Wright Axcess-ultralow	N51F	1998
60113	BM	R879HRF	Scania L113CRL	Wright Axcess-ultralow	N40F	1998
60115	BNu	R881HRF	Scania L113CRL	Wright Axcess-ultralow	N40F	1998
60128	NE	S105TNB	Scania L94UB	Wright Axcess Floline	N40F	1998
60131	BM	R178GSX	Scania L113CRL	Wright Axcess-ultralow	N40F	1997
60133	BM	N414ENW	Scania L113CRL	Wright Axcess-ultralow	N48F	1996
60135	NEt	R177GSX	Scania L113CRL	Wright Axcess-ultralow	tv	1998
60136	AG	R179GSX	Scania L113CRL	Wright Axcess-ultralow	N40F	1998

60161-60168

		Scania L94UB			Wright Axcess Floline		N40F	1998	
60161	BNu	S108TNB	60165	BK	S112TNB	60167	LT	S114TNB	60168	BK	S115TNB
60163	BK	S110TNB	60166	BK	S113TNB						

60170-60194

		Scania L94UB			Wright Axcess Floline		N42F*	1999-2000	*60170-172 are N40F
60170	NE	T917SSF	60175	AG	V330DBU	60182	LT	V130DND	60189	NE	V137DND
60171	AG	T918SSF	60176	AG	V124DND	60184	BNu	V132DND	60192	BK	V140DND
60172	HP	T919SSF	60178	BK	V126DND	60187	LT	V135DND	60193	NE	V141DND
60173	AG	V142DND	60180	BK	V128DND	60188	LTt	V136DND	60194	NEu	W142PSH
60174	AG	V122DND	60181	LVt	V129DND						

Now a training bus at Livingston, Scania 60204, X272USH was pictured while operating route 38 which links Falkirk to Stirling. *Mark Doggett*

60195-60214

Scania L94UB   Wright Axcess Floline   N43F   2001

60195	LT	Y343XBN	**60199**	LT	X256USH	**60204**	LVt	X272USH	**60212**	HP	Y633RTD
60196	NE	X253USH	**60201**	NE	X257USH	**60205**	NE	X261USH	**60213**	BM	X269USH
60197	BK	Y597KNE	**60202**	NE	Y346XBN	**60206**	CO	Y598KNE	**60214**	BM	Y634RTD
60198	LT	Y344XBN	**60203**	BK	Y632RTD	**60208**	NEu	Y347XBN			

60215-60222

Scania L94UB   Wright Axcess Floline   N40F   1998-99

60215	NE	S561JSE	**60220**	BK	T566BSS	**60221**	BK	T567BSS	**60222**	HP	S560JSE
60217	HP	T563BSS									

60223-60282

Mercedes-Benz O530 Citaro   Mercedes-Benz   N38F   2000

60223	OM	W301JND	**60239**	BY	W317JND	**60254**	BY	W332RJA	**60270**	BY	W348RJA
60224	OM	W302JND	**60240**	OM	W338JND	**60255**	BY	W363RJA	**60271**	BY	W349RJA
60225	OM	W303JND	**60241**	BY	W319JND	**60256**	BY	W334RJA	**60272**	BY	W362RJA
60226	OM	W304JND	**60242**	BY	W337JND	**60257**	BY	W335RJA	**60273**	BY	W351RJA
60227	OM	W335JND	**60243**	BY	W341JND	**60258**	BY	W336RJA	**60274**	BY	W352RJA
60228	OM	W336JND	**60244**	OM	W322JND	**60259**	BY	W337RJA	**60275**	BY	W353RJA
60229	OM	W307JND	**60245**	BY	W339JND	**60260**	BY	W338RJA	**60276**	BY	W354RJA
60230	OM	W308JND	**60247**	BY	W378JNE	**60261**	BY	W339RJA	**60277**	BY	W366RJA
60233	BY	W311JND	**60248**	OM	W326JND	**60262**	BY	W361RJA	**60278**	BY	W356RJA
60234	OM	W312JND	**60249**	BY	W327JND	**60264**	BY	W342RJA	**60279**	BY	W357RJA
60235	BY	W313JND	**60250**	BY	W379JNE	**60267**	BY	W365RJA	**60280**	BY	W358RJA
60236	OM	W314JND	**60251**	BY	W329JND	**60268**	BY	W346RJA	**60281**	BYu	W359RJA
60237	BY	W315JND	**60252**	BY	W331JND	**60269**	BY	W347RJA	**60282**	BY	W364RJA
60238	BY	W334JND	**60253**	BY	W331RJA						

60283	BY	W179BVP	Mercedes-Benz O530 Citaro	Mercedes-Benz	N38F	2000 Evobus demonstrator, 2001

60299-60340

Volvo B10B   Wright Endurance   tv   1994-96

60299	HOt	M504PNA	**60304**	CMt	M509PNA	**60311**	WRt	M516PNA	**60322**	BNt	N527WVR
60301	BYt	M506PNA	**60305**	CMt	M510PNA	**60316**	AGt	M521WVR	**60337**	HOt	N542WVR
60302	BNt	M507PNA	**60308**	BNt	M513PNA	**60317**	AGt	N522WVR	**60340**	WRt	N545WVR
60303	OMt	M508PNA									

60361-60373

Volvo B10BLE   Wright Renown   N41F   1997

60361	ROt	R571YNC	**60367**	ROu	R577SBA	**60369**	QS	R579SBA	**60371**	QS	R581SBA
60366	ROu	R576SBA	**60368**	ROt	R578SBA	**60370**	QS	R580SBA	**60373**	QS	R583SBA

60374	LEt	J461OVU	Volvo B10M-50	Northern Counties Paladin	tv	1991

Split between Bury and Oldham is the batch of sixty Mercedes-Benz O530 Citaro buses supplied in 2000. Representing them is 60234, W312JND, an example in the new livery as it works route 149 in Manchester.
Richard Godfrey

60376-60386

		Volvo B10BLE			Wright Renown		N41F	1998	
60376	QS	R621CVR	60379	QS	R624CVR	60381	QS	R626CVR	60386 QS R631CVR
60377	QS	R622CVR	60380	QS	R625CVR	60385	QS	R630CVR	

60405	QS	X699ADK	Volvo B10BLE		Wright Renown	N41F	2000	
60406	DN	Y774TNC	Volvo B7L		Wrightbus Eclipse	N41F	2001	

60457-60487

		Volvo B10M-55			Alexander PS		tv	1990	
60457	ROt	G602NWA	60464	LFt	G609NWA	60468	BMt	G623NWA	60474 HGtu G629NWA
60458	ROt	G603NWA	60466	LFt	G613NWA	60472	BMt	G627NWA	60486 HUt G641NWA
60460	LEt	G605NWA	60467	BMt	G622NWA	60473	RAtu	G628NWA	60487 ROt H642RKU

60600	BAt	N763CKY	Volvo B10M-55		Alexander PS	tv	1996

60618-60627

		Volvo B10BLE			Wright Renown		N44F	1997-98	
60618	BD	R781WKW	60620	OGw	R783WKW	60622	RDu	R785WKW	60626 RDu R789WKW
60619	OGu	R782WKW	60621	BD	R784WKW	60624	RDu	R787WKW	60627 DN R790WKW

60628-60632

		Volvo B10BLE			Wright Renown		N41F	1998	
60628	HX	S810RWG	60630	OG	S812RWG	60631	OG	S813RWG	60632 OG S814RWG
60629	OG	S811RWG							

60633-60682

		Volvo B10BLE			Wright Renown		N41F	1999	
60633	RO	T815MAK	60646	OG	T828MAK	60659	OG	T841MAK	60672 RO T854MAK
60634	RO	T816MAK	60647	OG	T829MAK	60660	OG	T842MAK	60673 RO T855MAK
60635	RO	T817MAK	60648	OG	T830MAK	60661	OG	T843MAK	60674 RO T856MAK
60636	RO	T818MAK	60649	OG	T831MAK	60662	OG	T844MAK	60675 RO T857MAK
60637	RO	T819MAK	60650	OG	T832MAK	60663	BNu	T845MAK	60676 RO T858MAK
60638	RO	T820MAK	60651	OG	T833MAK	60664	RO	T846MAK	60677 RO T859MAK
60639	RO	T821MAK	60653	OGu	T835MAK	60665	RO	T847MAK	60678 RO T860MAK
60640	RO	T822MAK	60654	OG	T836MAK	60666	RO	T848MAK	60679 RO T861MAK
60641	OGu	T823MAK	60655	OG	T837MAK	60668	RO	T850MAK	60680 RO T862MAK
60642	OG	T824MAK	60656	OG	T838MAK	60669	RO	T851MAK	60681 RO T863MAK
60643	OG	T825MAK	60657	OG	T839MAK	60670	RO	T852MAK	60682 RO T864MAK
60644	OG	T826MAK	60658	OG	T840MAK	60671	RO	T853MAK	

The Volvo B7L featured a low-floor chassis with rear engine mounted vertically on the near-side rear overhang and on all First's vehicles Wrightbus Eclipse bodywork has been built. Illustrating the type is 60898, YJ51RFX, pictured in the grounds of the University of York. *Richard Godfrey*

60683-60702

			Volvo B10BLE			Wright Renown			N41F	1999	
60683	RO	T865ODT	60688	OG	T870ODT	60693	OG	T875ODT	60698	OG	T880ODT
60684	OG	T866ODT	60689	OG	T871ODT	60694	OG	T876ODT	60699	OG	T881ODT
60685	OG	T867ODT	60690	OG	T872ODT	60695	OG	T877ODT	60700	OG	T882ODT
60686	OG	T868ODT	60691	OG	T873ODT	60696	OG	T878ODT	60701	OG	T883ODT
60687	OG	T869ODT	60692	OG	T874ODT	60697	OG	T879ODT	60702	OG	T884ODT

60703	OG	Y661UKU	Volvo B7L			Wrightbus Eclipse			N41F	2001	

60704-60745

			Volvo B7L			Wrightbus Eclipse			N41F	2002	
60704	DN	MV02VAA	60714	OG	MV02VBF	60725	OG	MV02VCE	60736	RO	MV02VDK
60705	DN	MV02VAD	60715	OG	MV02VBG	60726	RO	MV02VCF	60737	RO	MV02VDL
60706	DN	MV02VAE	60716	OG	MV02VBJ	60727	RO	MV02VCG	60738	RO	MV02VDM
60707	OG	MV02VAF	60717	OG	MV02VBK	60728	RO	MV02VCJ	60739	RO	MV02VDN
60708	OG	MV02VAH	60718	OG	MV02VBL	60729	RO	MV02VCK	60740	RO	MV02VDO
60709	OG	MV02VAJ	60719	OG	MV02VBM	60730	RO	MV02VCL	60741	RO	MV02VDP
60710	OG	MV02VAK	60720	RO	MV02VBN	60731	RO	MV02VDD	60742	RO	MV02VDR
60711	OG	MV02VAM	60721	RO	MV02VBO	60733	RO	MV02VDF	60743	RO	MV02VDT
60712	OG	MV02VAO	60722	RO	MV02VBP	60734	RO	MV02VDG	60744	DN	MV02VDX
60713	OG	MV02VAU	60724	RO	MV02VCD	60735	RO	MV02VDJ	60745	DN	MV02VDY

60766	BS	R644CVR	Volvo B10BLE			Wright Renown			N41F	1998	
60767	BS	S657RNA	Volvo B10BLE			Wright Renown			N41F	1998	

60798-60806

			Volvo B10BLE			Wright Renown			N41F	1998	
60798	RO	R131JYG	60801	RO	R134JYG	60803	RO	R136JYG	60805	OG	R138JYG
60799	RO	R132JYG	60802	RO	R135JYG	60804	OG	R137JYG	60806	OG	R139JYG
60800	ROu	R133JYG									

60807-60816

			Volvo B10BLE			Wright Renown			N41F	1998	
60807	YA	S658RNA	60810	CM	S661RNA	60813	YA	S664RNA	60815	HX	S667RNA
60808	YA	S659RNA	60811	BS	S662RNA	60814	YA	S665RNA	60816	HX	S668RNA
60809	CM	S660RNA									

60818	HXu	S675SVU	Volvo B10BLE			Wright Renown			N41F	1998	
60819	HX	S676SVU	Volvo B10BLE			Wright Renown			N41F	1998	
60820	HX	S677SVU	Volvo B10BLE			Wright Renown			N41F	1998	

The Volvo B7L was the successor to the B10BLE which First purchased in large numbers at the turn of this century. Bodywork on the type was the Wright Renown, represented in this view by 60865, R643CVR, from the Chelmsford allocation. *Mark Doggett*

60821-60825
Volvo B10BLE — Wright Renown — N44F — 1999

60821	BD	T154OUB	60823	BD	T156OUB	60824	BD	T157OUB	60825	BD	T158OUB
60822	BD	T255GUG									

60826-60840
Volvo B10BLE — Wright Renown — N44F — 2000

60826	BD	V759UVY	60830	BD	V763UVY	60834	BD	V767UVY	60838	BD	V771UVY
60827	HX	V760UVY	60831	BD	V764UVY	60835	BD	V768UVY	60839	BD	V772UVY
60828	BD	V721UVY	60832	BD	V765UVY	60836	BD	V769UVY	60840	BD	V773UVY
60829	BD	V762UVY	60833	BD	W766HBT	60837	BD	V770UVY			

60841-60855
Volvo B10BLE — Wright Renown — N44F — 2000

60841	BD	W801DWX	60845	BD	W805DWX	60849	BD	W809DWX	60853	BD	W814DWX
60842	BD	W802DWX	60846	BD	W806DWX	60850	BD	W811DWX	60854	BD	W815DWX
60843	BD	W803DWX	60847	BD	W807DWX	60851	BD	W812DWX	60855	BD	W816DWX
60844	BD	W804DWX	60848	BD	W808DWX	60852	BD	W813DWX			

60856-60865
Volvo B10BLE — Wright Renown — N41F — 1998

60856	OG	R634CVR	60859	RO	R637CVR	60861	OG	R639CVR	60863	BS	R641CVR
60857	OG	R635CVR	60860	OG	R638CVR	60862	OG	R640CVR	60865	CM	R643CVR
60858	OG	R636CVR									

60876-60928
Volvo B7L — Wrightbus Eclipse — N41F — 2001-02

60876	YK	Y445CUB	60890	OG	YJ51RHK	60903	BD	YG02DHM	60916	TN	YG02DKU
60877	BD	Y446CUB	60891	OG	YJ51RGZ	60904	BD	YG02DHL	60917	TN	YG02DKV
60878	BD	Y447CUB	60892	OG	YJ51RHF	60905	BD	YG02DHO	60918	TN	YG02DLJ
60880	YK	Y449CUB	60893	OG	YJ51RGY	60906	BD	YG02DHN	60919	YK	YG02DLX
60881	YK	Y451CUB	60894	OG	YJ51REU	60907	BD	YG02DHV	60920	YK	YG02DLU
60882	YK	YJ51PZT	60895	BW	YJ51RFE	60908	BD	YG02DHA	60921	YK	YG02DLN
60883	YK	YJ51PZU	60896	YK	YJ51RFF	60909	YK	YG02DGZ	60922	YK	YG02DHJ
60884	YK	YJ51PZV	60897	YK	YJ51RFY	60910	TN	YJ51RFK	60923	BD	YG02DHF
60885	OG	YJ51PZW	60898	YK	YJ51RFX	60911	TN	YG02DLO	60924	BD	YG02DHE
60886	OG	YJ51PZX	60899	YK	YJ51RFL	60912	TN	YG02DLD	60925	BD	YG02DHD
60887	OG	YJ51PZY	60900	YK	YJ51RFN	60913	TN	YG02DLY	60926	YK	YG02DGY
60888	DN	YJ51RDZ	60901	YK	YJ51RFO	60914	TN	YG02DKO	60927	YK	YG02DHC
60889	DN	YJ51RHE	60902	YK	YG02DHK	60915	TN	YG02DLZ	60928	YK	YG02DHU

60944	BMt	M406VWW	Dennis Lance 11m	Plaxton Verde	tv	1995

61017-61021 — Scania L94UB — Wright Axcess Floline — N40F — 1999

61017	DU	S116CSG	61019	DU	S118CSG	61020	LFu	S119CSG	61021	LFu	S220GKS
61018	DU	S117CSG									

61017 DU S116CSG · 61019 DU S118CSG · 61020 LFu S119CSG · 61021 LFu S220GKS
61018 DU S117CSG

61022-61044 — Scania L94UB — Wright Axcess Floline — N43F* — 1999 — *61037-42 are N37F

No.			No.			No.			No.		
61022	DU	T421GUG	61029	HP	T428GUG	61035	HP	V134ESC	61040	BM	V139ESC
61024	DU	T423GUG	61030	HP	T429GUG	61036	HP	V135ESC	61041	BM	V140ESC
61025	LF	T424GUG	61031	HP	T430GUG	61037	BM	V136ESC	61042	BM	V141ESC
61026	DU	T425GUG	61032	HP	T431GUG	61038	BM	V137ESC	61043	LFu	V142ESC
61027	LF	T426GUG	61034	HP	V133ESC	61039	BM	V138ESC	61044	LFu	V143ESC
61028	DU	T427GUG									

No.			Chassis	Body	Layout	Year
61054	CN	R434GSF	Scania L113CRL	Wright Axcess-ultralow	N40F	1997
61056	BM	P436YSH	Scania L113CRL	Wright Axcess-ultralow	N40F	1997
61057	CN	R437GSF	Scania L113CRL	Wright Axcess-ultralow	N40F	1997

61058-61078 — Scania L113CRL — Wright Axcess-ultralow — N40F — 1998

No.			No.			No.			No.		
61058	BM	S644BSG	61065	BM	R451JSG	61070	BM	R456JFS	61074	BM	R460JFS
61059	BM	S445BSG	61066	BM	R452JSG	61071	BM	R457JFS	61076	BM	R462JFS
61060	BM	S446BSG	61067	BM	R453JFS	61072	BM	R458JFS	61077	BM	R463JFS
61061	BM	S447BSG	61068	BM	R454JFS	61073	BM	R459JFS	61078	BM	R464JFS
61062	BM	S448BSG	61069	BM	R455JFS						

No.			Chassis	Body	Layout	Year
61135	BL	YS51JVA	Bluebird A3 RE	Bluebird	S60F	2002
61136	BL	YS51JVK	Bluebird A3 RE	Bluebird	S60F	2002
61137	BNu	S101CSG	Scania L94UB	Wright Axcess Floline	N40F	1998
61140	BNu	S105CSG	Scania L94UB	Wright Axcess Floline	N40F	1998
61141	BNu	S359MFP	Scania L94UB	Wright Axcess Floline	N40F	1998
61142	BNu	S360MFP	Scania L94UB	Wright Axcess Floline	N40F	1998
61143	NE	S361MFP	Scania L94UB	Wright Axcess Floline	N40F	1998
61145	AG	S690BFS	Scania L113CRL	Wright Axcess-ultralow	N40F	1998
61148	VN	MV02VBU	Volvo B7L	Wrightbus Eclipse	N41F	2002
61158	LFu	R175GSX	Scania L113CRL	Wright Axcess-ultralow	N40F	1998
61160	AG	S684BFS	Scania L113CRL	Wright Axcess-ultralow	N40F	1998

61192-61211 — Volvo B7L — Wrightbus Eclipse — N41F — 2002

No.			No.			No.			No.		
61192	DN	YU52VXH	61197	DN	YU52VXN	61202	DN	YU52VXT	61207	DN	JDZ2339
61193	DN	YU52VXJ	61198	DN	YU52VXO	61203	DN	YU52VXV	61208	DN	JDZ2340
61194	DN	YU52VXK	61199	DN	YU52VXP	61204	DN	YU52VXW	61209	DN	JDZ2391
61195	DN	YU52VXL	61200	DN	YU52VXR	61205	DNu	YU52VXX	61210	DN	NDZ3162
61196	DN	YU52VXM	61201	DN	YU52VXS	61206	DN	YU52VXY	61211	DN	NDZ3164

61214-61233 — Scania L94UB — Wrightbus Solar — N43F — 2003

No.			No.			No.			No.		
61214	BK	YM52UVK	61219	LV	YM52UVR	61224	MU	YM52UVZ	61229	LT	YM52UWG
61215	LV	YM52UVL	61220	LV	YM52UVS	61225	LV	YM52UWA	61230	MU	YM52UWH
61216	LV	YM52UVN	61221	LV	YM52UVT	61226	MU	YM52UWB	61231	LT	YM52UWJ
61217	LV	YM52UVO	61222	LT	YM52UVU	61227	MU	YM52UWD	61232	MU	YM52UWK
61218	BK	YM52UVP	61223	LT	YM52UVW	61228	BK	YM52UWF	61233	LT	YM52UWN

No.			Chassis	Body	Layout	Year
61235	AG	S680BFS	Scania L113CRL	Wright Axcess-ultralow	N40F	1998
61237	AG	S681BFS	Scania L113CRL	Wright Axcess-ultralow	N40F	1998
61238	AG	S683BFS	Scania L113CRL	Wright Axcess-ultralow	N40F	1998
61239	AG	S689BFS	Scania L113CRL	Wright Axcess-ultralow	N40F	1998
61240	QS	R340GHS	Volvo B10BLE	Wright Renown	N43F	1998
61241	QS	R339GHS	Volvo B10BLE	Wright Renown	N43F	1998
61243	AG	R126GSF	Scania L113CRL	Wright Axcess-ultralow	N40F	1997
61244	AG	R124GSF	Scania L113CRL	Wright Axcess-ultralow	N40F	1997
61245	AG	R127GSF	Scania L113CRL	Wright Axcess-ultralow	N40F	1997
61246	AG	S686BFS	Scania L113CRL	Wright Axcess-ultralow	N40F	1998
61256	LFt	G601NWA	Volvo B10M-55	Alexander PS	B51F	1990
61266	LFtu	G621NWA	Volvo B10M-55	Alexander PS	B51F	1990
61288	HX	S808RWG	Volvo B10BLE	Wright Renown	N41F	1998
61289	HX	S809RWG	Volvo B10BLE	Wright Renown	N41F	1998

61291-61300 — Scania L94UB — Wright Axcess Floline — N40F — 1998

No.			No.			No.			No.		
61291	DUu	S106CSG	61294	LFu	S109CSG	61296	DU	S211CSG	61299	LFu	S114CSG
61292	LFu	S107CSG	61295	LFu	S110CSG	61298	DU	S113CSG	61300	LFu	S115CSG
61293	LFu	S108CSG									

No.			Chassis	Body	Layout	Year
61306	LF	SJ51DJZ	Volvo B7L	Wrightbus Eclipse	N42F	2001

61351	BYt	L204KSX	Volvo B10B	Alexander Strider	tv	1993	
61356	OMt	L209KSX	Volvo B10B	Alexander Strider	tv	1993	
61359	QSt	L212KSX	Volvo B10B	Alexander Strider	tv	1993	
61363	BMt	L304VSU	Volvo B10B	Alexander Strider	B51F	1993	
61365	QSt	L306VSU	Volvo B10B	Alexander Strider	B51F	1993	
61366	OMt	L307VSU	Volvo B10B	Alexander Strider	B51F	1993	
61391	PHtu	N123OGG	Volvo B10M-55	Alexander PS	B49F	1996	
61478	LFt	P106MFS	Scania L113CRL	Wright Axcess-ultralow	N47F	1996	
61499	PHtu	P529TYS	Volvo B10M-55	Alexander PS	B49F	1996	

61524-61540   Scania L113CRL   Wright Axcess-ultralow   N40F   1997

61524	LFu	R110GSF	61531	AG	R119GSF	61534	LFu	R122GSF	61540	LFu R131GSF
61529	AG	R117GSF	61533	BR	R121GSF	61537	LFu	R128GSF		

61543-61557   Scania L113CRL   Wright Axcess-ultralow   N40F   1997

61543	LFu	R158GSF	61548	LFu	R163GSF	61553	AG	R168GSF	61557	LFu R172GSX
61545	LFu	R160GSF								

61558	LFu	R195GSX	Scania L94UB	Wright Axcess Floline	N43F	1998
61559	LFu	R211GSF	Scania L113CRL	Wright Axcess-ultralow	N40F	1997
61562	LFu	R342SUT	Scania L113CRL	Wright Axcess-ultralow	N40F	1998
61564	LFu	R344SUT	Scania L113CRL	Wright Axcess-ultralow	N40F	1998
61565	LFu	R345SUT	Scania L113CRL	Wright Axcess-ultralow	N40F	1998

61567-61576   Scania L94UB   Wright Axcess Floline   N40F   1999

61567	LFu	S550JSE	61572	LFu	S555JSE	61574	LFu	S557JSE	61576	LFu S559JSE
61568	LFu	S551JSE	61573	LFu	S556JSE	61575	DUu	S558JSE		

61579-61586   Scania L94UB   Wright Axcess Floline   N40F   1998

61579	DU	S692BFS	61581	LFu	S694BFS	61584	DU	S698BFS	61586	LFu S701BFS
61580	LFu	S693BFS	61582	LFu	S696BFS					

61587-61596   Volvo B7L   Wrightbus Eclipse   N40F   2002

61587	PH	SA02BZD	61590	PH	SA02BZG	61593	PH	SA02BZK	61595	PH SA02BZM
61588	PH	SA02BZE	61591	PH	SA02BZH	61594	PH	SA02BZL	61596	PH SA02BZN
61589	LF	SA02BZF	61592	PH	SA02BZJ					

61597-61614   Volvo B10BLE   Wrightbus Renown   N42F   2001

61597	B	SF51YAA	61602	B	SF51YAJ	61607	B	SF51YAW	61611	B SF51YBB
61598	B	SF51YAD	61603	B	SF51YAK	61608	B	SF51YAX	61612	O SF51YBC
61599	B	SF51YAE	61604	B	SF51YAO	61609	B	SF51YAY	61613	O SF51YBD
61600	B	SF51YAG	61605	B	SF51YAU	61610	B	SF51YBA	61614	O SF51YBE
61601	B	SF51YAH	61606	B	SF51YAV					

61615	LF	SF51YBG	Volvo B7L	Wrightbus Eclipse	N42F	2001

61616-61626   Volvo B10BLE   Wrightbus Renown   N42F   2001

61616	O	SF51YBH	61619	O	SF51YBL	61622	O	SF51YBO	61625	O SF51YBS
61617	O	SF51YBJ	61620	O	SF51YBM	61623	O	SF51YBP	61626	O SF51YBT
61618	O	SF51YBK	61621	O	SF51YBN	61624	O	SF51YBR		

61627-61635   Volvo B7L   Wrightbus Eclipse   N42F   2001

61627	LF	SH51MHY	61630	LF	SH51MJF	61632	LF	SH51MKG	61634	LF SH51MKK
61628	LF	SH51MHZ	61631	OG	SH51MKF	61633	OG	SH51MKJ	61635	LF SH51MKL
61629	LF	SH51MJE								

61636-61651   Volvo B7L   Wrightbus Eclipse   N40F   2001

61636	OG	SJ51DHD	61640	LF	SJ51DHK	61644	LF	SJ51DHO	61648	LF SJ51DHZ
61637	LF	SJ51DHE	61641	LF	SJ51DHL	61645	LF	SJ51DHP	61649	LF SJ51DJD
61638	OG	SJ51DHF	61642	LF	SJ51DHM	61646	LF	SJ51DHV	61650	LF SJ51DJE
61639	OG	SJ51DHG	61643	LF	SJ51DHN	61647	LF	SJ51DHX	61651	LF SJ51DJF

61652	O	SJ51DJK	Volvo B10BLE	Wrightbus Renown	N42F	2001
61653	O	SJ51DJO	Volvo B10BLE	Wrightbus Renown	N42F	2001
61654	O	SJ51DJU	Volvo B10BLE	Wrightbus Renown	N42F	2001

61656-61664   Volvo B7L   Wrightbus Eclipse   N40F   2001

61656	LF	SJ51DJX	61659	LF	SJ51DKD	61661	LF	SJ51DKF	61663	PH SJ51DKL
61657	LF	SJ51DJY	61660	LF	SJ51DKE	61662	OG	SJ51DKK	61664	PH SJ51DKN
61658	LF	SJ51DKA								

61667-61673 Scania L94UB Wright Axcess Floline N40F 1999

61667	LF	V116FSF	61669	LF	V118FSF	61671	LF	V120FSF	61673 LF V221GLS
61668	LFu	V117FSF	61670	LFu	V119FSF	61672	LF	V122FSF	

61675-61704 Scania L94UB Wright Axcess Floline N43F 2000

61675	LF	X424UMS	61682	LF	X433UMS	61689	LF	X441UMS	61697	LF	X451UMS
61676	LF	X425UMS	61683	DU	X434UMS	61690	LF	X442UMS	61698	LF	X452UMS
61677	LF	X426UMS	61684	LF	X435UMS	61691	LF	X443UMS	61699	LF	X453UMS
61678	LF	X427UMS	61685	DU	X436UMS	61693	DU	X446UMS	61700	LF	X454UMS
61679	LF	X429UMS	61686	LF	X437UMS	61694	LF	X447UMS	61701	LF	X457UMS
61680	LF	X431UMS	61687	LF	X438UMS	61695	LF	X448UMS	61702	LF	X458UMS
61681	LF	X432UMS	61688	LF	X439UMS	61696	LF	X449UMS	61704	LF	X461UMS

61705-61710 Volvo B10BLE Wrightbus Renown N42F 2001

61705	O	Y301RTD	61707	O	Y303RTD	61709	O	Y307RTD	61710 O Y949RTD
61706	O	Y302RTD	61708	O	Y304RTD				

62118	HX	S672SVU	Volvo B10BLE	Wright Renown	N40F	1998
62121	ABs	RG1173	Albion PMA28	Walker	B31R	1930 *Aberdeen Corporation*

62122-62141 Volvo B10BLE Wright Renown N43F 2000

62122	AB	X601NSS	62127	AB	X606NSS	62132	AB	X611NSS	62137	AB	X616NSS
62123	AB	X602NSS	62128	AB	X607NSS	62133	AB	X612NSS	62138	AB	X617NSS
62124	AB	X603NSS	62129	O	X608NSS	62134	AB	X613NSS	62139	AB	X618NSS
62125	AB	X604NSS	62130	O	X609NSS	62135	AB	X614NSS	62140	AB	X619NSS
62126	AB	X605NSS	62131	LT	X69NSS	62136	AB	X615NSS	62141	AB	X944NSO

62142	DN	R588SBA	Volvo B10BLE	Wright Renown	N40F	1998
62143	BD	R589SBA	Volvo B10BLE	Wright Renown	N40F	1998

62149-62169 Volvo B10BLE Wright Renown N43F 1998-2001

62149	AB	X621NSS	62154	AB	Y626RSA	62159	O	R334GHS	62166	AB	Y631RSA
62150	AB	X622NSS	62155	AB	Y627RSA	62163	AB	Y628RSA	62167	AB	Y632RSA
62151	AB	X623NSS	62156	LTu	R330GHS	62164	AB	Y629RSA	62168	AB	Y633RSA
62152	AB	X624NSS	62157	LT	R331GHS	62165	AB	Y701RSA	62169	AB	Y634RSA
62153	AB	X477NSS	62158	LT	R332GHS						

62170-62176 Volvo B10BLE Alexander ALX300 N40F 2000

62170	AB	W577RFS	62172	AB	W579RFS	62174	ABu	W582RFS	62176 AB W584RFS
62171	AB	W578RFS	62173	AB	W581RFS	62175	AB	W583RFS	

62177-62183 Volvo B10BLE Wright Renown N44F 2000-01

62177	AB	Y635RSA	62179	AB	Y637RSA	62181	AB	Y639RSA	62183 AB X684ADK
62178	AB	Y636RSA	62180	AB	Y638RSA	62182	AB	X683ADK	

62184-62190 Volvo B10BLE Alexander ALX300 N40F 2000

62184	GS	W585RFS	62186	LT	W587RFS	62188	BF	W589RFS	62190 LT W592RFS
62185	LT	W586RFS	62187	GS	W588RFS	62189	BF	W591RFS	

62191-62204 Volvo B10BLE Wright Renown N43F 2000

62191	AB	X685ADK	62195	AB	X689ADK	62199	AB	X694ADK	62202	AB	X697ADK
62192	AB	X686ADK	62196	AB	X691ADK	62200	AB	X695ADK	62203	AB	X698ADK
62193	BA	X687ADK	62197	AB	X692ADK	62201	AB	X696ADK	62204	AB	W681RNA
62194	BA	X688ADK	62198	AB	X693ADK						

62205-62211 Volvo B10BLE Alexander ALX300 N40F 2000

62205	LT	W593RFS	62207	LT	W595RFS	62209	LT	W597RFS	62211 BF W599RFS
62206	BF	W594RFS	62208	LT	W596RFS	62210	LT	W598RFS	

62212-62218 Volvo B10BLE Wright Renown N43F 1998-2000

62212	BK	W682RNA	62214	QS	S673SVU	62216	QS	R585SBA	62218 QS R587SBA
62213	BK	W683RNA	62215	QS	R584SBA	62217	QS	R586SBA	

62219-62227 Volvo B10BLE Alexander ALX300 N40F 2000

62219	BF	W601RFS	62222	GS	W604RFS	62224	LT	X606RFS	62226 LT W608RFS
62220	BF	W602RFS	62223	GS	W605RFS	62225	LT	W607RFS	62227 GS W609RFS
62221	LT	W603RFS							

62228	AB	YS51JVD	Blue Bird AARE	Blue Bird	S60F	2002

Sunshine in Aberdeen in June 2013 and Volvo B10BLE 62139, X618NSS, shows off its Aberdeen Tramway's retro-livery for the 115th anniversary of transport in the Granite City. *Steve Rice*

62231-62245

						Volvo B10BLE			Wrightbus Renown		N44F	2001	
62231	BN	Y941CSF	62235	OG	Y946CSF	62239	OG	Y948CSF	62243	OG	Y953CSF		
62232	OG	Y937CSF	62236	BN	Y944CSF	62240	OG	Y949CSF	62244	OG	Y952CSF		
62233	BN	Y942CSF	62237	OG	Y945CSF	62241	BN	Y951CSF	62245	MS	Y938CSF		
62234	OG	Y943CSF	62238	BA	Y947CSF	62242	MS	Y939CSF					

62302-62312

						Scania L113CRL			Wright Axcess-ultralow		N40F	1998	
62302	BK	R445ALS	62304	BK	R447ALS	62309	BK	S523UMS	62312	BK	S526UMS		
62303	BK	R446ALS	62305	BK	R448ALS	62310	BKu	R524BMS					

62345	LTs	P578DMS	Scania L113CRL		Wright Axcess-ultralow	N47F	1996

62355-62358

					Scania L94UB		Wrightbus Solar	NC43F	2001	
62355	BK	SN51MSV	62356	BK	SN51MSU	62357	BK	SN51MSY	62358	MU	SN51MSX

62359	BK	R154GSF	Scania L113CRL	Wright Axcess-ultralow	NC40F	1998
62383	BK	S520UMS	Scania L113CRL	Wright Axcess-ultralow	N40F	1998

62385-62392

					Scania L94UB		Wright Axcess Floline	N43F	1999	
62385	LV	V527ESH	62387	LV	V529ESH	62389	LV	V531ESH	62392	LV	V35ESC
62386	LV	V528ESH	62388	LV	V530ESH	62390	LV	V532ESH			

62394	BK	R583YMS	Scania L113CRL	Wright Axcess-ultralow	N40F	1998

62406-62410

					Scania L94UB		Wrightbus Solar	N44F	2003	
62406	CO	YS03ZKA	62408	CO	YS03ZKE	62409	CO	YS03ZKD	62410	CO	YS03ZKF
62407	CO	YS03ZKB									

62411	LT	SN03WMJ	TransBus E300	TransBus Enviro 300	N44F	2003
62412	LT	SN03WMU	TransBus E300	TransBus Enviro 300	N44F	2003

The Wrightbus Streetlite Max was launched in 2012 as an 11.5 metre option with a capacity of up to forty-five seated passengers. The initial deliveries for First are now working in Sheffield, Bath and Portsmouth with further orders having been placed for delivery in 2014. From the Bath allocation, 63077, SM13NBK, is seen working route X39 to Bristol. *Mark Lyons*

63001-63041   Wrightbus Streetlite Max DF   Wrightbus   N41F   2013

63001	OG	SM13NDJ	63012	OG	SM13NEJ	63022	OG	SK63KGY	63032	OG	SK63KHJ
63002	OG	SM13NDK	63013	OG	SM13NEN	63023	OG	SK63KGZ	63033	OG	SK63KHL
63003	OG	SM13NDL	63014	OG	SM13NEO	63024	OG	SK63KHA	63034	OG	SK63KHM
63004	OG	SM13NDN	63015	OG	SM13NEU	63025	OG	SK63KHB	63035	OG	SK63KHO
63005	OG	SM13NDO	63016	OG	SM13NEY	63026	OG	SK63KHC	63036	OG	SK63KHP
63006	OG	SM13NDU	63017	OG	SK63KGO	63027	OG	SK63KHD	63037	OG	SK63KHR
63007	OG	SM13NDV	63018	OG	SK63KGP	63028	OG	SK63KHE	63038	RO	LK62HJD
63008	OG	SM13NDX	63019	OG	SK63KGU	63029	OG	SK63KHF	63039	RO	LK62FUJ
63009	OG	SM13NDY	63020	OG	SK63KGV	63030	OG	SK63KHG	63040	RO	LK62HKG
63010	OG	SM13NDZ	63021	OG	SK63KGX	63031	OG	SK63KHH	63041	RO	LK62HJX
63011	OG	SM13NEF									

63042-63067   Wrightbus Streetlite Max DF   Wrightbus   N41F   2013

63042	HI	SK63KHT	63049	HI	SK63KJA	63056	HI	SK63KJV	63062	HI	SK63KKC
63043	HI	SK63KHU	63050	HI	SK63KJE	63057	HI	SK63KJX	63063	HI	SK63KKD
63044	HI	SK63KHV	63051	HI	SK63KJF	63058	HI	SK63KJY	63064	HI	SK63KKE
63045	HI	SK63KHW	63052	HI	SK63KJJ	63059	HI	SK63KJZ	63065	HI	SK63KKF
63046	HI	SK63KHX	63053	HI	SK63KJN	63060	HI	SK63KKA	63066	HI	SK63KKG
63047	HI	SK63KHY	63054	HI	SK63KJO	63061	HI	SK63KKB	63067	HI	SK63KKH
63048	HI	SK63KHZ	63055	HI	SK63KJU						

63068-63078   Wrightbus Streetlite Max DF   Wrightbus   NC41F   2013

63068	BA	SM13NAE	63071	BA	SM13NBB	63074	BA	SM13NBF	63077	BA	SM13NBK
63069	BA	SM13NAO	63072	BA	SM13NBD	63075	BA	SM13NBG	63078	BA	SM13NBL
63070	BA	SM13NBA	63073	BA	SM13NBE	63076	BA	SM13NBJ			

63079-63095   Wrightbus Streetlite Max DF   Wrightbus   N41F   2014

63079	PT	SN14DTX	63084	PT	SN14DUJ	63088	PT	SN14DVB	63092	PT	SN14DVH
63080	PT	SN14DTY	63085	PT	SN14DUU	63089	PT	SN14DVC	63093	PT	SN14DVJ
63081	PT	SN14DTZ	63086	PT	SN14DUV	63090	PT	SN14DVF	63094	PT	SN14DVK
63082	PT	SN14DUA	63087	PT	SN14DUY	63091	PT	SN14DVG	63095	PT	SN14DVL
63083	PT	SN14DUH									

Featuring The Star livery is Portsmouth's 63052, SK63KJJ, one of twenty-six Streetlites that formed their 2013 delivery. It is seen on route 8 on the Waterlooville corridor. *Richard Godfrey*

63096-63118

Wrightbus Streetlite Max DF   Wrightbus   N41F   2013

63096	OX	SM13NBN	63102	OX	SM13NCC	63108	OX	SM13NCO	63114	BN	SK63KGE
63097	OX	SM13NBO	63103	OX	SM13NCD	63109	OX	SM13NCU	63115	BN	SK63KGF
63098	OX	SM13NBX	63104	OX	SM13NCE	63110	OX	SM13NCV	63116	BN	SK63KGG
63099	OX	SM13NBY	63105	OX	SM13NCF	63111	OX	SK63KFY	63117	BN	SK63KGJ
63100	OX	SM13NBZ	63106	OX	SM13NCJ	63112	OX	SK63KFZ	63118	BN	SK63KGN
63101	OX	SM13NCA	63107	OX	SM13NCN	63113	OX	SK63KGA			

63119-63170

Wrightbus Streetlite Max DF   Wrightbus   N41F   2014

63119	OG	SN14DVN	63132	OG	-	63145	OG	-	63158	Scotland East
63120	OG	SN14DVO	63133	OG	-	63146	OX	-	63159	Scotland East
63121	OG	SN14DVP	63134	OG	-	63147	OX	-	63160	Scotland East
63122	OG	-	63135	OG	-	63148	OX	-	63161	HH	-
63123	OG	SN14DVT	63136	OG	-	63149	OX	-	63162	HH	-
63124	OG	SN14DVU	63137	OG	-	63150	OX	-	63163	HH	-
63125	OG	SN14DVV	63138	OG	-	63151	OX	-	63164	HH	-
63126	OG	SN14DVW	63139	OG	-	63152	OX	-	63165	HH	-
63127	OG	-	63140	OG	-	63153	OX	-	63166	HH	-
63128	OG	-	63141	OG	-	63154	OX	-	63167	HH	-
63129	OG	-	63142	OG	-	63155	OX	-	63168	HH	-
63130	OG	-	63143	OG	-	63156	OX	-	63169	HH	-
63131	OG	-	63144	OG	-	63157	Scotland East		63170	HH	-

63171-63240

Wrightbus Streetlite Max DF   Wrightbus   N41F   2014

63171	LE	-	63189	WH	-	63207	AB	-	63224	B	-
63172	LE	-	63190	SH	-	63208	AB	-	63225	B	-
63173	LE	-	63191	SH	-	63209	AB	-	63226	B	-
63174	LE	-	63192	SH	-	63210	AB	-	63227	B	-
63175	LE	-	63193	AB	-	63211	AB	-	63228	B	-
63176	LE	-	63194	AB	-	63212	AB	-	63229	B	-
63177	LE	-	63195	AB	-	63213	AB	-	63230	B	-
63178	LE	-	63196	AB	-	63214	AB	-	63231	B	-
63179	LE	-	63197	AB	-	63215	AB	-	63232	B	-
63180	LE	-	63198	AB	-	63216	AB	-	63233	B	-
63181	WH	-	63199	AB	-	63217	AB	-	63234	B	-
63182	WH	-	63200	AB	-	63218	AB	-	63235	B	-
63183	WH	-	63201	AB	-	63219	Scotland East		63236	B	-
63184	WH	-	63202	AB	-	63220	Scotland East		63237	B	-
63185	WH	-	63203	AB	-	63221	Scotland East		63238	B	-
63186	WH	-	63204	AB	-	63222	Scotland East		63239	B	-
63187	WH	-	63205	AB	-	63223	Scotland East		63240	B	-
63188	WH	-	63206	AB	-						

64000	D	02D78371	Mercedes-Benz O530 Citaro	Mercedes-Benz Citaro	N38D	2002	Transport for London, 2005

64001-64011
Mercedes-Benz O530 Citaro — Mercedes-Benz — N36D* — 2002 — *64001/2/5 are N40F

64001	BL	LT02NTV	64004	LV	LT02NUA	64007	LV	LT02NUE	64010	LV	LT02NUJ
64002	SH	LT02NTX	64005	BL	LT02NUB	64008	LV	LT02NUF	64011	LV	LT02NVY
64003	LV	LT02NTY									

64012-64019
Mercedes-Benz O530 Citaro — Mercedes-Benz — N40F — 2003

64012	BL	LT52WXA	64014	BL	LT52WXL	64016	BL	LT52WXO	64018	BL	LK03LNE
64013	BL	LT52WXB	64015	BL	LT52WXN	64017	BL	LT52WXP	64019	BL	LK03LNF

64020	BL	BU04EZF	Mercedes-Benz O530 Citaro	Mercedes-Benz	N40F	2004	
64021	BL	BU04EZG	Mercedes-Benz O530 Citaro	Mercedes-Benz	N40F	2004	
64029	BY	BX02CMK	Mercedes-Benz O530 Citaro	Mercedes-Benz	N38F	2002	Evobus demonstrator, 2004

64030-64042
Mercedes-Benz O530 Citaro — Mercedes-Benz — N40F — 2007-08

64030	SH	LK07CCA	64033	SH	LK07CCF	64036	SH	LK07CCO	64039	SH	LK07CCX
64031	SH	LK07CCD	64034	SH	LK07CCJ	64037	SH	LK07CCU	64042	SH	LK08FNL
64032	SH	LK07CCE	64035	SH	LK07CCN	64038	SH	LK07CCV			

64043-64048
Mercedes-Benz O530 Citaro — Mercedes-Benz — N38F — 2008

64043	SH	LK08FMC	64045	SH	LK08FME	64047	SH	LK08FMG	64048	SH	LK08FMJ
64044	SH	LK08FMD	64046	SH	LK08FMF						

64049	CE	WK08ESV	Mercedes-Benz O530 Citaro	Mercedes-Benz	N38F	2008	Western Greyhound, 2013
64050	CE	WK10AZU	Mercedes-Benz O530 Citaro	Mercedes-Benz	N38F	2010	Western Greyhound, 2013
64504	CF	YJ61MMA	Optare Tempo X1200	Optare	NC35F	2011	operated for Ceredigion CC
64505	CF	YJ61MME	Optare Tempo X1200	Optare	NC35F	2011	operated for Ceredigion CC
64506	CF	YJ61MMF	Optare Tempo X1200	Optare	NC35F	2011	operated for Ceredigion CC
64507	CF	YA13AAF	Optare Tempo X1260	Optare	NC35F	2013	operated for Ceredigion CC
64508	CF	YA13AAJ	Optare Tempo X1260	Optare	NC35F	2013	operated for Ceredigion CC
64509	CF	YD63UZM	Optare Tempo X1260	Optare	NC35F	2013	operated for Ceredigion CC
64818	Hlt	M818PGM	Scania L113 CRL	Northern Counties Paladin	B51F	1995	
64994	AB	-	Van Hool A330 fuel cell 13.1m	Van Hool	N44F	2014	
64995	AB	-	Van Hool A330 fuel cell 13.1m	Van Hool	N44F	2014	
64996	AB	-	Van Hool A330 fuel cell 13.1m	Van Hool	N44F	2014	
64997	AB	-	Van Hool A330 fuel cell 13.1m	Van Hool	N44F	2014	

65001-65005
Scania OmniCity CN94UB — Scania — N42F — 2004

65001	AG	YN04YJC	65003	AG	YN04YJE	65004	AG	YN04YJF	65005	AG	YN04YJG
65002	AG	YN04YJD									

65006-65025
Scania OmniCity CN94UB — Scania — N44F — 2004

65006	HO	YN54NZA	65011	HO	YN54NZG	65016	HO	YN54NZO	65021	HO	YN54NZV
65007	HO	YN54NZC	65012	HO	YN54NZH	65017	HO	YN54NZP	65022	HO	YN54NZW
65008	HO	YN54NZD	65013	HO	YN54NZJ	65018	HO	YN54NZR	65023	HO	YN54NZX
65009	HO	YN54NZE	65014	HO	YN54NZK	65019	HO	YN54NZT	65024	HO	YN54NZY
65010	HO	YN54NZF	65015	HO	YN54NZM	65020	HO	YN54NZU	65025	HO	YN54NZZ

65026-65042
Scania OmniCity CN94UB — Scania — N44F* — 2005-06 — *65028-32 are NC41F

65026	AG	YN54OCK	65031	CM	YN06TDX	65035	AG	YN06WMG	65039	AG	YN06WMM
65027	AG	YN05HCL	65032	CM	YN06TDZ	65036	AG	YN06WMJ	65040	AG	YN06WMO
65028	CM	YN06TDO	65033	AG	YN06WME	65037	AG	YN06WMK	65041	AG	YN06WMP
65029	CM	YN06TDU	65034	AG	YN06WMF	65038	AG	YN06WML	65042	AG	YN06WMT
65030	CM	YN06TDV									

65527-65540
Scania L113CRL — Wright Axcess-ultralow — N40F — 1997

65527	CN	R147GSF	65530	LFu	R150GSF	65535	LFw	R135GSF	65538	CN	R138GSF
65528	IPw	R148GSF	65532	CN	R152GSF	65536	LFu	R136GSF	65540	IPw	R140GSF
65529	IPw	R149GSF									

65551-65564
Scania L113CRL — Wright Axcess-ultralow — N40F — 1998

65551	CN	R551CNG	65557	u	R257DVF	65560	u	R260DVF	65563	u	R263DVF
65554	CN	R554CNG	65558	u	R258DVF	65561	AG	R261DVF	65564	AG	R264DVF
65556	CN	R556CNG	65559	u	R259DVF	65562	AG	R262DVF			

First operates three batches of the Scania Omnicity single-deck vehicles, principally in the Potteries and Portsmouth areas. Carrying branding for the service from Hanley to Stafford is 65042, YN06WMT. Interestingly, these buses have all spent their entire lives at their current allocations. *Richard Godfrey*

65565-65574

			Scania L94UB			Wright Axcess Floline		N40F	1999		
65565	CO	S565TPW	65568	u	S568TPW	65571	u	S571TPW	65573	CO	S573TPW
65566	CO	S566TPW	65569	CO	S569TPW	65572	AG	S572TPW	65574	CO	S574TPW
65567	u	S567TPW	65570	CO	S570TPW						

65575-65580

			Scania L94UB			Wright Axcess Floline		N40F	1999		
65575	u	T575JNG	65577	u	T577JNG	65579	IP	T579JNG	65580	u	T580JNG
65576	CO	T576JNG	65578	u	T578JNG						

65586-65601

			Scania L94UB			Wright Axcess Floline		N40F	1999-2000		
65586	CO	V586DVF	65590	IP	V590DVF	65594	BK	W594SNG	65598	BK	W598SNG
65587	CO	V587DVF	65591	LF	W591SNG	65595	LT	W595SNG	65599	LT	W599SNG
65588	IP	V588DVF	65592	LF	W592SNG	65596	DU	W596SNG	65601	LT	W601SNG
65589	IP	V589DVF	65593	LF	W593SNG	65597	LT	W597SNG			

65602	BL	S102CSG	Scania L94UB	Wright Axcess Floline	N40F	1998
65621	BL	T821JBL	Scania L94UB	Wright Axcess Floline	N40F	1999
65622	BL	T822JBL	Scania L94UB	Wright Axcess Floline	N40F	1999
65624	BLw	T824JBL	Scania L94UB	Wright Axcess Floline	N40F	1999

65626-65632

			Scania L94UB			Wright Axcess Floline		N43F	2000		
65626	CO	V826FSC	65628	IP	V828FSC	65631	IP	V831FSC	65632	IP	V832FSC
65627	CO	V827FSC	65630	IP	V830FSC						

65650-65654

			Scania L94UB			Wright Axcess Floline		N43F	1999		
65650	CO	T650SSF	65652	CO	T652SSF	65653	CO	T653SSF	65654	CO	T654SSF
65651	CO	T651SSF									

65662	LT	V362CNH	Scania L94UB	Wright Axcess Floline	N43F	1999
65663	LT	V363CNH	Scania L94UB	Wright Axcess Floline	N43F	1999
65664	LT	V364CNH	Scania L94UB	Wright Axcess Floline	N43F	1999

65665-65677   Scania L94UB   Wrightbus Solar   N43F   2001

65665	CO	SN51UXX	65669	CO	SN51UYB	65672	IP	SN51UYE	65675	IP	SN51UYJ
65666	CO	SN51UXY	65670	IP	SN51UYC	65673	IP	SN51UYG	65676	CO	SN51UYK
65667	CO	SN51UXZ	65671	CO	SN51UYD	65674	IP	SN51UYH	65677	CO	SN51UYL
65668	CO	SN51UYA									

65678-65692   Scania L94UB   Wrightbus Solar   N44F   2002-03

65678	CO	YP02ABN	65682	CO	YR52VEP	65686	CO	YS03ZKC	65690	IP	YS03ZKK
65679	CO	YR52VEH	65683	CO	YR52VEU	65687	CO	YS03ZKG	65691	IP	YS03ZKL
65680	CO	YR52VEK	65684	CO	YR52VEY	65688	CO	YS03ZKH	65692	IP	YS03ZKM
65681	CO	YR52VEL	65685	CO	YR52VFO	65689	CO	YS03ZKJ			

65693-65699   Scania L94UB   Wrightbus Solar   N43F   2003

65693	LF	SN53KHH	65695	BK	SN53KHK	65697	LF	SN53KHM	65699	LT	SN53KHP
65694	BK	SN53KHJ	65696	LF	SN53KHL	65698	LT	SN53KHO			

65700-65706   Scania L94UB   Wrightbus Solar   N43F   2004

65700	MU	SN04CKY	65702	MU	SN04CLF	65705	NE	YN04GME	65706	NE	YN04GMF
65701	MU	SN04CKX	65703	LV	SN04CNK						

65708-65723   Scania L94UB   Wrightbus Solar   N43F   2004-05

65708	BF	SN54KDF	65712	BK	SN54KDU	65716	BK	SN54KEJ	65720	BK	SN54KFC
65709	BK	SN54KDJ	65713	BK	SN54KDV	65717	BK	SN54KEK	65721	BK	SN54KFD
65710	BK	SN54KDK	65714	BK	SN54KDX	65718	BK	SN54KEU	65722	BK	SN54KFE
65711	BK	SN54KDO	65715	BK	SN54KDZ	65719	BK	SN54KFA	65723	BK	SN54KFF

65724-65733   Scania L94UB   Wrightbus Solar   N43F   2005

65724	SH	LK55ABZ	65727	NE	YN05HCO	65730	NE	YN05HCV	65732	NE	YN05HCY
65725	SH	LK55ACF	65728	NE	YN05HCP	65731	NE	YN05HCX	65733	NE	YN05HCZ
65726	SH	LK55ACJ	65729	NE	YN05HCU						

65742-65754   Scania L94UB   Wrightbus Solar   N43F   2005-06

65742	GS	SN55JVG	65746	GS	SN55JVL	65749	GS	SN55JVP	65752	LT	SN55JVD
65743	GS	SN55JVH	65747	GS	SN55JVM	65750	GS	SN55JVA	65753	LT	SN55JVE
65744	GS	SN55JVJ	65748	GS	SN55JVO	65751	BF	SN55JVC	65754	LT	SN06AHK
65745	GS	SN55JVK									

65755	LF	SK02ZYG	Scania L94UB	Wrightbus Solar	N43F	2002	Hutchison, Overtown, 2007
65756	LF	SK02ZYH	Scania L94UB	Wrightbus Solar	N43F	2002	Hutchison, Overtown, 2007
65757	LF	SN03CLX	Scania L94UB	Wrightbus Solar	N43F	2003	Hutchison, Overtown, 2007
65758	LF	SN03CLY	Scania L94UB	Wrightbus Solar	N43F	2003	Hutchison, Overtown, 2007

65759-65762   Scania L94UB   Wrightbus Solar   N44F   2005   Reading Buses, 2013

65759	CE	YN05GXF	65760	CE	YN05GXR	65761	CE	YN06NXP	65762	CE	YN06NXW

66100	WS	R460VOP	Volvo B10BLE	Wright Renown	N44F	1997	Volvo demonstrator, 1999

66101-66120   Volvo B10BLE   Wright Renown   N47F   1998

66101	HU	R901BOU	66107	WS	R907BOU	66113	OGu	R913BOU	66117	MS	R917BOU
66102	LH	R902BOU	66108	WS	R908BOU	66114	OGu	R914BOU	66118	MS	R918BOU
66104	LH	R904BOU	66109	LH	R909BOU	66115	LH	R915BOU	66119	OGu	R919BOU
66105	LH	R905BOU	66110	LH	R910BOU	66116	LH	R916BOU	66120	MS	R920COU
66106	WS	R906BOU	66112	RO	R912BOU						

66121-66130   Volvo B10BLE   Wright Renown   N41F   1998-99

66121	HO	S121JTP	66126	YA	S116JTP	66128	HO	S118JTP	66130	HO	S120JTP
66122	HO	S122UOT	66127	HO	S117JTP						

66151-66163   Volvo B10BLE   Wright Renown   N44F   1998-99

66151	HI	S351NPO	66154	HO	S354NPO	66158	HO	S358XCR	66161	MS	S361XCR
66152	HO	S352NPO	66156	HO	S356XCR	66159	LH	S359XCR	66162	LH	S362XCR
66153	HO	S353NPO	66157	HO	S357XCR	66160	WS	S360XCR	66163	WS	S363XCR

66164-66181   Volvo B10BLE   Wright Renown   N44F   2000

66164	HO	W364EOW	66168	BR	W368EOW	66174	WS	W374EOW	66178	LH	W378EOW
66165	BS	W365EOW	66169	BS	W369EOW	66176	HO	W376EOW	66179	BS	W379EOW
66166	MS	W366EOW	66171	MS	W371EOW	66177	BS	W377EOW	66181	HO	W381EOW
66167	LH	W367EOW	66173	WS	W373EOW						

Norwich is the location for this view of 66301, KV02VVC, a Volvo B7L with Wrightbus Eclipse bodywork.
Mark Doggett

66191-66207

											Volvo B10BLE			Wright Renown		N41F	1998

66191	QS	S791RWG	66195	QS	S795RWG	66199	HO	S799RWG	66204	HO	S804RWG
66192	QS	S792RWG	66196	HO	S796RWG	66201	HO	S801RWG	66205	HO	S805RWG
66193	QS	S793RWG	66197	HO	S797RWG	66202	HO	S802RWG	66206	WS	S806RWG
66194	BN	S794RWG	66198	HO	S798RWG	66203	HO	S803RWG	66207	WS	S807RWG

66233	B	X303JGE	Volvo B10BLE	Alexander ALX300	N44F	2000	Hutchison, Overtown, 2007
66234	B	X304JGE	Volvo B10BLE	Alexander ALX300	N44F	2000	Hutchison, Overtown, 2007
66281	O	Y181BGB	Volvo B10BLE	Wrightbus Renown	N44F	2001	Hutchison, Overtown, 2007
66282	O	Y182BGB	Volvo B10BLE	Wrightbus Renown	N44F	2001	Hutchison, Overtown, 2007

66301-66323

Volvo B7L   Wrightbus Eclipse   N41F   2002

66301	VN	KV02VVC	66307	LE	KV02VVJ	66313	LE	KV02VVP	66319	LE	KV02VVX
66302	LE	KV02VVD	66308	LE	KV02VVK	66314	LE	KV02VVR	66320	LE	KV02VVY
66303	LE	KV02VVE	66309	LE	KV02VVL	66315	LE	KV02VVS	66321	LE	KV02VVZ
66304	LE	KV02VVF	66310	LE	KV02VVM	66316	LE	KV02VVT	66322	LE	KV02VWA
66305	LE	KV02VVG	66311	LE	KV02VVN	66317	LE	KV02VVU	66323	LE	KV02VWB
66306	LE	KV02VVH	66312	LE	KV02VVO	66318	LE	KV02VVW			

66324-66348

Volvo B7L   Wrightbus Eclipse   N41F   2002

66324	VN	MV02VAX	66330	VN	MV02VBE	66337	VN	MV02VCM	66343	VN	MV02VCW
66325	VN	MV02VAY	66332	VN	MV02VBX	66338	VN	MV02VCN	66344	VN	MV02VCX
66326	VN	MV02VBA	66333	BR	MV02VBY	66339	VN	MV02VCO	66345	VN	MV02VCY
66327	VN	MV02VBB	66334	VN	MV02VBZ	66340	VN	MV02VCP	66346	VN	MV02VCZ
66328	VN	MV02VBC	66335	VN	MV02VCA	66341	VN	MV02VCT	66347	VN	MV02VDA
66329	VN	MV02VBD	66336	VN	MV02VCC	66342	VN	MV02VCU	66348	VN	MV02VDC

66349-66356

Volvo B7L   Wrightbus Eclipse   N41F   2002

66349	PH	MV02VDZ	66351	BW	MV02VEB	66353	BW	MV02VEH	66355	BW	MV02VEL
66350	BW	MV02VEA	66352	BW	MV02VEF	66354	BW	MV02VEK	66356	BW	MV02VEM

Arriving in Glasgow from Hamilton is 66952, WX55TZO, a Volvo B7RLE with Wrightbus Eclipse Urban bodywork. The Volvo B7RLE was introduced in 2003 as a replacement for the B7L. *Steve Rice*

66358	LN	Y186HNH	Volvo B7L	Wrightbus Eclipse	N26D	2001	Dawson Rentals, 2007
66651	BDt	K114PRV	Volvo B10B	Northern Counties Paladin	tv	1993	
66652	BDt	M967GDU	Volvo B10B	Plaxton Verde	tv	1994	Plaxton demonstrator, 1995
66691	WR	CN07HVG	Volvo B7RLE	Plaxton Centro	N45F	2007	Veolia, 2012

66692-66699

			Volvo B7RLE		Plaxton Centro	N45F*	2007	Veolia, 2011 *66697 is NC45F
66692	WR	CN07HVH	66694	WR	CN07HVJ	66696	WR	CN57EFE	66698	WR	CN07HVL
66693	WR	CN07HVK	66695	WR	CN57EFB	66697	WR	CN57EFF	66699	WR	CN07HVM

66707-66715

Volvo B7RLE   Wrightbus Eclipse Urban   N43F   2003-04

66707	HX	YK53GXR	66710	HX	YK53GXV	66712	HX	YK04EZL	66714	BD	YK04EZM
66708	HX	YK53GXT	66711	HX	YK04EZJ	66713	HX	YK04EZG	66715	BD	YK04EZH
66709	HX	YK53GXU									

66716-66737

Volvo B7RLE   Wrightbus Eclipse Urban   NC43F   2004

66716	RA	WX54XDA	66722	WS	WX54XDL	66728	MS	WX54XCN	66733	BA	WX54XCU
66717	RA	WX54XDD	66723	WS	WX54XDH	66729	MS	WX54XCO	66734	BA	WX54XCV
66718	RA	WX54XDB	66724	WS	WX54XDG	66730	BA	WX54XCP	66735	B	WX54XCW
66719	BA	WX54XDC	66725	WS	WX54XDJ	66731	BA	WX54XCR	66736	B	WX54XCY
66720	WS	WX54XDF	66726	WS	WX54XDK	66732	BA	WX54XCT	66737	B	WX54XCZ
66721	WS	WX54XDE	66727	WS	WX54XCM						

66738-66758

Volvo B7RLE   Wrightbus Eclipse Urban   N43F   2005

66738	HX	YJ54XVM	66744	HX	YJ54XVU	66749	HX	YJ54XWA	66754	YK	YJ05KNV
66739	HX	YJ54XVN	66745	HX	YJ54XVW	66750	HX	YJ05KOB	66755	HX	YJ05KNW
66740	HX	YJ54XVO	66746	HX	YJ54XVX	66751	HU	YJ05KOD	66756	YK	YJ05KNX
66741	HX	YJ54XVP	66747	HX	YJ54XVY	66752	HU	YJ05KOE	66757	YK	YJ05KNY
66742	HX	YJ54XVR	66748	HX	YJ54XVZ	66753	HU	YJ05KOH	66758	YK	YJ05KNZ
66743	HX	YJ54XVT									

66759-66792 — Volvo B7RLE — Wrightbus Eclipse Urban — N43F — 2005

Fleet	Code	Reg	Fleet	Code	Reg	Fleet	Code	Reg	Fleet	Code	Reg
66759	YK	YJ05VVA	66768	HU	YJ05VVL	66777	HX	YJ05VVW	66785	HU	YK05FPA
66760	YK	YJ05VVB	66769	HU	YJ05VVM	66778	HX	YJ05VVX	66786	HU	YK05FLC
66761	YK	YJ05VVC	66770	B	YJ05VVN	66779	HX	YJ05VVY	66787	HU	YK05FOV
66762	YK	YJ05VVD	66771	B	YJ05VVO	66780	HX	YJ05VVZ	66788	HU	YK05FOU
66763	HX	YJ05VVE	66772	HU	YJ05VVP	66781	HX	YK05FJJ	66789	HX	YK05FOT
66764	HU	YJ05VVF	66773	HU	YJ05VVR	66782	HX	YK05FLB	66790	HX	YA05SOU
66765	HU	YJ05VVG	66774	HU	YJ05VVS	66783	HX	YK05FJF	66791	HU	YK05FOP
66766	HU	YJ05VVH	66775	HU	YJ05VVT	66784	HU	YK05FJE	66792	HU	YA05SOJ
66767	HU	YJ05VVK	66776	HX	YJ05VVU						

66794-66933 — Volvo B7RLE — Wrightbus Eclipse Urban — N43F — 2005

Fleet	Code	Reg	Fleet	Code	Reg	Fleet	Code	Reg	Fleet	Code	Reg
66794	CM	MX05CBF	66826	BS	MX05CFA	66858	OM	MX05CHO	66896	BN	MX55FFG
66795	CM	MX05CBU	66827	BS	MX05CFD	66859	OM	MX05CHV	66897	BY	MX55FFH
66796	CM	MX05CBV	66828	HH	MX05CFE	66860	OM	MX05CHY	66898	QS	MX55FFJ
66797	CM	MX05CBY	66829	CM	MX05CFG	66861	BN	MX05CHZ	66899	BN	MX55FFK
66798	HH	MX05CCA	66830	CM	MX05CFJ	66862	OM	MX05CJE	66900	BY	MX55FFL
66799	CM	MX05CCD	66831	QS	MX05CFK	66863	OM	MX05CJF	66901	BN	MX55FFM
66800	HH	MX05CCF	66832	QS	MX05CFL	66864	OM	MX05CJJ	66902	BN	MX55FFO
66801	HH	MX05CCJ	66833	QS	MX05CFM	66865	OM	MX05CJO	66903	BN	MX55FFP
66802	CM	MX05CCK	66834	QS	MX05CFN	66866	OM	MX05CJU	66904	BN	MX55FFR
66803	HH	MX05CCN	66835	QS	MX05CFO	66867	BN	MX05CJV	66905	BN	MX55FFS
66804	HH	MX05CCO	66836	OM	MX05CFP	66868	OM	MX05CJY	66906	BN	MX55FFT
66805	BS	MX05CCU	66837	CM	MX05CFU	66869	OM	MX05CJZ	66907	BN	MX55FFU
66806	BS	MX05CCV	66838	NE	MX05CFV	66870	BN	MX05CKA	66908	QS	MX55FFV
66807	HH	MX05CCY	66839	NE	MX05CFY	66871	OM	MX05CKC	66909	BY	MX55FFW
66808	CM	MX05CCZ	66840	NE	MX05CGE	66872	BY	MX05CKD	66910	QS	MX55FFY
66809	HH	MX05CDE	66841	LE	MX05CGF	66873	BY	MX05CKE	66911	QS	MX55FFZ
66810	HH	MX05CDF	66842	NE	MX05CGG	66874	QS	MX05CKF	66912	QS	MX55FGA
66811	CM	MX05CDK	66843	NE	MX05CGK	66875	QS	MX55NWE	66913	QS	MX55FGC
66812	CM	MX05CDN	66844	OM	MX05CGO	66876	BN	MX05CKJ	66914	BY	MX55FGE
66813	BS	MX05CDO	66845	LE	MX05CGU	66880	BY	MX05CKO	66915	BY	MX55FGF
66814	CM	MX05CDU	66846	OM	MX05CGV	66881	SO	MX05CKP	66916	BY	MX55FGG
66815	CM	MX05CDV	66847	NE	MX05CGY	66882	SO	MX55HHR	66917	BY	MX55FGJ
66816	HH	MX05CDY	66848	OM	MX05CGZ	66883	SO	MX55HHP	66918	BY	MX55FGK
66817	CM	MX05CDZ	66849	LE	MX05CHC	66884	SO	MX55HHO	66919	BY	MX55FGM
66818	CM	MX05CEA	66850	IP	MX05CHD	66885	SO	MX05CLF	66920	QS	MX55FGN
66819	BS	MX05CEF	66851	NE	MX05CHF	66886	SO	MX55LHL	66922	BY	MX55FGP
66820	BS	MX05CEJ	66852	NE	MX05CHG	66890	QS	MX55NWH	66923	BY	MX55FGU
66821	BS	MX05CEK	66853	OM	MX05CHH	66891	QS	MX55UAA	66928	BY	MX55FHC
66822	BS	MX05CEO	66854	OM	MX05CHJ	66892	BY	MX55LDJ	66929	BY	MX55FHD
66823	BS	MX05CEU	66855	OM	MX05CHK	66893	QS	MX55LDK	66930	BY	MX55FHE
66824	BS	MX05CEV	66856	OM	MX05CHL	66894	BN	MX55FFD	66931	BN	MX55FHF
66825	BS	MX05CEY	66857	OM	MX05CHN	66895	BN	MX55FFE	66933	QS	MX55FHH

66934-66961 — Volvo B7RLE — Wrightbus Eclipse Urban — N43F — 2005

Fleet	Code	Reg	Fleet	Code	Reg	Fleet	Code	Reg	Fleet	Code	Reg
66934	WS	WX55UAA	66941	BA	WX55TZC	66948	B	WX55TZK	66955	O	WX55TZS
66935	WS	WX55UAB	66942	BA	WX55TZD	66949	B	WX55TZL	66956	WS	WX55TZT
66936	WS	WX55UAC	66943	BA	WX55TZE	66950	VN	WX55TZM	66957	VN	WX55TZU
66937	BA	WX55UAD	66944	SO	WX55TZF	66951	B	WX55TZN	66958	PT	WX55TZV
66938	BA	WX55TYZ	66945	SO	WX55TZG	66952	O	WX55TZO	66959	VN	WX55TZW
66939	BA	WX55TZA	66946	B	WX55TZH	66953	SO	WX55TZP	66960	PT	WX55TZY
66940	BA	WX55TZB	66947	B	WX55TZJ	66954	O	WX55TZR	66961	PT	WX55TZZ

66962-66987 — Volvo B7RLE — Wrightbus Eclipse Urban — N43F — 2005

Fleet	Code	Reg	Fleet	Code	Reg	Fleet	Code	Reg	Fleet	Code	Reg
66962	LE	KX05MHY	66969	LE	KX05MJU	66976	CO	KX05MGZ	66982	CO	KX05MHL
66963	LE	KX05MHZ	66970	LE	KX05MJV	66977	CO	KX05MHA	66983	CO	KX05MHM
66964	LE	KX05MJE	66971	LE	KX05MJY	66978	CO	KX05MHE	66984	CO	KX05MHN
66965	LE	KX05MJF	66972	LE	KX05AOC	66979	CO	KX05MHF	66985	CO	KX05MHO
66966	LE	KX05MJJ	66973	LE	KX05AOD	66980	CO	KX05MHJ	66986	CO	KX05MHU
66967	LE	KX05MJK	66974	LE	KX05AOE	66981	IP	KX05MHK	66987	IP	KX05MHV
66968	LE	KX05MJO	66975	LE	KX05MGY						

66988-66999 — Volvo B7RLE — Wrightbus Eclipse Urban — N43F — 2006-07 — *66992-4 N34D

Fleet	Code	Reg	Fleet	Code	Reg	Fleet	Code	Reg	Fleet	Code	Reg
66988	B	SF56GYP	66991	B	SF56GYT	66994	D	06D85192	66997	HP	YJ07LWE
66989	B	SF56GYR	66992	BA	RKZ4761	66995	YK	YJ07LWC	66998	HP	YJ07LWF
66990	B	SF56GYS	66993	BA	RKZ4760	66996	YK	YJ07LWD	66999	BD	YK57FCL

Alexander's Enviro 300 featured in the 2013 orders, with 67414, SN13CKO representing the batch. It is seen leaving Manchester for the Derker district of Oldham where it is allocated. *Steve Rice*

67401-67430

ADL E30D · ADL Enviro 300 · N41F · 2013

67401	BN	SN13CJV	67409	BN	SN13CKF	67417	OM	SN13CKV	67424	OM	SN13CLV
67402	BN	SN13CJX	67410	BN	SN13CKG	67418	OM	SN13CKX	67425	OM	SN13CLX
67403	BN	SN13CJY	67411	BN	SN13CKJ	67419	OM	SN13CKY	67426	OM	SN13CLY
67404	BN	SN13CJZ	67412	BN	SN13CKK	67420	OM	SN13CLF	67427	OM	SN13CLZ
67405	BN	SN13CKA	67413	OM	SN13CKL	67421	OM	SN13CLJ	67428	OM	SN13CME
67406	BN	SN13CKC	67414	OM	SN13CKO	67422	OM	SN13CLO	67429	OM	SN13CMF
67407	BN	SN13CKD	67415	OM	SN13CKP	67423	OM	SN13CLU	67430	OM	SN13CMK
67408	BN	SN13CKE	67416	OM	SN13CKU						

67431-67439

ADL E30D · ADL Enviro 300 · N44F · 2013-14

67431	RA	SL63GBF	67434	RA	SL63GBV	67436	RA	SL63GBY	67438	RA	SL63GCF
67432	RA	SL63GBO	67435	RA	SL63GBX	67437	RA	SL63GBZ	67439	RA	SL63GCK
67433	RA	SL63GBU									

67501	RAs	M626XWS	Dennis Javelin 12m	Wadham Stringer Vanguard III tv	1995	Abus, Bristol, 2005
67600	WRu	SN53KKY	TransBus Enviro 300	TransBus Enviro 300	N47F	2003

67601-67604

TransBus Enviro 300 · TransBus Enviro 300 · N44F · 2004

67601	WR	VX53VJV	67602	WR	VX53VJZ	67603	WR	VX53VKA	67604	WR	VX53VKB

67631-67651

ADL E30D · ADL Enviro 300 · N43F · 2005

67631	WR	VX54MOV	67636	WR	VX54MPV	67641	WR	VX54MRV	67648	WR	VX54MTJ
67632	WR	VX54MPE	67637	WR	VX54MPY	67642	WR	VX54MRY	67649	WR	VX54MTK
67633	WR	VX54MPF	67638	WR	VX54MPZ	67643	WR	VX54MSO	67650	WR	VX54MTO
67634	WR	VX54MPO	67639	WR	VX54MRO	67647	WR	VX54MTF	67651	WR	VX54MTU
67635	WR	VX54MPU	67640	WR	VX54MRU						

First Glasgow's *one* network links the city centre with Balloch and Dumbarton. Displaying the *one* logo and additional lettering is 67721, SN62AEK, pictured in Stockwell Street. *Mark Lyons*

67652-67664

			ADL E30D			ADL Enviro 300			N44F	2005			
67652	WR	VX05LVS	67656	WR	VX05LVW	67659	WR	VX05LWC	67662	WR	VX05LWF
67653	WR	VX05LVT	67657	WR	VX05LVY	67660	WR	VX05LWD	67663	WR	VX05LWG
67654	WR	VX05LVU	67658	WR	VX05LVZ	67661	WR	VX05LWE	67664	WR	VX05LWH
67655	WR	VX05LVV									

67665	WR	FN08AZZ	ADL E300			ADL Enviro 300			N44F	2008	Premiere, Nottingham, '13
67699	WR	PT59JPT	ADL E300			ADL Enviro 300			N44F	2010	JP Travel, Middleton, 2013

67701-67710

			ADL E300			ADL Enviro 300			NC37F	2010			
67701	LF	SN60EAA	67704	LF	SN60EAF	67707	LF	SN60EAM	67709	LF	SN60EAP
67702	LF	SN60EAC	67705	LF	SN60EAG	67708	LF	SN60EAO	67710	LF	SN60EAW
67703	LF	SN60EAE	67706	LF	SN60EAJ						

67711-67750

			ADL E30D			ADL Enviro 300			N41F	2012			
67711	DU	SN62ABU	67721	DU	SN62AEK	67731	DU	SN62AGV	67741	DU	SN62AKJ
67712	DU	SN62ABV	67722	DU	SN62AET	67732	DU	SN62AGY	67742	DU	SN62AKO
67713	DU	SN62ABX	67723	DU	SN62AEU	67733	DU	SN62AHD	67743	DU	SN62AKP
67714	DU	SN62ABZ	67724	DU	SN62AEY	67734	DU	SN62AHF	67744	DU	SN62AMV
67715	DU	SN62ACX	67725	DU	SN62AFE	67735	DU	SN62AHL	67745	DU	SN62ANR
67716	DU	SN62ACZ	67726	DU	SN62AFJ	67736	DU	SN62AHV	67746	DU	SN62ANU
67717	DU	SN62ADU	67727	DU	SN62AFK	67737	DU	SN62AHX	67747	DU	SN62AOA
67718	DU	SN62ADV	67728	DU	SN62AFU	67738	DU	SN62AJU	67748	DU	SN62AOC
67719	DU	SN62AEA	67729	DU	SN62AFY	67739	DU	SN62AJV	67749	SN	SN62AOF
67720	DU	SN62AEF	67730	DU	SN62AFZ	67740	DU	SN62AKG	67750	SN	SN62AOG

67751-67772

			ADL E30D			ADL Enviro 300			N41F	2013			
67751	PH	SN62AOZ	67757	PH	SN62ASX	67763	PH	SN62AUJ	67768	PH	SN13CGK
67752	PH	SN62APF	67758	PH	SN62ASZ	67764	PH	SN62AUU	67769	PH	SN13CGO
67753	PH	SN62APO	67759	PH	SN62ATZ	67765	PH	SN62AUW	67770	PH	SN13CGU
67754	PH	SN62APZ	67760	PH	SN62AUC	67766	PH	SN13CGF	67771	PH	SN13CGV
67755	PH	SN62ASO	67761	PH	SN62AUH	67767	PH	SN13CGG	67772	PH	SN13CGX
67756	PH	SN62ASU	67762	PH	SN62AUK						

Aberdeen's 67785, SN13CMV, carries Northern Lights names alongside lettering for routes 17/18. It was pictured shortly after delivery. *Murdoch Currie*

67773-67782

			ADL E30D			ADL Enviro 300		NC41F	2013		
67773	GS	SN62AXH	67776	GS	SN62AXU	67779	GS	SN62AXZ	67781	GS	SN62AYB
67774	GS	SN62AXK	67777	GS	SN62AXW	67780	GS	SN62AYA	67782	GS	SN62AYJ
67775	GS	SN62AXO	67778	GS	SN62AXY						

67783-67805

			ADL E30D			ADL Enviro 300		N41F	2013		
67783	AB	SN13CMO	67789	AB	SN13CNA	67795	AB	SN13CNO	67801	AB	SN13COA
67784	AB	SN13CMU	67790	AB	SN13CNC	67796	AB	SN13CNU	67802	AB	SN13COH
67785	AB	SN13CMV	67791	AB	SN13CNE	67797	AB	SN13CNV	67803	AB	SN13COJ
67786	AB	SN13CMX	67792	AB	SN13CNF	67798	AB	SN13CNX	67804	AB	SN13COU
67787	AB	SN13CMY	67793	AB	SN13CNJ	67799	AB	SN13CNY	67805	AB	SN13CPE
67788	AB	SN13CMZ	67794	AB	SN13CNK	67800	AB	SN13CNZ			

67806-67894

			ADL E30D			ADL Enviro 300		N41F	2013		
67806	SN	SN13EAY	67829	SN	SN13ECW	67851	B	SN13EES	67873	SN	SN63MYT
67807	SN	SN13EBA	67830	SN	SN13ECX	67852	B	SN13EET	67874	SN	SN63MYU
67808	SN	SN13EBC	67831	SN	SN13ECY	67853	B	SN13EEU	67875	SN	SN63MYV
67809	SN	SN13EBD	67832	SN	SN13ECZ	67854	B	SN13EEV	67876	SN	SN63MYW
67810	SN	SN13EBF	67833	B	SN13EDC	67855	B	SN13EEW	67877	SN	SN63MYX
67811	SN	SN13EBG	67834	B	SN13EDF	67856	B	SN13EEX	67878	SN	SN63MYY
67812	SN	SN13EBJ	67835	B	SN13EDJ	67857	B	SN13EEY	67879	SN	SN63MYZ
67813	SN	SN13EBK	67836	B	SN13EDK	67858	B	SN13EEZ	67880	SN	SN63MZD
67814	SN	SN13EBL	67837	B	SN13EDL	67859	B	SN13EFA	67881	SN	SN63MZE
67815	SN	SN13EBM	67838	B	SN13EDO	67860	B	SN13EFB	67882	SN	SN63MZF
67816	SN	SN13EBO	67839	B	SN13EDP	67861	B	SN13EFC	67883	SN	SN63MZG
67817	SN	SN13EBP	67840	B	SN13EDR	67862	B	SN13EFD	67884	SN	SK63ATY
67818	SN	SN13EBU	67841	B	SN13EDU	67863	B	SN13EFE	67885	SN	SK63ATZ
67819	SN	SN13EBV	67842	B	SN13EDV	67864	SN	SN13EFF	67886	SN	SK63AUA
67820	SN	SN13EBX	67843	B	SN13EDX	67865	SN	SN13EFG	67887	SN	SK63AUC
67821	SN	SN13EBZ	67844	B	SN13EEF	67866	SN	SN13EFH	67888	SN	SK63AUE
67822	SN	SN13ECA	67845	B	SN13EEG	67867	SN	SN13EFJ	67889	SN	SK63AUF
67823	SN	SN13ECC	67846	B	SN13EEH	67868	SN	SN13EFK	67890	SN	SK63AUH
67824	SN	SN13ECD	67847	B	SN13EEJ	67869	SN	SN13EFL	67891	SN	SK63AUJ
67825	SN	SN13ECF	67848	B	SN13EEM	67870	SN	SN63MYP	67892	SN	SK63AUL
67826	SN	SN13ECJ	67849	B	SN13EEO	67871	SN	SN63MYR	67893	SN	SK63AUM
67827	SN	SN13ECT	67850	B	SN13EEP	67872	SN	SN63MYS	67894	SN	SK63AUN
67828	SN	SN13ECV									

The 2014 First Bus Handbook

Four Alexander Dennis Enviro 350s are based at Chelmsford. The Alexander Dennis Enviro E35H is a heavyweight hybrid-electric bus chassis using hybrid technology. It uses a BAe Systems hybrid power train. 67903, SN13CHX, is shown. *Dave Heath*

67901-67904

			ADL E35H			ADL Enviro 350		N41F	2013		
67901	CM	SN13CHO	67902	CM	SN13CHV	67903	CM	SN13CHX	67904	CM	SN13CHY

68000	BRs	Q275LBA	Blue Bird		Blue Bird		B60F	1999		

68001-68006

			Blue Bird AARE			Blue Bird		S60F	2002		
68001	BL	RD51FKV	68003	BL	RD51FKZ	68005	BL	YS51JVE	68006	BL	YS51JVH
68002	BL	RD51FKW	68004	BL	RD51FLA						

68225-68229

			Irisbus Scolabus 24			Vehixel		S63F	2005	*Operated for GMPTE*	
68225	BN	FJ55KNB	68227	BN	FJ55KMY	68228	OM	FJ55KMZ	68229	BN	FN55EDV
68226	QS	FJ55KMO									

68301	SO	BX55NZV	Autosan Eagle A1012T		Autosan		S67D	2006	Truronian, 2008
68302	SO	BX06NZT	Autosan Eagle A1012T		Autosan		S67D	2006	Truronian, 2008

68503-68548

			BMC 1100FE Student			BMC		S60F	2004-05	*68515/6/27-30/45-8 WYPTE	
68503	LL	BX54VUN	68512	SO	RX54AOY	68522	BL	RX54OGZ	68534	CM	LK54FNL
68504	MU	CU54CYX	68513	LL	CU54DCE	68527	HX	YA54WBL	68535	CM	EU05DXR
68505	LL	CU54CYY	68514	BF	CU54DCF	68528	HX	YA54WBK	68536	SO	LK54FNF
68506	LL	CU54CYZ	68515	HX	YJ54YCO	68529	HX	YA54WBO	68537	SO	LK54FNH
68507	WR	KX54AHP	68516	HX	YJ54YCP	68530	HX	YA54WBN	68545	HX	YJ05VWA
68508	BR	KX54AHU	68518	AB	SV54CFY	68531	CM	LK54FNC	68546	HX	YJ55CAO
68509	BR	KX54AHY	68519	AB	SV54CFZ	68532	CM	LK54FNE	68547	HX	YJ55CAV
68510	CM	KX54ANR	68520	BR	KP54AZU	68533	SO	LK54FNJ	68548	HX	YJ55CAU
68511	SO	RX54AOV	68521	CM	KP54AZV						

68550-68566

			BMC 1100FE Student			BMC		S55F	2005-06		
68550	SO	HX05BUO	68555	CM	MX55NWS	68559	WR	LK55ABV	68563	SO	HX55AOK
68551	CM	EU05DXS	68556	LT	MX55NWC	68560	LT	LK55ABX	68564	SO	SF55TXA
68552	CM	EU05DXT	68557	SO	MX55NWD	68561	LT	HX55AOJ	68565	SO	SF55TXB
68553	SO	HX05BUJ	68558	GS	LK55ABU	68562	SO	HX55AOH	68566	GS	SF55TXC
68554	SO	LK05FCE									

68567-68571

			BMC 1100FE Student			BMC		S55F	2007-08		
68567	CFu	BV57MSO	68569	RAt	BV57MSX	68570	CFu	BV57MSY	68571	PLt	BG57ZGJ
68568	RAt	BV57MSU									

The First Student brand was originally used in the United States for school transport and is now used in Britain, predominantly in the Yorkshire area. A BMC 1100, 68534, LK54FNL, is one of nine allocated to Chelmsford. *Steve Rice*

68603-68648   BMC Condor 220   BMC   NC57F   2005-06   *Operated for Metro WYPTE*

68603	BD	YK55AAJ	68616	HU	YK55AUH	68628	BD	YJ06WTV	68640	BD	YJ06XEK
68606	BD	YK55AUP	68621	BD	YK55AVF	68630	BD	YJ06WTZ	68641	HX	YJ06XEL
68608	HX	YJ06XFR	68622	BD	YK55AVG	68631	BD	YJ06WUA	68642	HX	YK06ATO
68609	HX	YK55AUU	68623	BD	YK55AVJ	68635	HX	YK06DYJ	68643	HX	YK06CZZ
68610	HX	YK55AAN	68625	HX	YK55AVM	68638	HX	YK06DNN	68646	BD	YK06DAA
68614	HU	YK55AUE	68626	BD	YJ06WTX	68639	BD	YK06DTZ	68648	BD	YK06EHE
68615	HX	YK55AUF									

68651-68683   BMC Condor 220   BMC   NC57F   2006-07   *Operated for Metro WYPTE*

68651	BD	YJ56LJE	68659	HX	YJ56LLN	68668	HX	YJ56LKD	68675	HX	YJ56ZMU
68652	BD	YJ56LJF	68660	HX	YJ56LLO	68669	HX	YJ56LMX	68676	HX	YK07FTU
68653	BD	YJ56LJK	68662	BD	YJ56LNA	68670	HX	YJ56LRU	68677	HX	YK07FUD
68654	HX	YJ56LJN	68663	HX	YJ56LKE	68671	HX	YJ56LRN	68680	HX	YK07FUA
68655	HX	YJ56LJL	68664	HX	YJ56LJY	68672	BD	YJ56LRL	68682	HX	YK07FTP
68656	HX	YJ56LLG	68667	HX	YJ56LKC	68674	HX	YJ56WGA	68683	HX	YK07FTT
68657	HX	YJ56LLK									

68684-68700   BMC Condor 225   BMC   NC57F   2007-08   *Operated for Metro WYPTE*

68684	HU	YJ57VYX	68689	HU	YJ08XCR	68693	HU	YJ08XCS	68697	BD	YJ07XMB
68685	HU	YJ57VTV	68690	HU	YJ08XCO	68694	HU	YK07BJX	68698	BD	YJ07XWG
68686	HU	YJ57VVA	68691	HU	YJ08XCP	68695	HU	YK07BJY	68699	BD	YK07FTX
68687	HU	YJ57VYY	68692	HU	YJ08XCN	68696	HU	YK07BJZ	68700	BD	YJ07WBL

68701-68708   BMC Condor 220   BMC   NC57F   2005-07   *Operated for Metro WYPTE*

68701	HX	YK55JCN	68703	HX	YK06EFS	68705	HX	YJ57NFF	68707	HX	YJ57WKB
68702	HX	YK06EFR	68704	HX	YJ56ZTM	68706	HX	YJ57WKC	68708	HX	YJ07XND

68709	BD	YJ07FLP	BMC Condor 225	BMC	NC57F	2007	*Operated for Metro WYPTE*
68710	BD	YJ07XWF	BMC Condor 225	BMC	NC57F	2007	*Operated for Metro WYPTE*
68711	BD	YJ07WBK	BMC Condor 225	BMC	NC57F	2007	*Operated for Metro WYPTE*

69000-69011   Volvo B7RLE   Wrightbus Eclipse Urban   N43F*   2005   **69000-4 are N40F*

69000	YK	YK54ENP	69003	YK	YK54ENN	69006	VN	AU05DMF	69009	IP	AU05DMX
69001	YK	YK54ENL	69004	YK	YK54ENO	69007	IP	AU05DMO	69010	IP	AU05DMY
69002	YK	YK54ENM	69005	IP	AU05DME	69008	IP	AU05DMV	69011	VN	AU05DMZ

Representing the large order of Volvo B7RLEs for Scotland placed in 2006 is 69133, SV07EHK which is based in Aberdeen. It is seen in August 2013 while operating city service 3 from Mastrick to Cove.
Mark Bailey

69012-69134   Volvo B7RLE   Wrightbus Eclipse Urban   N43F   2006-07

69012	OG	SF55UAD	69043	RO	SF55UBC	69074	SN	SF06GXX	69105	SN	SF06GZP
69013	OG	SF55UAE	69044	RO	SF55UBD	69075	SN	SF06GXY	69106	SN	SF06GZR
69014	O	SF55UAG	69045	RO	SF55UBE	69076	O	SF06GXZ	69107	SN	SF06GZS
69015	O	SF55UAH	69046	RO	SF55UBG	69077	O	SF06GYA	69108	SN	SF06GZT
69016	O	SF55UAJ	69047	RO	SF55UBH	69078	O	SF06GYJ	69109	SN	SF06GZV
69017	OG	SF55UAK	69048	RO	SF55UBJ	69079	O	SF06GYK	69110	AB	SV06GRF
69018	OG	SF55UAL	69049	RO	SF55UBK	69080	O	SF06GYN	69111	PH	SF06GZX
69019	O	SF55UAM	69050	RO	SF55UBL	69081	O	SF06GYO	69112	PH	SF06GZY
69020	OG	SF55UAN	69051	RO	SF55UBM	69082	O	SF06GYP	69113	PH	SF06GZZ
69021	O	SF55UAO	69052	RO	SF55UBN	69083	O	SF06GYR	69114	PH	SF06HAA
69022	OG	SF55UAP	69053	RO	SF55UBO	69084	O	SF06GYS	69115	PH	SF06HAE
69023	OG	SF55UAR	69054	RO	SF55UBP	69085	PH	SF06GYT	69116	PH	SF06HAO
69024	OG	SF55UAS	69055	RO	SF55UBR	69086	SN	SF06GYU	69117	PH	SF06HAU
69025	OG	SF55UAT	69056	RO	SF55UBS	69087	SN	SF06GYV	69118	PH	SF06HAX
69026	OG	SF55UAU	69057	LF	SF06GXM	69088	SN	SF06GYW	69119	PH	SF06HBA
69027	LF	SF55UAV	69058	LF	SF06GXN	69089	SN	SF06GYX	69120	PH	SF06HBB
69028	OG	SF55UAW	69059	LF	SF06GXH	69090	SN	SF06GYY	69121	PH	SF06HBC
69029	OG	SF55UAX	69060	LF	SF06GXO	69091	SN	SF06GYZ	69122	AB	SV06GRK
69030	OG	SF55UAY	69061	LF	SF06GXP	69092	SN	SF06GZA	69123	AB	SV06GRU
69031	OG	SF55UAZ	69062	LF	SF06GXR	69093	O	SF06GZB	69124	AB	SV06GRX
69032	RO	SF55UBA	69063	LF	SF06GXS	69094	SN	SF06GZC	69125	AB	SV07EHB
69033	RO	SF55UBT	69064	LF	SF06GXT	69095	SN	SF06GZD	69126	AB	SV07EHC
69034	O	SF55UBU	69065	SN	SF06GXU	69096	SN	SF06GZE	69127	AB	SV07EHD
69035	O	SF55UBV	69066	SN	SF06GYB	69097	SN	SF06GZG	69128	AB	SV07EHE
69036	O	SF55UBW	69067	SN	SF06GYC	69098	SN	SF06GZH	69129	AB	SV07EHF
69037	O	SF55UBX	69068	SN	SF06GYD	69099	SN	SF06GZJ	69130	AB	SV07EHG
69038	O	SF06GXJ	69069	SN	SF06GYE	69100	SN	SF06GZK	69131	AB	SV07EHH
69039	B	SF06GXG	69070	SN	SF06GYG	69101	SN	SF06GZL	69132	AB	SV07EHJ
69040	B	SF06GXK	69071	SN	SF06GYH	69102	SN	SF06GZM	69133	AB	SV07EHK
69041	LF	SF06GXL	69072	SN	SF06GXV	69103	SN	SF06GZN	69134	AB	SV07EHL
69042	LF	SF55UBB	69073	SN	SF06GXW	69104	SN	SF06GZO			

69135-69244 Volvo B7RLE — Wrightbus Eclipse Urban — N43F — 2006

Fleet	Code	Reg	Fleet	Code	Reg	Fleet	Code	Reg	Fleet	Code	Reg
69135	BY	MV06CZS	69164	BN	MX06VNV	69191	B	MX56ADZ	69218	CE	MX56AEG
69136	BY	MV06CZG	69165	BY	MX06VMW	69192	B	MX56AEA	69219	CE	MX56AEJ
69137	BY	MV06CZT	69166	BY	MX06VMZ	69193	B	MX56AEB	69220	CE	MX56AEK
69138	BY	MV06CXB	69167	BY	MX06VNB	69194	B	MX56AEC	69221	CE	MX56AEL
69139	BN	MX06VOP	69168	BN	MX06VNC	69195	QS	MX06VPR	69222	CE	MX56AEM
69141	BN	MX06VOU	69169	BN	MX06VND	69196	QS	MX06VPT	69223	CE	MX56AEN
69142	BN	MX06VOV	69170	BN	MX06VNE	69197	QS	MX06VPU	69224	CE	MX56AEO
69143	BN	MX06VOY	69171	BN	MX06VNF	69198	QS	MX06VPV	69225	CE	MX56AEP
69144	BN	MX06VPA	69172	BN	MV06CZJ	69199	QS	MX06VPW	69226	CE	MX56AET
69145	BN	MX06VNW	69173	BN	MV06DWZ	69200	QS	MX06VPY	69227	CE	MX56AEU
69146	BN	MX06VNY	69174	BN	MX06VNK	69201	BN	MX06VPZ	69228	CE	MX56AEV
69147	BN	MX06VNZ	69175	BN	MX06VPO	69202	QS	MX06VRC	69229	CE	MX56AEW
69148	BN	MX06VOA	69176	QS	MX06VPP	69203	QS	MX06VPC	69230	CE	MX56AEY
69149	BN	MX06VOB	69177	OM	MX06YXJ	69204	OM	MX06VPD	69231	PT	MX56AEZ
69150	BN	MX06VOC	69178	BY	MX06YXK	69205	OM	MX06VPE	69232	PT	MX56AFA
69151	BN	MX06VOD	69179	QS	MX06YXL	69206	CE	MV06DYU	69233	PT	MX56AFE
69152	BN	MX06VOF	69180	QS	MX06YXM	69207	CE	MX06VPG	69234	PT	MX56AFF
69153	BN	MX06VOG	69181	B	MX06YXN	69208	CE	MX06VPJ	69235	PT	MX56AFJ
69154	BN	MX06VOH	69182	B	MX06YXO	69209	CE	MX06VPK	69236	PT	MX56AFK
69155	BN	MX06VNL	69183	B	MX06YXP	69210	WH	MX06VPL	69237	PT	MX56AFN
69156	BN	MX06VNM	69184	B	MX06YXR	69211	WH	MX06VPM	69238	PT	MX56AFO
69157	BN	MX06VNN	69185	QS	MX56ACV	69212	WH	MX06VPN	69239	RA	MX56AFU
69158	BN	MX06VNO	69186	BY	MX56ACY	69213	WH	MX06YXS	69240	LL	MX56AFV
69159	BN	MX06VNR	69187	B	MX56ACZ	69214	WH	MX06YXT	69241	LL	MX56AFY
69160	BN	MX06VNR	69188	B	MX56ADO	69215	WH	MX56AED	69242	LL	MX56AFZ
69161	BN	MX06VNS	69189	B	MX56ADU	69216	WH	MX56AEE	69243	LL	MX56AGO
69162	BN	MX06VNT	69190	B	MX56ADV	69217	WH	MX56AEF	69244	LL	MX56AGU
69163	BN	MX06VNU									

69245-69294 Volvo B7RLE — Wrightbus Eclipse Urban — N43F — 2007

Fleet	Code	Reg	Fleet	Code	Reg	Fleet	Code	Reg	Fleet	Code	Reg
69245	SO	YJ07WFM	69258	LT	SK57ADU	69271	BD	YJ07WFX	69283	LT	SN57JCO
69246	SO	YJ07WFN	69259	LT	SK57ADV	69272	BD	YJ07WFY	69284	LT	SN57JCU
69247	SO	YJ07WFO	69260	LT	SK57ADX	69273	BD	YJ07WFZ	69285	LT	SN57JCV
69248	SO	YJ07WFP	69261	LT	SK57ADZ	69274	BD	YJ07WGA	69286	LT	SN57JCX
69249	LL	YJ07WFR	69262	LT	SK57AEA	69275	YK	YJ57YSN	69287	LT	SN57JCY
69250	LL	YJ07WFS	69263	LT	SK57AEB	69276	YK	YJ57YSM	69288	LT	SN57JCZ
69251	LL	YJ07WFT	69264	LT	SK57AEC	69277	YK	YJ57YSO	69289	LT	SN57JDF
69252	LL	YJ07WFU	69265	AB	SV57EYH	69278	YK	YJ57YSP	69290	LT	SN57JDJ
69253	BA	YJ07WFV	69266	AB	SV57EYJ	69279	YK	YJ57YSR	69291	LT	SN57JDK
69254	LT	SK07JVN	69267	AB	SV57EYK	69280	LT	SN57MSU	69292	LT	SN57HZX
69255	LT	SK07JVO	69268	YK	YJ57YSK	69281	LT	SN57JBZ	69293	LT	SN57HZY
69256	LT	SK07JVP	69269	YK	YJ57YSL	69282	LT	SN57JCJ	69294	LT	SN57HZZ
69257	LT	SK57ADO	69270	BD	YJ07WFW						

69295-69298 Volvo B7RLE — Wrightbus Eclipse Urban — N38F — 2004 — Hutchison, Overtown, 2007

Fleet	Code	Reg	Fleet	Code	Reg	Fleet	Code	Reg	Fleet	Code	Reg
69295	B	SF04HXW	69296	B	SF04HXX	69297	B	SF04ZPE	69298	B	SF04ZPG

69299-69328 Volvo B7RLE — Wrightbus Eclipse Urban — N43F — 2008-09

Fleet	Code	Reg	Fleet	Code	Reg	Fleet	Code	Reg	Fleet	Code	Reg
69299	BD	YJ08GWX	69305	LL	CU08AHX	69317	BD	YJ09FWM	69323	HU	YJ09FWT
69300	BD	YJ08GWY	69306	YK	YJ09FWA	69318	BD	YJ09FWN	69324	HU	YJ09FWU
69301	LL	CU08AHN	69307	HU	YJ09FWB	69319	BD	YJ09FWO	69325	OM	YJ09FWV
69302	LL	CU08AHO	69308	HU	YJ09FWC	69320	BD	YJ09FWP	69326	QS	YJ09FWW
69303	LL	CU08AHP	69315	BD	YJ58RVA	69321	BD	YJ09FWR	69327	QS	YJ09FWX
69304	LL	CU08AHV	69316	BD	YJ09FWL	69322	BD	YJ09FWS	69328	OM	YJ09FWY

69329-69350 Volvo B7RLE — Wrightbus Eclipse Urban — N43F — 2008

Fleet	Code	Reg	Fleet	Code	Reg	Fleet	Code	Reg	Fleet	Code	Reg
69329	HU	YJ08CDE	69335	BM	YJ08CDV	69341	BM	YJ08CEK	69346	BM	YJ08CEX
69330	HU	YJ08CDF	69336	BM	YJ08CDX	69342	BM	YJ08CEN	69347	BM	YJ08CEY
69331	BM	YJ08CDK	69337	BM	YJ08CDY	69343	BM	YJ08CEO	69348	BM	YJ08CFA
69332	BM	YJ08CDN	69338	BM	YJ08CDZ	69344	BM	YJ08CEU	69349	BM	YJ08CFD
69333	BM	YJ08CDO	69339	BM	YJ08CEA	69345	BM	YJ08CEV	69350	BM	YJ08CFE
69334	BM	YJ08CDU	69340	BM	YJ08CEF						

Route 3 from Lords Hill to Thornhill in Southampton has been re-branded in an all-over red scheme and is now named *the three*. Illustrating the scheme is 69390, HY09AOS from the 2009 batch. *Mark Lyons*

69351-69379   Volvo B7RLE   Wrightbus Eclipse Urban   N43F   2008

69351	AB	SV08FHA	69359	YK	YJ08ZGM	69366	YK	YJ08XYE	69373	YK	YJ08XYN
69352	AB	SV08FHB	69360	YK	YJ08ZGN	69367	YK	YJ08XYF	69374	YK	YJ08XYO
69353	AB	SV08FHC	69361	YK	YJ08ZGO	69368	YK	YJ08XYG	69375	YK	YJ08XYP
69354	AB	SV08FHD	69362	YK	YJ08ZGP	69369	YK	YJ08XYH	69376	YK	YJ08XYR
69355	AB	SV08FHE	69363	YK	YJ08XYB	69370	YK	YJ08XYK	69377	YK	YJ08XYS
69356	AB	SV08FHF	69364	YK	YJ08XYC	69371	YK	YJ08XYL	69378	YK	YJ08XYT
69357	AB	SV08FHG	69365	YK	YJ08XYD	69372	YK	YJ08XYM	69379	YK	YJ08XXW
69358	YK	YJ08ZGL									

69380-69401   Volvo B7RLE   Wrightbus Eclipse Urban   N38F   2009

69380	LL	HY09AJX	69386	SO	HY09AZB	69392	SO	HY09AOR	69397	SO	HY09AZL
69381	LL	HY09AKG	69387	SO	HY09AUW	69393	SO	HY09AZD	69398	SO	HY09AUX
69382	LL	HY09AOU	69388	SO	HY09AOT	69394	SO	HY09AZC	69399	SO	HY09AZN
69383	LL	HY09AZA	69389	SO	HY09AUO	69395	SO	HY09AZF	69400	SO	HY09AZJ
69384	LL	HY09AKF	69390	SO	HY09AOS	69396	SO	HY09AZO	69401	SO	HY09AZG
69385	SO	HY09AJV	69391	SO	HY09AUV						

69402-69420   Volvo B7RLE   Wrightbus Eclipse Urban   N43F   2009

69402	LT	SN09EZW	69407	LT	SN09FBC	69413	HP	YJ09FXA	69417	HP	YJ09FXE
69403	LT	SN09EZX	69408	LT	SN09FBD	69414	HP	YJ09FXB	69418	HP	YJ09FXF
69404	LT	SN09FAU	69409	LT	SN09FBE	69415	HP	YJ09FXC	69419	HU	YJ09FXG
69405	LT	SN09FBA	69410	LT	SN09FBF	69416	HP	YJ09FXD	69420	OM	YJ09FXH
69406	LT	SN09FBB	69412	HP	YJ09FWZ						

69421-69434   Volvo B7RLE   Wrightbus Eclipse Urban   N43F   2009

69421	CO	AU58FFH	69425	IP	AU58FFM	69429	IP	AU58FFR	69432	IP	AU58FFV
69422	IP	AU58FFJ	69426	IP	AU58FFN	69430	CO	AU58FFS	69433	IP	AU58FFW
69423	IP	AU58FFK	69427	IP	AU58FFO	69431	IP	AU58FFT	69434	CM	EU58JWZ
69424	IP	AU58FFL	69428	IP	AU58FFP						

In October 2011 Volvo launched the 7900 Hybrid bus in left-hand drive format and in 2013 just First and Lothian Buses took this new model in right-hand drive format into stock in Britain. Registered by Volvo in the Midlands with index marks starting with B have been supplied to recent deliveries. Nineteen are allocated to Basildon including 69903, BV13ZBE, seen passing through Billericay. *Dave Heath*

69435-69460

Volvo B7RLE — Wrightbus Eclipse Urban 2 — NC43F — 2009

69435	BA	WX59BYM	69442	WS	WX59BYU	69449	LH	WX59BZC	69455	LH	WX59BZJ
69436	BA	WX59BYN	69443	WS	WX59BYV	69450	LH	WX59BZD	69456	LH	WX59BZK
69437	BA	WX59BYO	69444	WS	WX59BYW	69451	LH	WX59BZE	69457	LH	WX59BZL
69438	WS	WX59BYP	69445	WS	WX59BYY	69452	LH	WX59BZF	69458	LH	WX59BZM
69439	WS	WX59BYR	69446	WS	WX59BYZ	69453	LH	WX59BZG	69459	WS	WX59BZN
69440	WS	WX59BYS	69447	WS	WX59BZA	69454	LH	WX59BZH	69460	WS	WX59BZO
69441	WS	WX59BYT	69448		WX59BZB						

69461-69485

Volvo B7RLE — Wrightbus Eclipse Urban — N43F — 2009

69461	DN	YN09HFH	69468	BD	YJ09NYC	69474	BD	YJ09NYM	69480	BD	YJ09NYT
69462	DN	YN09HFJ	69469	BD	YJ09NYD	69475	BD	YJ09NYN	69481	BD	YJ09NYU
69463	DN	YN09HFK	69470	BD	YJ09NYF	69476	BD	YJ09NYO	69482	BD	YJ09NYV
69464	DN	YN09HFL	69471	BD	YJ09NYG	69477	BD	YJ09NYP	69483	BD	YJ09NYW
69465	DN	YN09HFM	69472	BD	YJ09NYH	69478	BD	YJ09NYR	69484	BD	YJ09NYX
69466	BD	YJ09NYA	69473	BD	YJ09NYK	69479	BD	YJ09NYS	69485	BD	YJ09NYY
69467	BD	YJ09NYB									

69500-69531

Volvo B7RLE — Wrightbus Eclipse Urban 2 — NC37F — 2010-11

69500	HG	BJ10VGA	69508	HG	BJ11EBX	69516	CM	BJ11ECE	69524	BN	BD11CEV
69501	HG	BJ10VGD	69509	HG	BJ11XHZ	69517	CM	BJ11ECD	69525	BN	BD11CFA
69502	HG	BJ10VGC	69510	HG	BJ11EBU	69518	CM	BJ11ECT	69526	BN	BD11CEY
69503	HG	BJ10VGE	69511	HG	BJ11EBZ	69519	CM	BJ11ECV	69527	BN	BD11CEX
69504	HG	BJ10VGF	69512	CM	BJ11ECA	69520	CM	BJ11ECW	69528	BN	BD11CFG
69505	HG	BJ10VGG	69513	CM	BJ11ECC	69521	BN	BD11CEN	69529	BN	BD11CFJ
69506	HG	BJ11XHY	69514	CM	BJ11ECF	69522	BN	BD11CEU	69530	BN	BD11CFF
69507	HG	BJ11EBV	69515	CM	BJ11ECN	69523	BN	BD11CEO	69531	BN	BD11CFE

69532	IP	PL05UBS	Volvo B7RLE	Wrightbus Eclipse Urban	NC--F	2005	Transbus, 2013
69533	IP	PL05UBR	Volvo B7RLE	Wrightbus Eclipse Urban	NC--F	2005	Transbus, 2013

69537-69555

Volvo B7RLE — Wrightbus Eclipse Urban 2 — NC42F — 2012-13

69537	HO	BF63HDN	69544	HO	BF12KWD	69548	HO	BF12KWJ	69552	HO	BF12KWP
69538	HO	BF63HDU	69545	HO	BF12KWC	69549	HO	BF12KWK	69553	HO	BF12KWM
69539	HO	BF63HDO	69546	HO	BF12KWL	69550	HO	BF12KWO	69554	HO	BF12KWS
69542	HO	BF12KWE	69547	HO	BF12KWH	69551	HO	BF12KWN	69555	HO	BF12KWR
69543	HO	BF12KWG									

The 2014 First Bus Handbook

Built in Wroclaw, Poland, the Volvo 7900 is the successor to the heavier 7700 model. This new bus is proving to be considerably more fuel efficient. The side panels are manufactured from fibreglass and various plastic materials and are glued together, while the aluminium and the patented assembly method makes it more resistant to corrosion. The vehicle has the same hybrid drive-line as the B5LH double-deck with a five litre diesel engine, an electric motor and the Volvo I-shift transmission. The buses at Slough are in a blue livery and are dedicated to the service that links the town with Heathrow Airport. 69922, BV13ZCK, is shown. *Mark Lyons*

69556-69587   Volvo B7RLE   Wrightbus Eclipse Urban 2   N43F   2013

69556	HU	BV13ZDH	69564	HU	BD13NFK	69572	BY	BD13OHL	69580	HX	BT13YVW
69557	HU	BV13ZDJ	69565	HU	BD13NFO	69573	BY	BD13OHN	69581	HX	BT13YVX
69558	HU	BV13ZDK	69566	BY	BD13NFP	69574	BD	BD13OHO	69582	HX	BT13YVY
69559	HU	BV13YZZ	69567	BY	BD13NFM	69575	BD	BD13OHP	69583	HX	BT13YVZ
69560	HU	BG13VUD	69568	BY	BD13NFN	69576	BD	BD13OHR	69584	HX	BT13YWA
69561	HU	BG13VUC	69569	BD	BD13NFR	69577	BD	BD13OHS	69585	HX	BT13YWB
69562	HU	BG13VUE	69570	BD	BD13NFV	69578	HX	BD13OHT	69586	HX	BT13YWC
69563	HU	BD13NFL	69571	BY	BD13OHK	69579	HX	BT13YVV	69587	HX	BT13YWD

69901-69919   Volvo 7900 Hybrid   Volvo   N40F   2013

69901	BS	BV13ZBC	69906	BS	BV13ZBJ	69911	BS	BV13ZBR	69916	BS	BV13ZBY
69902	BS	BV13ZBD	69907	BS	BV13ZBL	69912	BS	BV13ZBT	69917	BS	BV13ZBZ
69903	BS	BV13ZBE	69908	BS	BV13ZBN	69913	BS	BV13ZBU	69918	BS	BV13ZCA
69904	BS	BV13ZBF	69909	BS	BV13ZBO	69914	BS	BV13ZBW	69919	BS	BV13ZCE
69905	BS	BV13ZBG	69910	BS	BV13ZBP	69915	BS	BV13ZBX			

69920-69934   Volvo 7900 Hybrid   Volvo   NC37F   2013-14

69920	SH	BV13ZCF	69924	SH	BV13ZCN	69928	SH	BV13ZCX	69932	SH	BJ63UJW
69921	SH	BV13ZCJ	69925	SH	BV13ZCO	69929	SH	BV13ZCY	69933	SH	BJ63UJX
69922	SH	BV13ZCK	69926	SH	BV13ZCT	69930	SH	BJ63UHZ	69934	SH	BJ63UJZ
69923	SH	BV13ZCL	69927	SH	BV13ZCU	69931	SH	BJ63UJV			

90092	ROs	OWJ782A	Leyland Titan PD3	Roe		RV	1963	
90489	HUs	RL02FYX	Dennis Dart SLF 10.3m	Marshall Capital 2	N--F	2002	St Helen's College, 2012	
90557	SOs	EHO228	Guy Arab I	Weymann	H32/26R	1942	Provincial	

Allocations - March 2014

Aberdeen

Aberdeen (King Street) - AB

Volvo B10BLA	10045							
Volvo B7LA	10047	10048	10049	10050	10051	10052	10136	10138
	10141	10144	10148	10154	10155	10156	10157	10158
	10159	10160	10161	10162	10163	10164	10165	10166
	10167	10168	10169	10170	10171	10172	10173	10183
Volvo B12B	20021							
Volvo B12T	20205	20207						
Volvo B7R	20351	20352	20353	20367	20372	20373	20374	
Volvo B12M	20505							
Scania coach	23021	23305	23306	23330	23401	23402		
Temsa Safari	29004	29005	29006	29007				
Trident	32845	32897	32898	32918	32923	32927	32962	32973
	32974	32975	32976	32994				
Volvo B9TL	37633	37634	37635	37636	37637	37638	37639	37640
	37641	37642	37643	37644				
Mercedes-Benz Vario	56001	56005	56006	56007	56008	56009		
Mercedes-Benz Atego	56501							
Volvo B10BLE	62122	62123	62124	62125	62126	62127	62128	62132
	62133	62134	62135	62136	62137	62138	62139	62140
	62141	62149	62150	62151	62152	62153	62154	62155
	62163	62164	62165	62166	62167	62168	62169	62170
	62171	62172	62174	62175	62176	62177	62178	62179
	62180	62181	62182	62183	62191	62192	62195	62196
	62197	62198	62199	62200	62201	62202	62203	62204
Bluebird Schoolbus	62228							
Enviro 300	67783	67784	67785	67786	67787	67788	67789	67790
	67791	67792	67793	67794	67795	67796	67797	67798
	67799	67800	67801	67802	67803	67804	67805	
BMC Schoolbus	68518	68519						
Volvo B7RLE	69110	69122	69123	69124	69125	69126	69127	69128
	69129	69130	69131	69132	69133	69134	69265	69266
	69267	69351	69352	69353	69354	69355	69356	69357

Ancillary / Reserve / Specials:

Volvo B10BLA	10044	10108
Volvo B12M	20507	
Atlantean	31528	31577
Daimler CVG6	31529	
Trident	32928	32970
Volvo B10BLE	62173	
Albion	62121	

Scotland East

Balfron (Dunmore Street) - BF

Olympian	30745	30746	30748	30749	30750	
Scania N94UD	36022					
Dart	40946	41754	41755			
Optare Solo	53704	53705				
Volvo B10BLE	62188	62189	62206	62211	62219	62220
Scania L94UB	65708	65751				
BMC Schoolbus	68514					

Bannockburn (Cowie Road, Stirling) - BK

Volvo B7R	20355	20358					
Olympian	30560	30740	30743	30744	30751	31497	34015	34066
	34067	34075	34076	34290			
Scania N94	36013	36021	36026	36028	36029		
Dart	41487						
Scania L94 UB	60163	60165	60166	60168	60178	60180	60192	60197
	60203	60220	60221	61214	61218	61228	62355	62356
	62357	65712	65713	65714	65715	65716	65717	65718
	65719	65720	65721	65722	65723		
Scania L113 CRL	62302	62303	62304	62305	62309	62312	62359	62383
	62394	65594	65598	65694	65695	65709	65710	65711
Volvo B10BLE	62212	62213					

Ancillary / Reserve / Specials:
Dart   40938
Scania   62310

Galashiels (Stirling Street) - GS

Volvo B7R	20300	20301	20326	20327	20368	20371	
Olympian	31446	31447	31684	31687	31688	34048	
Volvo B7TL	31790	31791	31792	32669	32670	32671	32672
Volvo B9TL	37133	37134					
Dart	40899	40911	40915	41751	41752	41753	41756
Optare Solo	50275						
Mercedes-Benz	56003						
Volvo B10BLE	62184	62187	62222	62223	62227		
Scania L94UB	65742	65743	65744	65745	65746	65747	65748	65749
	65750						
Enviro 300	67773	67774	67775	67776	67777	67778	67779	67780
	67781	67782					
BMC Schoolbus	68558	68566					

Ancillary / Reserve / Specials:
Dart   40703

Larbert (Stirling Road) - LT

Volvo B7R	20302	20307	20360	20369			
Olympian	30826	30827	30828	30829	31440	31441	
Volvo B7TL	31558	31559	31560	31561	31562	31563	
Trident	32830	32831	32834	32841	32842	32889	32892	32893
	32895	32896	32904	32907	32909	32910	32914	32919
	32921	32922	32924	32949	32968	32995	
Dart	41337	41488	43834	43842	43844		
Optare Solo	50283	50460	50468	53702	53703	53706	
Plaxton Primo	57001	57002					
Scania L94UB	60167	60182	60187	60195	60198	60199	61222	61223
	61229	61231	61233	65595	65597	65599	65601	65662
	65663	65664	65698	65699	65752	65753	65754	
Volvo B10BLE	62131	62157	62158	62185	62186	62190	62205	62207
	62208	62209	62210	62221	62224	62225	62226	
Enviro 300	62411	62412					
BMC Schoolbus	68556	68560	68561				
Volvo B7RLE	69254	69255	69256	69257	69258	69259	69260	69261
	69262	69263	69264	69280	69281	69282	69283	69284
	69285	69286	69287	69288	69289	69290	69291	69292
	69293	69294	69402	69403	69404	69405	69406	69407
	69408	69409	69410				

Ancillary / Reserve / Specials:

Olympian	30741	31445	31572	31656	31660	31663	31666	31667
	31669						
Trident	32824						
Scania	60188	62345					
Volvo B10BLE	62156						

Livingston (Deans Road) - LV

Volvo B7R	20354	20356	20359	20361	20362	20363	20364	20366
	20370							
Volvo B7TL	32221	32225	32226	32227	32228	32294	32295	32296
	32297	32298	32299	32673	32674	32675	32676	32677
	32678	32679	32680	32681	32682	32683		
Trident	32811	32813	32814	32821	32837	32838	32870	32917
	32934	32948	32951	32967				
Scania OmniDekka	36009	36012	36014	36015	36016	36017	36018	36019
	36020	36024	36027					
Volvo B9TL	37135	37136	37137	37138	37139	37140	37141	37142
	37143	37144	37145	37266	37267	37268	37269	37270
	37271	37272	37273					
Scania L94UB	61215	61216	61217	61219	61220	61221	61225	62385
	62386	62387	62388	62389	62390	62392	65703	
Mercedes Benz Citaro	64003	64004	64007	64008	64010	64011		

Ancillary / Reserve / Specials:
Volvo B10M 20405
Dart 43835
Scania 60181 60204

Musselburgh (The Mall) - MU

Volvo B7R	20357	20365						
Olympian	30832							
Volvo B7TL	32222	32223	32224					
Trident	33037	33050	33059	33093	33131	33135	33137	33138
	33139	33140						
Scania OmniDekka	36007	36008	36010	36011	36023	36025	36030	
Mercedes-Benz	56002	56004						
Scania L94UB	61224	61226	61227	61230	61232	62358	65700	65701
	65702							
BMC Schoolbus	68504							

Glasgow

Blantyre (Station Road) - B

Volvo B7TL	31787	31788	31789	31793	31794	31795	31796	31797
	31798	31799	31800	31801	31802	31803	31804	32604
	32605	32606	32607	32608	32609	32610	37180	37181
	37182	37183	37184	37185				
Trident	32960	32977	32982	32983	32984	32987	32988	32989
	32990	32991	32992	32997	32999			
Volvo B9TL	37238	37239	37240	37241	37242	37243	37244	37245
	37278							
Dart	41217	41221	41242	41306	41307	41310	41314	41410
	41426	41683	41773	41775	41776	41777	41778	41779
VW Transporter	54302	54304	54307					
Fiat Ducato	54403							
Volvo B10BLE	61597	61598	61599	61600	61601	61602	61603	61604
	61605	61606	61607	61608	61609	61610	61611	66233
	66234							
Volvo B7RLE	66735	66736	66737	66770	66771	66946	66947	66948
	66949	66951	66988	66989	66990	66991	69039	69040
	69181	69182	69183	69184	69187	69188	69189	69190
	69191	69192	69193	69194	69295	69296	69297	69298
Enviro 300	67833	67834	67835	67836	67837	67838	67839	67840
	67841	67842	67843	67844	67845	67846	67847	67848
	67849	67850	67851	67852	67853	67854	67855	67856
	67857	67858	67859	67860	67861	67862	67863	

Ancillary / Reserve / Specials:
Volvo B12M	20506			
Olympian	31486			
Trident	32888	32890		
Volvo B6BLE	40562			
Dart	41216	41222	41236	41246

Cumbernauld (Glencryan Road) - CD (works & store)

Ancillary / Reserve / Specials:
Olympian	31200	31469	31477	31481	31483	31489	31491	31492
Trident	32816	32839	32840	32844	32848	32865	32868	32871
	32891	32958	32965					

Dumbarton (Birch Road, Broadmeadow Industrial Estate) - DU

Volvo B12M	20502	20503	20504	20508	20509			
Olympian	31444							
Scania L94UB	61017	61018	61019	61022	61024	61026	61028	61296
	61298	61579	61584	61683	61685	61693	65596	
Enviro 300	67711	67712	67713	67714	67715	67716	67717	67718
	67719	67720	67721	67722	67723	67724	67725	67726
	67727	67728	67729	67730	67731	67732	67733	67734
	67735	67736	67737	67738	67739	67740	67741	67742
	67743	67744	67745	67746	67747	67748		

Ancillary / Reserve / Specials:
Olympian	31438	31442	31448
Scania	61291	61575	

Glasgow (Victoria Road, Larkfield) - LF

Olympian	31435	31449						
Volvo B7TL	32543	32544	32546	32547	32549	32551	32561	32562
	32564	32565	32569	32571	32572	32574	32583	32598
	32599	32600	32601	32602	32603	32611	32612	32614
	32622	32623	32624	32625	32626	32657	37166	37167
	37168	37169	37170	37171	37172	37173	37174	37175
	37176	37177	37178	37179				
Trident	32961	33000	33008	33009	33010	33011	33012	33013
	33014	33015	33016	33017	33018	33019	33040	33046
	33053	33054	33089	33091	33092	33094	33096	33097
	33114	33115	33116	33117	33118	33119	33120	33121
	33122							
Volvo B9TL	37186	37187	37188	37189	37190	37191	37192	37193
	37194	37195	37196	37197	37198	37199	37200	37201
	37202	37203	37204	37205	37206	37207	37208	37209
	37210	37211	37212	37213	37214	37215	37216	37217
	37218	37219	37220	37221	37222	37223	37224	37225
	37226	37227	37530	37531	37532	37533	37534	37535
	37536	37537	37538	37539	37540	37541	37542	37543
	37544	37736	37737	37738	37739	37740	37741	37742
	37743	37744	37745	37746	37747	37748	37749	37750
	37751							
Enviro 400	33904	33905	33906	33907	33908	33909	33910	33911
	33912	33913	33914	33915	33916	33917	33918	33919
	33920	33921	33922	33923				
Enviro 500	38201	38202	38203	38204	38205	38206	38207	38208
	38209	38210	38211	38212	38213	38214	38215	38216
	38217	38218	38219	38220	38221	38222	38223	38224
	38225							
Fiat	54404	54405	54406	54407				
Scania L94UB	61025	61027	61667	61669	61671	61672	61673	61675
	61676	61677	61678	61679	61680	61681	61682	61684
	61686	61687	61688	61689	61690	61691	61694	61695
	61696	61697	61698	61699	61700	61701	61702	61704
	65591	65592	65593	65693	65696	65697	65755	65756
	65757	65758						
Volvo B7L	61306	61589	61615	61627	61628	61629	61630	61632

	61634	61635	61637	61640	61641	61642	61643	61644
	61645	61646	61647	61648	61649	61650	61651	61656
	61657	61658	61659	61660	61661			
Enviro 300	67701	67702	67703	67704	67705	67706	67707	67708
	67709	67710						
Volvo B7RLE	69027	69041	69042	69057	69058	69059	69060	69061
	69062	69063	69064					

Ancillary / Reserve / Specials:

Olympian	31443							
Volvo B7TL	32052	32563						
Trident	32824	32825	32826	32827	32828	32829	32920	32971
Dart	41243	41245	41681	41682				
Volvo B6	48045							
Volvo B10M	60464	60466	61256	61266				
Scania	61020	61021	61043	61044	61158	61292	61293	61294
	61295	61299	61300	61478	61524	61534	61537	61540
	61543	61545	61548	61557	61558	61559	61562	61564
	61565	61567	61568	61572	61573	61574	61576	61580
	61581	61582	61586	61668	61670	65530	65535	65536

Glasgow (Tollcross Road, Parkhead) - PH

Volvo B7TL	32556	32557	32558	32559	32560	32566	32567	32568
	32573	32577	32578	32579	32580	32581	32584	32585
	32587	32589	32613	32615	32616	32617	32618	32619
	32620	32621						
Trident	32845	32931	32935	32936	32937	32939	32940	32941
	32942	32946	32947	32950	32964	32978	32980	32996
	32998	33020	33021	33022	33023	33024	33025	33026
	33027	33028	33033	33034	33035	33343	33344	33345
	33346	33347	33348	33349	33350	33351	33352	33353
	33354	33355	33356	33357	33358	33359	33360	33361
	33362	33363	33364	33365	33366	33367	33368	33369
	33370	33371	33372	33374	33375	33386		
Volvo B7TL	37147	37148	37149	37150	37151	37152	37153	37154
	37155							
Dart	41405	41406	41414	41415	41416	41417	41418	42885
	42886	42887	42888					
Volvo B7L	61587	61588	61590	61591	61592	61593	61594	61595
	61596	61663	61664	66349				
Enviro 300	67751	67752	67753	67754	67755	67756	67757	67758
	67759	67760	67761	67762	67763	67764	67765	67766
	67767	67768	67769	67770	67771	67772		
Volvo B7RLE	69085	69111	69112	69113	69114	69115	69116	69117
	69118	69119	69120	69121				

Ancillary / Reserve / Specials:

Olympian	30107	31478						
Trident	32805	32815	32820	32832	32833	32835	32836	32843
	32866	32952						
Volvo B6BLE	40560							
Volvo B10M	61391	61499						

Glasgow (South Street, Scotstoun) - SN

Volvo B7TL	32300	32301	32302	32303	32304	32305	32545	32548
	32550	32552	32553	32554	32555	32570	32575	32576
	32582	32586	32588	32590	32591	32592	32593	32594
	32595	32596	32597					
Trident	32925	32956	32969	32979	32981	32985	32986	32993
Enviro 400	33901	33902	33903					
Enviro 400 Hybrid	39101	39102	39103	39104	39105	39106	39107	39108
	39109	39110						
Dart	40828	40830	41244	41278	41279	41288	41301	41302
	41303	41304	41311	41312	41313	41407	41408	41409
	41684	41685						
Optare Solo	40965	40966	50461	50462	50463	50464	50465	53201
	53202	53203						
Enviro 300	67749	67750	67806	67807	67808	67809	67810	67811

The 2014 First Bus Handbook

	67812	67813	67814	67815	67816	67817	67818	67819
	67820	67821	67822	67823	67824	67825	67826	67827
	67828	67829	67830	67831	67832	67864	67865	67866
	67867	67868	67869	67870	67871	67872	67873	67874
	67875	67876	67877	67878	67879	67880	67881	67882
	67883	67884	67885	67886	67887	67888	67889	67890
	67891	67892	67893	67894				
Volvo B7RLE	69065	69066	69067	69068	69069	69070	69071	69072
	69073	69074	69075	69086	69087	69088	69089	69090
	69091	69092	69094	69095	69096	69097	69098	69099
	69100	69101	69102	69103	69104	69105	69106	69107
	69108	69109						

Ancillary / Reserve / Specials:

Volvo B10BLA	10103	10104	10105	10106	10107	10109	10110
Volvo B7LA	10133						
Trident	32930						

Overtown (Castlehill Road) - O

Dart	40809	40819	40820	41422	41446	41447	41448	41449
	42376							
Fiat	54401	54402						
Volvo B10BLE	61612	61613	61614	61616	61617	61618	61619	61620
	61621	61622	61623	61624	61625	61626	61652	61653
	61654	61705	61706	61707	61708	61709	61710	62129
	62130	62159	66281	66282				
Volvo B7RLE	66952	66954	66955	69014	69015	69016	69019	69021
	69034	69035	69036	69037	69038	69076	69077	69078
	69079	69080	69081	69082	69083	69084	69093	

Ancillary / Reserve / Specials:

Dart	40722	40803	41308	41309

West Yorkshire

Bradford (Bowling Back Lane) - BD

Olympian	30791	30796	30817	30834	31677	31760	31761	31762
	31763	31764	31765	31766	31767	31768	31769	31770
Volvo B7TL	30857	30866	30867	30868	30869	30870	30890	30891
	30892	30893	30894	30895	30896	30897	30908	30909
	30910	30911	30912	30913	30914	30915	30939	30940
	32528	32529	32530	32531	32532	32533	32534	32535
	32536	32537	32538	37055	37056	37057	37058	37059
Volvo B9TL	37065	37066	37067	37068	37069	37070	37071	37072
	37073	37074	37075	37076	37077	37078	37079	37080
	37081	37082	37083	37084	37085	37086	37087	37088
	37089	37090	37091	37092	37093	37094	37095	37096
	37097	37098	37099	37100	37101	37102	37360	37361
	37362	37363	37364	37365	37366	37732	37733	37734
	37735							
Optare Solo	50286	50290	50291	50292	50294	50295	53101	53104
	53910	53911	53912					
Volvo B10BLE	60621	60821	60822	60823	60824	60825	60826	60828
	60829	60830	60831	60832	60833	60834	60835	60836
	60837	60838	60839	60840	60841	60842	60843	60844
	60845	60846	60847	60848	60849	60850	60851	60852
	60853	60854	60855	62143				
Volvo B7L	60877	60878	60903	60904	60905	60906	60907	60908
	60923	60924	60925					
Volvo B7RLE	66714	66715	66999	69270	69271	69272	69273	69274
	69299	69300	69315	69316	69317	69318	69319	69320
	69321	69322	69466	69467	69468	69469	69470	69471
	69472	69473	69474	69475	69476	69477	69478	69479
	69480	69481	69482	69483	69484	69485	69569	69570
	69574	69575	69576	69577				

BMC Schoolbus	68603	68606	68621	68622	68623	68626	68628	68630
	68631	68639	68640	68646	68648	68651	68652	68653
	68672	68697	68698	68699	68700	68709	68710	68711

Ancillary / Reserve / Specials:

Volvo B10BLE	66112							
Volvo B10B	66651	66652						

Bramley (Headconner Lane, Bramley, Leeds) - BM

Volvo B7LA	19001	19002	19003	19004	19005	19006	19007	19008
	19009	19010	19011	19012	19013	19014	19015	19016
	19017	19018	19019	19020	19021	19022	19023	19024
	19025	19026	19027	19028				
Olympian	30239	30790						
Volvo B7TL	30922	30923	30924	30925	30926	30927	30928	30929
	30930	30931	30932	30933	30934	32431	32432	32433
	32434	32435	32436	32437	32438	32439	32440	32441
	32442	32443	32444	32445	32446	32447	32448	32449
	32450	32451	32452	32461	32462	32463	32464	32465
	32466	32467	32468	32469	32470	32471	32472	32473
Volvo B9TL	37063	37064	37645	37646	37647	37648	37649	37650
	37651	37652	37653	37654	37655	37656	37657	37658
	37659	37660	37661	37662	37663	37664	37665	37666
	37680	37682	37687	37688	37689	37706	37707	37708
	37709	37710	37711	37712	37713	37714	37715	37716
	37717	37718	37719	37720	37721	37722	37723	37724
	37725	37726	37727	37728	37729	37730	37731	37752
	37753	37754	37755	37756				
Volvo B6BLE	40565	40466	40576	40577	40578	40579	40587	
Scania L113CRL	60113	60131	60133	61056	61058	61059	61060	61061
	61062	61065	61066	61067	61068	61069	61070	61071
	61072	61073	61074	61076	61077	61078		
Scania L94UB	60065	60066	60213	60214	61037	61038	61039	61040
	61041	61042						
Volvo B7RLE	69331	69332	69333	69334	69335	69336	69337	69338
	69339	69340	69341	69342	69343	69344	69345	69346
	69347	69348	69349	69350				

Ancillary / Reserve / Specials:

Olympian	31806							
Volvo B10M	60467	60468	60472					
Lance	60944							
Volvo B10B	61363							

Leeds (Hunslet Park) - HP

Volvo B7LA	10038	10039	10040	10041	10042	10043		
Volvo B7TL	32697	37036	37037	37038	37039	37040	37041	
	37042	37043	37044	37060	37061	37062		
Volvo B9TL	36181	36182	36183	36184	36185	36186	36187	36188
	36189	36190	36191	36192	36193	36194	36195	36196
	36197	36198	36199	36200	36201	36202	36203	36204
	36205	36206	36207	36208	36209	36210	36211	36212
	36213	36214	36215	36216	36217	36218	36219	36220
	36221	36222	36223	36224	36225	36226	36227	36228
	36229	36230	36231	36232	36233	36234	36235	36236
	36237	36238	36239	36240	36241	36242	36243	36244
	36245	36246	36247	36248	36249	36250	36251	36252
	36253	36254	36255	36256	36257	36258	36259	36260
	36261	36262	36263	36264	36265	36266	36267	36268
	36269	36270	36271	36272	36273	36274	36275	36276
	36277	36278	37123	37124	37125	37126	37127	37128
	37129	37130	37131	37132	37667	37668	37669	37670
	37671	37672	37673	37674	37675	37676	37677	37678
	37679	37681	37683	37684	37685	37686	37690	37691
	37692	37693	37694	37695	37696	37697	37698	37699
	37700	37701	37702	37703	37704	37705		
Volvo B5LH	39201	39202	39203	39204	39205	39206	39221	39222
	39223	39224	39225	39226	39227	39228	39229	39230
	39231	39232	39233	39234	39235	39236		

Optare Solo	53904	53905	53906	53907	53909			
Scania L94UB	60067	60131	60172	60212	60217	60222	61029	61030
	61032	61034	61035	61036				
Volvo B7RLE	66997	66998	69412	69413	69414	69415	69416	69417
	69418							

Ancillary / Reserve / Specials:

Olympian	31771	31773

Halifax (Skircoat Lane) - HX

Olympian	30800	30802	30805	30806	30808	30809	30810	30811
	30812	30813	30844	30845	31774	31775	31807	31808
	34107	34211	34214					
Volvo B7TL	30849	30855	30856	30858	30859	30860		32520
	32521	32522	32523	32524	32525	32526	32527	32539
	32540	32541	32542	32692	32693	32694	32695	32696
	37046	37047	37048	37049	37050	37051	37052	37053
	37054							
Dart	41281	41282	41283	41315	41316	41317		
Optare Solo	50319	50407	53301	53302	53303			
Volvo B10BLE	60628	60815	60816	60819	60820	60827	61288	61289
	62118							
Volvo B7RLE	66707	66708	66709	66710	66711	66712	66713	66738
	66739	66740	66741	66742	66743	66744	66746	66747
	66748	66749	66750	66755	66762	66776	66777	66778
	66779	66780	66781	66782	66783	66789	66790	66778
	69579	69580	69581	69582	69583	69584	69585	69586
	69587							
BMC Schoolbus	68515	68516	68527	68528	68529	68530	68545	68546
	68547	68548	68608	68609	68610	68615	68625	68635
	68638	68641	68642	68643	68654	68655	68656	68657
	68659	68660	68662	68663	68664	68667	68668	68669
	68670	68671	68574	68675	68676	68677	68680	68682
	68683	68701	68702	68703	68704	68705	68706	68707
	68708							

Ancillary / Reserve / Specials:

Olympian	30722
Volvo B7TL	32460
Volvo B10BLE	60818
Volvo B7RLE	66745

Huddersfield (Old Fieldhouse Lane) - HU

Olympian	30814	30815	30816	30818	30821	30822	30823	30840
	30841	30843						
Volvo B7TL	30847	30848	30850	30851	30852	30853	30854	30863
	30864	30865	30916	30917	30918	30919	30920	30921
	30935	30936	30941	30942	30943	30944	30945	30946
	30947	30948	30949	30950	30951	30952	30953	31143
	31146	31147	32503	32504	32505	32506	32507	32508
	32509	32510	32511	32512	32513	32514	32515	32516
	32517	32518	32519					
Volvo B10BLE	66101							
Volvo B7RLE	66751	66752	66753	66764	66765	66766	66767	66768
	66769	66772	66773	66774	66775	66784	66785	66786
	66787	66788	66791	66792	69307	69308	69323	69324
	69329	69330	69419	69556	69557	69558	69559	69560
	69561	69562	69563	69564	69565	69578		
BMC Schoolbus	68614	68616	68684	68685	68686	68687	68689	68690
	68691	68692	68693	68694	68695	68696		

Ancillary / Reserve / Specials:

Volvo B10M	60486
Dart	90489

York

York (James Street) - YK

Mercedes-Benz Citaro	11101	11102	11103	11104	11105	11106	11107	11108
	11109	11110	11111	11112	11113	11114	11115	
Volvo B7TL	30954	30955	30959	37045				
Volvo B9TL	37246	37247	37248	37249	37250	37251	37252	37253
	37254	37255	37256					
VDL/Wrightbus Hybrid	39001	39002	39003	39004	39005			
Volvo B6BLE	40571	40572	40573	40574	40575			
Volvo B7L	60876	60880	60881	60882	60883	60884	60896	60897
	60898	60899	60900	60901	60902	60909	60919	60920
	60921	60922	60926	60927	60928			
Volvo B7RLE	66754	66756	66757	66758	66759	66760	66761	66763
	66995	66996	69000	69001	69002	69003	69004	69268
	69269	69275	69276	69277	69278	69279	69306	69358
	69359	69360	69361	69362	69363	69364	69365	69366
	69367	69368	69369	69370	69371	69372	69373	69374
	69375	69376	69377	69378	69379			

South Yorkshire

Doncaster (Leger Way) - DN

Volvo B7TL	30881	30882	30883	30884	30885	30898	30899	30904
	30905	30906	30907	31148	31776	31777	31778	31779
	31780	31781	31782	31783	31784	31785	31786	32249
	32250	32260	32261	32262	32263	32264	32265	32266
	32267	32268	32269	32270	32271	32272	32273	32274
	32275	32276						
Volvo B9TL	37228	37230	37232	37233	37234	37235	37236	37237
	37257	37500	37501	37502	37503	37504	37505	37506
	37507	37508	37525					
Volvo B6	40502	40595	40596	40597	40598	40599		
Dart	40973	40974	40975	40976				
Optare Solo	50232	50233	50234	50235	50236	50237	50238	50239
	53034	53035						
Volvo B10BLE	60627	62142						
Volvo B7L	60406	60704	60705	60706	60744	60745	60888	60889
	61192	61193	61194	61195	61196	61197	61198	61199
	61200	61201	61202	61203	61204	61206	61207	61208
	61209	61210	61211					
Volvo B7RLE	69461	69462	69463	69464	69465			

Ancillary / Reserve / Specials:
Volvo B7L   61205

Sheffield (Olive Grove) - OG

Volvo B7TL	30571	30572	30573	30574	30576	30846	30861	30862
	30937	30938	31129	31130	31131	31132	31133	31134
	31135	31137	31138	31139	31140	31141	32108	32109
	32110	32111	32215	32216	32217	32218	32219	32220
	32308	32309	32310	32311	32312	37021	37022	37023
	37024	37025	37026	37027	37028	37029	37030	37031
	37032	37033	37034	37035				
Trident	32955	32957	33029	33030	33031	33032	33041	33052
	33061	33062	33063	33064	33065	33066	33067	33068
	33069	33070	33071	33079	33082	33083	33084	33099
	33124	33125	33126	33127	33128	33129	33230	

Volvo B9TL	37103	37104	37105	37106	37107	37108	37109	37110
	37111	37112	37113	37114	37115	37116	37117	37118
	37119	37120	37121	37122	37229	37472	37473	37474
	37475	37476	37477	37478	37479	37480	37481	37482
	37483	37484	37485	37486	37511	37512	37513	37514
	37515	37516	37517	37518	37519	37520	37521	37522
	37523	37524	37526	37527	37528	37529		
Enviro 200	44925	44926	44927					
Volvo B10BLE	60629	60630	60631	60632	60641	60642	60643	60644
	60646	60647	60648	60649	60650	60651	60653	60654
	60655	60656	60657	60658	60659	60660	60661	60662
	60684	60685	60686	60687	60688	60689	60690	60691
	60692	60693	60694	60695	60696	60697	60698	60699
	60700	60701	60702	60804	60805	60806	60856	60857
	60858	60860	60861	60862	62232	62234	62235	62237
	62239	62240	62243	62244				
Volvo B7L	60703	60707	60708	60709	60710	60711	60712	60713
	60714	60715	60716	60717	60718	60719	60725	60885
	60886	60887	60890	60891	60892	60893	60894	61631
	61633	61636	61638	61639	61662			
Wrightbus Streetlite Max	63001	63002	63003	63004	63005	63006	63007	63008
	63009	63010	63011	63012	63013	63014	63015	63016
	63017	63018	63019	63020	63021	63022	63023	63024
	63025	63026	63027	63028	63029	63030	63031	63032
	63033	63034	63035	63036	63037			
Volvo B7RLE	69012	69013	69017	69018	69020	69022	69023	69024
	69025	69026	69028	69029	69030	69031		

Ancillary / Reserve / Specials:

Olympian	34090	34099						
Trident	33123							
Volvo B10BLE	60618	60619	60620	60622	60624	60626	66113	66114
	66119							

Rotherham (Midland Road) - RO

Volvo B7TL	30561	30562	30563	30564	30565	30567	30568	30569
	30570	30575	30577	30578	31142	31144	31145	
Volvo B9TL	37231	37258	37259	37261	37262	37263	37264	37265
	37487	37488	37489	37490	37491	37492	37493	37494
	37495	37496	37497	37498	37499	37509	37510	
Volvo B10BLE	60633	60634	60635	60636	60637	60638	60639	60640
	60664	60665	60666	60668	60669	60670	60671	60672
	60673	60674	60675	60676	60677	60678	60679	60680
	60681	60682	60683	60798	60799	60801	60802	60803
	60859	66112						
Volvo B7L	60720	60721	60722	60724	60726	60727	60728	60729
	60730	60731	60733	60734	60735	60736	60737	60738
	60739	60740	60741	60742	60743			
Wrightbus Streetlite Max	63038	63039	63040	63041				
Volvo B7RLE	69032	69033	69043	69044	69045	69046	69047	69048
	69049	69050	69051	69052	69053	69054	69055	69056

Ancillary / Reserve / Specials:

Volvo B10M	60457	60458	60487		
Volvo B10BLE	60361	60366	60367	60368	60800
Leyland Titan PD3	90092				

Manchester

Bolton (Weston Street) - BN

Olympian	34104	34105	34219					
Volvo B7TL	30874	30875	30878	30960	30963			
Trident	32869	32899	32906	32908	32911	32912	32913	32915
	32916	32926	32972					
Enviro 400	33657	33673	33677	33691	33693	33695	33696	33697
	33699	33700	33704	33705	33707	33709	33710	33711
	33712	33713	33714	33715	33716	33717	33718	33719
	33720	33721	33722	33724	33725	33726	33727	33728
	33729	33730	33731	33732	33733	33734	33735	33736
	33737	33739	33740	33742	33743	33749	33753	
Volvo B9TL	37397	37402	37405	37407	37408	37409	37410	
	37415	37416	37430					
Optare Versa hybrid	49116	49117	49211	49214	49217	49227	49228	
Volvo B10BLE	60663	62231	62233	62236	62241	66194		
Streetlite Max	63114	63115	63116	63117	63118			
Volvo B7RLE	66861	66867	66870	66876	66894	66895	66896	66899
	66901	66902	66903	66904	66905	66906	66907	66931
	69139	69141	69142	69143	69144	69145	69146	69147
	69148	69149	69150	69151	69152	69153	69154	69155
	69156	69157	69158	69159	69160	69161	69162	69163
	69164	69168	69169	69170	69171	69172	69173	69174
	69175	69201	69521	69522	69523	69524	69525	69526
	69527	69528	69529	69530	69531			
Enviro 300	67401	67402	67403	67404	67405	67406	67407	67408
	67409	67410	67411	67412				
Irisbus Schoolbus	68225	68227	68229					

Ancillary / Reserve / Specials:

Olympian	34210							
Volvo B10B	60302	60308	60322					
Scania	60076	60112	60115	60161	60184	61137	61140	61141
	61142							

Bury (Rochdale Road) - BY

Scania L94 UA	10017							
Scania OmniCity G	12001	12002	12003	12004	12005	12006	12007	12008
	12009	12010	12011	12012	12013	12014	12015	12016
	12017	12018						
Volvo B7TL	30871	30872	30873	30876	30877	30879	30880	
Volvo B9TL	37291	37292	37293	37294	37295	37296	37297	37298
	37299	37300	37302	37391	37392	37393	37398	37399
	37400	37401	37403	37404	37406	37417	37418	37419
	37420	37421	37422	37423	37424	37425	37426	37427
	37428	37429	37431	37471	37551	37554		
Mercedes-Benz Citaro	60233	60235	60237	60238	60239	60241	60242	60243
	60245	60247	60249	60250	60251	60252	60253	60254
	60255	60256	60257	60258	60259	60260	60261	60262
	60264	60267	60268	60269	60270	60271	60272	60273
	60274	60275	60276	60277	60278	60279	60280	60282
	60283	64029						
Volvo B7RLE	66872	66873	66880	66892	66897	66900	66909	66914
	66915	66916	66917	66918	66919	66922	66923	66928
	66929	66930	69135	69136	69137	69138	69165	69166
	69167	69178	69186	69566	69567	69568	69571	69572
	69573							

Ancillary / Reserve / Specials:

Volvo B10B	60301	61351
Mercedes-Benz Citaro	60281	

Manchester (Ocford Street) - OX

Volvo B7TL	30956	30957	30958	30961	30962	30964		
Trident	32867	32959						
Streetlite Max	63096	63097	63098	63099	63100	63101	63102	63103
	63104	63105	63106	63107	63108	63109	63110	63111
	63112	63113						

Manchester (Queen's Road) - QS

Volvo B9TL	37279	37280	37281	37282	37283	37284	37285	37286
	37287	37288	37289	37290	37301	37303	37304	37367
	37368	37369	37370	37371	37372	37373	37374	37375
	37376	37377	37378	37379	37380	37381	37382	37384
	37385	37389	37390	37394	37395	37396	37411	37440
	37442	37452	37456					
Volvo B5LH	39207	39208	39209	39210	39211	39212	39213	39214
	39215	39216	39217	39218	39219	39220		
Volvo B6	40437	40438	40439	40440	40441	40443	40444	
Optare Versa	49101	49102	49103	49104	49105	49106	49107	49108
	49109	49110	49111	49112	49118	49119	49204	49208
	49213	49218	49220					
Solo Hybrid	59001	59002	59003	59004	59005	59006	59007	59008
	59012	59013						
Volvo B10BLE	60369	60370	60371	60373	60376	60377	60379	60380
	60381	60385	60386	60405	61240	61241	62214	62215
	62216	62217	62218	66191	66192	66193	66195	
Volvo B7RLE	66831	66832	66833	66834	66835	66874	66875	66890
	66891	66893	66898	66908	66910	66911	66912	66913
	66920	66933	69176	69179	69180	69185	69195	69196
	69197	69198	69199	69200	69202	69203	69326	69327
Irisbus Scolabus	68226							

Ancillary / Reserve / Specials:

Olympian	34206	34209		Volvo B10B	61359	61365

Oldham (Wallshaw Street) - OM

Olympian	34091	34092	34093	34094	34096	34097	34098	34100
	34102							
Enviro 400	33656	33663	33668	33669	33670	33671	33672	33674
	33675	33676	33678	33679	33680	33681	33682	33683
	33684	33685	33686	33687	33688	33689	33690	33692
	33694	33698	33701	33702	33703	33706	33708	33723
	33738	33741	33744	33745	33746	33747	33748	33750
	33751	33752	33754	33755	33788			
Volvo B9TL	36279	36280	37432	37439	37441	37443	37444	37445
	37446	37447	37448	37449	37450	37451	37453	37454
	37455	37457	37458	37459	37460	37461	37462	37463
	37467	37468	37469	37470	37545	37546	37547	37548
	37549	37550	37552	37553	37555	37556	37557	37558
	37559	37560	37561					
Optare Solo	40181	40308	40313	40314	40315	40316	40317	40318
	40319	40320	40321	40322	40323	40328	40329	40330
	40331	40332	40333	40334	40335	40336	40683	
Dart	40361	40364	40369	40406	40416	41782	41788	
Optare Versa hybrid	49202	49203	49205	49206	49209	49210	49212	49215
	49216	49222						
Mercedes-Benz	60223	60224	60225	60226	60227	60228	60229	60230
	60234	60236	60240	60244	60248			
Volvo B7RLE	66836	66844	66846	66848	66853	66854	66855	66856
	66857	66858	66859	66860	66862	66863	66864	66865
	66866	66868	66869	66871	69177	69204	69205	69325
	69328	69420						
Enviro 300	67413	67414	67415	67416	67417	67418	67419	67420
	67421	67422	67423	67424	67425	67426	67427	67428
	67429	67430						
Irisbus Scolabus	68228							

Ancillary / Reserve / Specials:

Olympian	34095			Dennis Arrow	31943	
Volvo B10B	60303	61356	61366			

The 2014 First Bus Handbook

Tameside (Broadway, Dukinfield) - TE

Dennis Arrow	31929							
Olympian	34088	34089						
Volvo B9TL	37383	37386	37387	37388	37412	37413	37414	37433
	37434	37435	37436	37437	37438	37464	37465	37466
Dart	40403	41780	41781	41783	41784	41785	41786	41787
	42940	42941	42944	42945				
Optare Solo	40324	40325	40326	40327	53143	53144	53145	53146
	53147	53148	53149	53150				
Optare Solo hybrid	59009	59010	59011	59014	59015	59016		
Versa	49113	49114	49115					

Ancillary / Reserve / Specials:
Dennis Arrow	31925	
Optare Solo	40312	

Midlands

Hereford (Friar Street) - HD

Trident	33042	33043					
Dart	40805	42351	42352	42353	42354	42356	
Optare Solo	50281	50282	50296	53040	53041	53042	53058	53059

Leicester (Abbey Park Road) - LE

Volvo B7TL	32055	32056	32057	32058	32059	32061	32064	32065
	32066	32067	32068	32069	32070	32071	32072	32073
	32074	32075	32076	32077	32078	32079	32080	32081
	32082	32083	32084	32085	32086	32087	32088	32089
	32090	32091	32092	32093	32094	32095	32096	32097
	32098	32099	32277	32629	32630	32643	32644	32645
	32646	32647	32648	32649	32650	37146		
Enviro 400	33504	33506	33507	33508	33544	33545	33546	33547
	33548	33549	33550	33551	33552	33553	33554	33555
	33556	33557	33558	33559	33560	33561	33562	33563
	33564	33565	33566	33567	33568	33569	33570	33571
	33572	33573	33574					
Volvo B7L	66302	66303	66304	66305	66306	66307	66308	66309
	66310	66311	66312	66313	66314	66315	66316	66317
	66318	66319	66320	66321	66322	66323		
Volvo B7RLE	66841	66845	66849	66962	66963	66964	66965	66966
	66967	66968	66969	66970	66971	66972	66973	66974
	66975							

Ancillary / Reserve / Specials:
Volvo B7TL	32055	32056
Volvo B10M	60374	60460

Newcastle-under-Lyme (Liverpool Road) - NE

Olympian	30031	30033	31518	34158	34286	34311		
Volvo B7TL	32053	32054	32627	32632	32633	32634	32635	32639
	37156	37157	37158	37159	37160			
Volvo Citybus	38125							
Optare Solo	40007	40010	40011	40015	40016	40017	40018	40019
	40020	40180	40304					
Dart	40137	40140	40147	40150	40151	40153	42892	42893
	42894	43875	43876	43877				
Scania L94UB	60013	60015	60068	60069	60072	60074	60081	60128
	60170	60189	60193	60196	60201	60202	60205	60215
	61143	65705	65706	65727	65728	65729	65730	65731
	65732	65733						
Volvo B7RLE	66838	66839	66840	66842	66843	66847	66851	66852

Ancillary / Reserve / Specials:
Olympian	30038	34285	34288
Scania	60135	60194	60208

Stoke-on-Trent (Dividy Road, Adderley Green) - AG

Dart	40003	40030	40154	40155	40173	40175	40367	40373
	40375	40376	40378	40383	41070	41492	41493	41494
	41495	41496	41497	41498	41499	41500	41501	41502
	41512	41514	41520	41521	41522	41540	42726	42727
Optare Solo	40009	40021	40022	40023	40024	40025	40026	40027
	40028	40029	53155	53207	53208	53209	53405	53828
	53829	53830						
Scania L113CRL	60004	60006	60011	60012	60057	60058	60059	60060
	60061	60062	60063	60075	60078	60079	60083	60136
	61145	61160	61235	61237	61238	61239	61243	61244
	61245	61246	61529	61531	61553	65561	65562	65564
Scania L94UB	60073	60171	60173	60174	60175	60176	65572	
Scania OmniCity	65001	65002	65003	65004	65005	65026	65027	65033
	65034	65035	65036	65037	65038	65039	65040	65041
	65042							

Ancillary / Reserve / Specials:
Dart	40179	
Iveco Daily	50019	
Volvo B10B	60316	60317

Worcester (Padmore Street) - WR

Volvo B12T	20201	20202						
Trident	32852	32854	33039	33401	33402	33403	33404	33405
Dart	43869	43870	43871	43872	43873	43874		
Enviro 200	44511	44512	44514	44515				
Optare Solo	53043	53044	53045	53046	53047	53048	53049	53050
	53051	53060	53061	53062	53063	53064		
Volvo B7RLE	66691	66692	66693	66694	66695	66696	66697	66698
	66699							
Enviro 300	67601	67602	67603	67604	67631	67632	67633	67634
	67635	67636	67637	67638	67639	67640	67641	67642
	67643	67647	67648	67649	67650	67651	67652	67653
	67654	67655	67656	67657	67658	67659	67660	67661
	67662	67663	67664	67665	67699			
BMC schoolbus	68507	68559						

Ancillary / Reserve / Specials:
Volvo B10B	60311	60340
Enviro 300	67600	

Eastern Counties

Ipswich (Foundation Street) - IP

Volvo B7TL	32479	32486	32487	32488	32489	32490	32491	32492
	32493	32494	32653	32655	32656			
Scania L94UB	65579	65588	65589	65590	65628	65630	65631	65632
	65670	65672	65673	65674	65675	65690	65691	65692
Volvo B7RLE	66850	66981	66987	69005	69007	69008	69009	69010
	69422	69423	69424	69425	69426	69427	69428	69429
	69431	69432	69433	69532	69533			

Ancillary / Reserve / Specials:
Dart	43488		
Scania	65528	65529	65540

King's Lynn (Vancouver Avenue) - KL

Enviro 400	33803	33804	33805	33806	33807	33808	33809	33810
	33811	33812	33813	33814	33815	33816	33817	33818
	33819	33820	33821	33822	33823	33824		

Lowestoft (Gas Works Road) - LO

Volvo B7TL	30886	30889	30900	30901				
Volvo B9TL	37563	37564	37565	37566	37567	37568	37569	37570
	37571							
Dart	43466	43481	43489	43865	43866	43867	43868	
Enviro 200	44513	44928	45116	45117	45118	45119		

Ancillary / Reserve / Specials:

Olympian	34155	34156

Norwich (Vulcan Road) - VN

Volvo B7TL	32100	32101	32102	32103	32104	32105	32106	32107
	32112	32203	32211					
Trident	33003	33004	33007	33055	33056	33057	33058	33060
	33113	33146	33149	33150	33151	33152	33154	33155
	33156	33157	33158	33159	33160	33161	33162	33163
	33164	33165	33166	33167	33168	33169	33170	33171
	33233	33234	33235	33236	33237	33238	33239	33240
	33242	33244	33245	33246	33247	33248		
Volvo B9TL	36166	36167	36168	36169	36170	36171	36172	36173
	36174	36175	36176	36177	36178	36179	36180	
Optare Solo	53118	53119	53120	53122	53123	53124		
Volvo B7L	61148	66301	66324	66325	66326	66327	66328	66329
	66330	66332	66334	66335	66336	66337	66338	66339
	66340	66341	66342	66343	66344	66345	66346	66347
	66348							
Volvo B7RLE	66950	66957	66959	69006	69011			

Ancillary / Reserve / Specials:

Volvo B10M	20122

Great Yarmouth (Caister Road) - YA

Volvo B10M	20514	20515						
Olympian	34108	34109	34186	34187				
Volvo B7TL	30888	32200	32201	32202	32204	32205	32206	32207
	32208	32209	32210	32212	32213	32214		
Enviro 400	33423							
Volvo B9TL	37562	37572	37573	37574	37575	37576	37577	37578
	37579							
Dart	42358	42919	42920	42921	42929	43681	43859	43860
	43861	43862	43863	43864				
Volvo B10BLE	60807	60808	60813	60814	66126			

Ancillary / Reserve / Specials:

Volvo B10M	20109				
Olympian	34110	34111	34112	34113	34114
Volvo B7TL	32062	32063			
Routemaster	39480	39623			

Essex

Basildon (Cherrydown East) - BS

Volvo B7TL	32628	32631	32640	32641	32642			
Trident	32801	32804	32818	32847	32849	32855	32859	32863
	32864	32883	32887	32905	33047	33077	33178	33188
	33192	33194						
Enviro 400	33424	33425						
Dart	41238	41239	41240	41241	41513	41523	41524	41525
	41527	41538	41539	41541	41542	41543	41544	42529
	42551	43845	43846	43847	43848			
Volvo B10BLE	60766	60767	60811	60863	66165	66169	66177	66179
Volvo B7RLE	66805	66806	66813	66819	66820	66821	66822	66823
	66824	66825	66826	66827				
Volvo 9700 Hybrid	69901	69902	69903	69904	69905	69906	69907	69908
	69909	69910	69911	69912	69913	69914	69915	69916
	69917	69918	69919					

Ancillary / Reserve / Specials:
Trident   32807

Braintree (Fairfield Road, Springfield Industrial Estate) - BR

Volvo B7TL	30887	30902	30903					
Trident	33044	33078	33080	33086	33087	33088	33184	33186
	33190	33195	33196					
Dart		42447	42482	42484	42485	42486	42487	42488
	42489	43448	43474	43480	43483	43485	43679	
Optare Solo	40008							
Scania L113CRL	61533							
Volvo B10BLE	66168							
Volvo B7L	66333							
BMC Schoolbus	68508	68509	68520					

Ancillary / Reserve / Specials:
Trident   33045
Dart   42483
Bluebird schoolbus 68000

Chelmsford (Duke Street) - CM

Volvo B10M	20463							
Volvo B12M	20500	20501						
Volvo B9R	20801	20802	20803	20804	20805			
Olympian	34305							
Dart	42918	42930	42931	42932	42933	42934	42935	42936
	43356	43360	43801	43802				
Enviro 200	44537	44538	44539	44540	44541	44542	44543	44544
	44545	44546	44547	44548	44549	44550	44551	44900
Optare Solo	53112	53113	53114	53115	53116	53117	53121	53125
	53126	53127	53128	53129	53130	53131	53132	53133
	53134	53135	53136	53137	53138	53139	53701	
Volvo B10BLE	60809	60810	60865					
Scania OmniCity	65028	65029	65030	65031	65032			
Volvo B7RLE	66794	66795	66796	66797	66799	66802	66808	66811
	66812	66814	66815	66817	66818	66829	66830	66837
	69434	69512	69513	69514	69515	69516	69517	69518
	69519	69520						
Enviro 350H	67901	67902	67903	67904				
BMC Schoolbus	68510	68521	68531	68532	68534	68535	68551	68552
	68555							

Ancillary / Reserve / Specials:
Volvo B10M   20128
Trident   32806
Volvo B10B   60304 | 60305

Clacton-on-Sea (Telford Road) - CN

Trident	32810	32856						
Dart	42937	43713	43741	43742	43854	43855	43856	43857
Enviro 200	44516	44517	44518	44519	44596	44597	44598	44599
Scania L113CRL	61054	61057	65527	65532	65538	65551	65554	65556

Ancillary / Reserve / Specials:
Dart   43743

Colchester (Queen Street) - CO

Outstation: Hythe

Olympian	34014							
Volvo B7TL	32475	32476	32477	32478	32480	32481	32482	32483
	32484	32485	32651	32652	32654			
Scania L94UB	60206	62406	62407	62408	62409	62410	65565	65566
	65569	65570	65573	65574	65576	65586	65587	65626
	65627	65650	65651	65652	65653	65654	65665	65666
	65667	65668	65669	65671	65676	65677	65678	65679
	65680	65681	65682	65683	65684	65685	65686	65687
	65688	65689						
Volvo B7RLE	66976	66977	66978	66979	66980	66982	66983	66984
	66985	66986	69421	69430				

Hadleigh (London Road) - HH

Trident	32809	32850	33001	33002	33072	33073	33074	33081
	33090	33095	33098	33132	33133	33134	33136	33229
	33232	33373	33376	33383	33384	33385		
Dart	41011	41730	41732	41735	41736	41737	41761	41762
	42439	42922	42923	42927	42928	43357	43359	43712
	43714	43715	43717	43719	43720	43721	43729	43731
	43732	43733	43734	43735	43736	43738		
Enviro 200	44001	44002	44003	44004	44005	44006	44076	44077
	44078	44079	44080	44081				
Volvo B7RLE	66798	66800	66801	66803	66804	66807	66809	66810
	66816	66828						

Luton Airport - LN

Volvo B7LA	10180	10181	10182	19031
Volvo B7L	66358			

Hampshire, Dorset & Berkshire

Bracknell (Market Street) - BL

Outstation: - Chertsey

Volvo B7TL	32348							
Trident	33141	33142	33143	33144	33145	33147	33148	33153
	33179	33180	33181	33182	33183			
Volvo B9TL	37274	37275	37276	37985	37986	37987	37997	37998
	37999							
Dart	40956	42113	42114	42115	42508			
Optare Solo	53065							
Mercedes-Benz Citaro	64001	64005	64012	64013	64014	64015	64016	64017
	64018	64019	64020	64021				
Scania L94UB	65602	65621	65622					
Bluebird Schoolbus	61135	61136	68001	68002	68003	68004	68005	68006

Ancillary / Reserve / Specials:

Olympian	34215	34216	34218
Routemaster	39735	39810	
Dart	40826		
Scania	65624		
BMC Schoolbus	68522		

Bridport (West Street) - BP

Scania OmniDekka	36001	36002
Volvo B9TL	37580	
Dart	42817	

Hilsea (London Road) - HI

Dart	40790	40823	40825	40827	40957	40959	41346	41348
	41387	41633	41643	42507	42728	42778		
Streetlite DF	47419	47420	47421	47431	47432	47433	47434	
Mercedes-Benz	52513	52533	52558	52560				
Optare Solo	50277	50278	53140	53151	53206			
Streetlite Max	63042	63043	63044	63045	63046	63047	63048	63049
	63050	63051	63052	63053	63054	63055	63056	63057
	63058	63059	63060	63061	63062	63063	63064	63065
	63066	63067						
Volvo B10BLE	66151							

Ancillary / Reserve / Specials:

Dart	41147	41165	41166	41634	41636	41646	42783	47015
Mercedes-Benz	52517	52559						
Optare Solo	53006							
Scania	64818							

Hoeford (Gosport Road) - HO

Olympian	34016	34017	34059	34170	34295			
Dart	42109	42116	42120	42124	42125	42126	42127	
	42128	42129	42130	42131	42132	42133	42134	42136
	42137	42138	42139	42140	42141	42142	42232	42234
	42754	42757	42759	42773				
Streetlite DF	47411	47412	47413	47414	47415	47416	47417	47418
Optare Solo	53008							
Scania OmniCity	65006	65007	65008	65009	65010	65011	65012	65013
	65014	65015	65016	65017	65018	65019	65020	65021
	65022	65023	65024	65025				
Volvo B10BLE	66121	66122	66127	66128	66130	66152	66153	66154
	66156	66157	66158	66164	66176	66181	66196	66197
	66198	66199	66201	66202	66203	66204	66205	
Volvo B7RLE	69537	69538	69539	69542	69543	69544	69545	69546
	69547	69548	69549	69550	69551	69552	69553	69554
	69555							

Ancillary / Reserve / Specials:

Volvo B10M	20417	20418	20457					
Olympian	34022							
Dart	40792	40961	41515	42111	42112	42118	42119	42121
	42122	42123						
Volvo B10B	60299	60337						

Reading (Reading Transport Ltd) - RG

Volvo B12B	20611	20612	20613			
Volvo B9R	20806	20807	20808	20809	20810	20811
Scania K114IB	23015					

Slough (Stoke Road) - SH

Dart	40721	41336	42338	42339	42341	42343	42344	42346
	42347	42654	42656	42659	42673			
Enviro 200	44560	44561	44562	44563	44564	44565	44566	44567
	44568							
Optare Solo	53052	53054	53055	53056	53057			
Mercedes-Benz Citaro	64002	64030	64031	64032	64033	64034	64035	64036
	64037	64038	64039	64042	64043	64044	64045	64046
	64047	64048						
Scania L94	65724	65725	65726					
Volvo 7900 Hybrid	69920	69921	69922	69923	69924	69925	69926	69927
	69928	69929	69930	69931	69932	69933	69934	

Ancillary / Reserve / Specials:

Dart	41403

Southampton (Portswood Road) - SO

Volvo B12B	20550	20551						
Olympian	34079	34129						
Trident	32704	32705	32706	32764	32767	32768		
Volvo B7TL	32031	32032	32033	32034	32035	32036	32038	32039
	32041	32042	32043	32044	32045	32046	32254	32255
	32256	32257	32258	32259	37161	37162	37163	37164
	37165							
Dart	42504	42505	42506	42509	42511	42513	42521	42522
	42523	42524	42525	42526	42527	46324	46325	
Enviro 200	44507	44508	44509	44510	44527	44528	44529	44530
	44531	44532	44533	44534	44535	44536		
Streetlite DF	47422	47423	47424	47425	47426	47427	47428	47429
	47430							
Volvo B7RLE	66881	66882	66883	66884	66885	66886	66944	66945
	66953	69245	69246	69247	69248	69385	69386	69387
	69388	69389	69390	69391	69392	69393	69394	69395
	69396	69397	69398	69399	69400	69401		
Autosan Eagle	68301	68302						
BMC Schoolbus	68511	68512	68533	68536	68537	68550	68553	68554
	68557	68562	68563	68564	68565			

Ancillary / Reserve / Specials:

Dart	40822	40824	41516	41517	42454	42510	42512	42514
Guy Arab	90557							

Weymouth (Edward Street) - WH

Olympian	34044	34165	34167	34168	34175			
Trident	32701	32702	32703	32707	32708	32763	32765	32766
Scania OmniDekka	36003	36004	36005	36006				
Volvo B9TL	37581	37582	37583	37584	37585	37586		
Dart	42350	42818	42819	42821	42822	42823	42826	42828
	42829							
Enviro 200	44502	44503	44504	44505	44506			
Streetlite DF	47405	47406	47407	47408	47409	47410		
Volvo B6BLE	48202	48204	48205	48207	48208	48209	48270	48272
	48273							
Mercedes-Benz	52540							
Optare Solo	40006	40012	50270	50272	50293	53002	53012	53028
	59100							
Volvo B7RLE	69210	69211	69212	69213	69214	69215	69216	69217

Ancillary / Reserve / Specials:

Olympian	34043	39920			
Dart	42221	42717	42820	42827	46727
Volvo B6BLE	48203				

West of England

Bath (Western Island, Lower Bristol Road) - BA

Outstations: Chippenham; Colerne; Devizes; Frome; Melksham; Radstock and Trowbridge

Volvo B7LA	10035	10036	10037	10174	10175	10176	10177	10178
	10179							
Volvo B7TL	32281	32282	32283	32284	32285	32349	32350	32351
	32352	32353	32354					
Volvo B9TL	37358	37359						
Enviro 400 Hybrid	39133	39134	39135	39137	39138	39139	39140	39141
Volvo B6BLE	40588	40589	40590	40591	40592	40593	40594	
Dart	40525	40529	40534	40535	40541	40542	40835	42552
	42553	42554	42555	42556	42557	42561	42643	42701
	42704	42824	42902	42903	42904	42905	42906	42907
	42908	42909	42910	42911	42914	42915	42916	42925
	42926	42938	42939	42968	43849	46259		
Enviro 200	44520	44521	44522	44523	44524	44525	44526	44902
	44903	44904	44913	44914	44915	44916	44917	44918
	44919	44920	44921					
Optare Versa	49300							
Optare Solo	50318	53102	53103	53204	53804	53805	53806	53807
	53808	53809	53810	53811	53812	53813	53814	53815
	53816	53817	53818	53819	53820			
Plaxton Primo	57000							
Volvo B10BLE	62193	62194	62238					
Streetlite Max	63068	63069	63070	63071	63072	63073	63074	63075
	63076	63077	63078					
Volvo B7RLE	66719	66730	66731	66732	66733	66734	66937	66938
	66939	66940	66941	66942	66943	66992	66993	69435
	69436	69437						

Ancillary / Reserve / Specials:

Dart	46225	46239
Volvo B10M	60600	
Lance	67341	

Bristol (Hengrove) - HG

Volvo B7TL	32279	32328	32329	32330	32331	32332	32333	32334
	32335	32336	32337	32338	32339	32340	32341	32342
	32343	32344	32345	32346	32347	32636	32637	32638
	37001	37002	37008	37009	37010	37015	37016	37017
	37018	37019	37020					
Volvo B9TL	37315	37316	37317	37318	37351	37587	37588	37589
	37590	37591	37592	37593	37594	37595	37596	37597
	37598	37599	37600	37601	37602	37603	37604	37605
	37606	37608	37609	37610	37611	37612		
Dart	42708	42709	42710	42711	42712	42718	42723	42732
	42733	42734	42735	42736	42737			
Streetlite DF	47435	47436	47437	47438	47439	47440	47441	47442
	47443	47444	47445	47446	47447	47448	47449	47450
	47451	47452	47453	47454	47455	47456	47457	47458
	47459	47460	47461	47462	47463	47464	47465	
Volvo B6BLE	48210	48211	48212	48213	48214	48215	48216	48217
	48218	48219	48221	48222	48223	48224		
Volvo B7RLE	69500	69501	69502	69503	69504	69505	69506	69507
	69508	69509	69510	69511				

Ancillary / Reserve / Specials:

Volvo B10M	20416	20460	60474		
Dart	41404	41420	41421	41423	46657
Ford Transit	54601				

Bristol (Easton Road, Lawrence Hill) - LH

Volvo B7TL	32002	32003	32004	32005	32008	32009	32011	32012
	32013	32014	32015	32016	32017	32018	32019	32021
	32022	32023	32024	32251	32252	32253	32280	32286
	32287	32288	32289	32290	32292	32355	32356	32357
	32358	32359	32360					
Volvo B9TL	37003	37004	37005	37006	37007	37011	37012	37013
	37014	37319	37320	37321	37322	37323	37324	37325
	37326	37327	37328	37329	37330	37331	37332	37333
	37334	37335	37336	37337	37338	37339	37340	37341
	37342	37343	37344	37345	37346	37347	37348	37349
	37350	37352	37353	37354	37355	37356	37357	37607
	37613	37614	37615	37616	37617	37618	37619	37620
	37621	37622	37623	37624	37625	37626	37627	37628
	37629	37630	37631	37632	37757	37758	37759	37760
	37761	37762	37763	37764	37765	37766	37767	37768
	37769	37770	37771	37772				
Dart	42703	42705	42706	42895	42896	42897	42898	42899
	42900	42901	42949	42950	42957	42958	42959	42961
Volvo B10BLE	66102	66104	66105	66109	66110	66115	66116	66159
	66162	66167	66178					
Volvo B7RLE	69449	69450	69451	69452	69453	69454	69455	69456
	69457	69458						

Ancillary / Reserve / Specials:

Dart	46616	46620	46651	46653	46902

Bristol (Marlborough Street) - MS

Volvo B7TL	32006	32007	32027	32278	32291	32684	32685	32686
	32687	32688	32689	32690	32691			
Dart	42947	42948	42951	42952	42953	42954	42955	42956
	42960	42962	42963	42964	42965	42966	42967	42969
	46264							
Volvo B10BLE	62242	62245	66117	66118	66120	66161	66166	66171
Volvo B7RLE	66728	66729						

Ancillary / Reserve / Specials:

Dart	42702	46244	46623

Weston-super-Mare (Searle Crescent) - WS

Volvo B7TL	32001							
Trident	33411	33412	33413	33414	33415	33416	33417	33418
	33419							
Enviro 400	33825	33826	33827	33828	33829	33830		
Dart	40517	41144	41332	41333	41334	41335	41686	41687
	42707	42730	42731	42738	46262	46603		
Enviro 200	44905	44906	44907	44908	44909	44910	44911	44912
Optare Solo	53401							
Volvo B10BLE	66100	66106	66107	66108	66160	66163	66173	66174
	66206	66207						
Volvo B7RLE	66720	66721	66722	66723	66724	66725	66726	66727
	66934	66935	66936	66956	69438	69439	69440	69441
	69442	69443	69444	69445	69446	69447	69448	69459
	69460							

Ancillary / Reserve / Specials:

Dart	46240	46252	46609

South West

Bridgwater (East Quay) - BW

Olympian	34171	34178	34179	34188	34189	34190		
Trident	32872	32873	32874					
Dart	43811							
Optare Solo	50466	50467	53001	53009	53013	53014		
Volvo B7L	60895	66350	66351	66352	66353	66354	66355	66356

Ancillary / Reserve / Specials:

Volvo B10M	20461	
Javelin	21032	
Mercedes-Benz	51590	51685

Camborne (Union Street) - CE

Outstations: Flambards, Helston; Trecerus Industrial Estate, Padstow; Long Rock Industrial Estate, Penzance; Bodmin; Camworthy Water; Delabole; Tregonnigie Industrial Estate, Falmouth; Tolcarne Street, Newquay; North Petherwin and Pelynt.

Mercedes-Benz Citaro	11036	11037	11038					
Volvo B12M	20108							
Volvo B12B	20556	20557	20558	20559	20560	20561	23208	
Scania coach	23008	23009	23010	23011	23012	23013	23014	
Olympian	31457	31458	31461	31820	31821	31826	31828	31830
	31836	31841	31846	31877	31878	34041	34049	34050
	34051	34052	34116	34138	34172	34173	34177	34181
	34182	34183	34184	34185	34191	34192	34193	34194
	34196	34197	34198	34199	34200	34259	34261	34615
	34629							
Trident	32802	32803	32808	32817	32819	32846	32853	32858
	32861	32875	32876	32878	32879	32880		
Dart	41132	41143	42207	42235	42255	42430	42469	42470
	42471	42472	42473	42474	42475	42476	42477	42558
	42559	42560	42719	42720	42725	42801	42802	42860
	42871	42872	42873	42874	42875	42876	42942	42943
	43812	46235	46647					
Mercedes-Benz	52526	52554	56000					
Optare Solo	50276	50284	50285	53007	53015	53107	53108	53402
	53403	53404	53801	53803	53826			
Transit	54602							
Mercedes-Benz	64049	64050						
Scania L94UB	65759	65760	65761	65762				
Volvo B7RLE	69206	69207	69208	69209	69218	69219	69220	69221
	69222	69223	69224	69225	69226	69227	69228	69229
	69230							

Ancillary / Reserve / Specials:

Volvo B10M	20412					
Scania	23019	23201	23202			
Olympian	34137	34195	34626			
Volvo Citybus	38000	38001	38002	38004	38005	38006
Dart	42252					

Plymouth (Chelson Meadow) - PL

Outstations: New Road, Callington; Little Cotton Farm, Dartmouth; Okehampton; Crowndale Road, Tavistock; Wills Road Industrial Estate, Totnes and Trevol Road, Torpoint.

Olympian	34003	34068						
Trident	32709	32711	32712	32713	32714	32715	32716	32717
	32751	32752	32753	32754	32755	32756	32757	32758
	32759	32760	32761	32762	32851	32954	33172	33173
	33174	33175	33176	33177				
Enviro 400	33420	33421	33422	33658	33659	33660	33661	33662
	33664	33665	33666	33667				
Dart	40002	40035	40036	40037	40039	40960	41291	42459
	42463	42562	42563	42752	42753	42758	42764	42777
	42779	42924	42946	43809				
Volvo B6	40570	40580	40581	40582	40583	40584	40585	40586
	48201	48225	48226	48227	48228	48229	48231	48232
	48233	48234	48261	48262	48263	48264	48265	48266
	48267	48269	48271					
Optare Solo	53011	53109	53110	53111	53154	53205	53827	

Ancillary / Reserve / Specials:								
Volvo B10M	20408							
Dart	40033	40034	40038	40958	41295	41795	42724	42784
BMC Schoolbus	68571							

Taunton (Hamilton Road) -TN

Outstations: Burnham-on-Sea; Chard; Honiton; Minehead; Martock; Wells; Willand and Wiveliscombe

Olympian	34064	34174	34176					
Trident	33377	33378	33379	33380	33381	33382		
Dart	41129	41134	41156	42634	42825	42830	42832	42833
	42834	42835	42841	42842	42843	42844	43810	43821
	43822	43823						
Enviro 200	44922	44923	44924	45111	45112	45113	45114	45115
Volvo B7L	60910	60911	60912	60913	60914	60915	60916	60917
	60918							

Ancillary / Reserve / Specials:			
Dart	40786	40788	42831

Cymru

Bridgend - BG

Dart	41162	41230	41265	42322	42331	42620	42685	42687
	42688	42689	42690	42692	42713	42715	42721	42722
Enviro 200	44569	44590	44591	44592	44593			
Optare Versa	49002	49003	49004	49005	49006	49007	49008	49009
	49010							

Ancillary / Reserve / Specials:	
Dart	42336

Cardiff - CF

Volvo B7R	20323	20324	20325					
Scania coach	23307	23308	23309	23320	23321	23322	23323	23324
Optare Tempo	64504	64505	64506	64507	64508	64509		

Ancillary / Reserve / Specials:		
BMC Schoobus	68567	68570

Haverfordwest (Withybush Industrial Estate) - HV

Dart	42861	42862	42869	42879	42880	42881	42882	42883
	42884							

Llanelli (Inkerman Street) - LL

Dart	41167	41186	41188	41191	41197	41233	41330	41331
	41340	41518	41519	42520	42613	42642	42674	42676
	42677	42678	42680	42681	42682	42683	42684	42693
	42694	42863	42864	42877	42878	42912	42913	43680
	43836	43837	43838	43839	43840	43841	43901	43902
	43903							
Optare Solo	53707	53708	53802					
BMC Schoolbus	68503	68505	68506	68513				
Volvo B7RLE	69240	69241	69242	69243	69244	69249	69250	69251
	69252	69301	69302	69303	69304	69305	69380	69381
	69382	69383	69384					

Ancillary / Reserve / Specials:

Dart	40891	40892	41171	41183	41192	41194	41198	41341
	41345	42449	42456	42599	43677			

Port Talbot (Acacia Avenue, Sandfields Estate) - PT

Olympian	34162	34163						
Volvo B7TL	32037							
Dart	41155	41174	41200	41338	41343	41344	41347	41381
	41382	41383	41385	41386	41388	41389	41391	41393
	41394	41395	41398	41399	41400	41489	41490	41718
	41719	41720	41721	41726	41727	41729	42134	42323
	42325	42326	42327	42328	42329	42330	42332	42333
	42334	42335	42337	42453	42478	42569	42573	42574
	42575	42631	42686	42691	42845	43850	43851	43852
	43853							
Enviro 200	44570	44582	44583	44584	44585	44586	44587	44588
	44589							
Optare Versa	49301	49302	49303	49304	49305	49306	49307	49308
	49309							
Volvo B7RLE	66958	66960	66961	69231	69232	69233	69234	69235
	69236	69237	69238					

Ancillary / Reserve / Specials:

Olympian	34161	34164						
Dart	40161	40935	41185	41190	41193	41397	41728	42215
	42218	42462						

Leeds allocation contains six Volvo B7LA articulated buses with 10038, W127DWX seen heading from the city centre on route 1 to Holt Park.
John Birtwistle

Swansea (Pentregethin Road, Ravenhill) - RA

Volvo B7LA	19000	19029	19030	19032	19033	19034	19035	19036
	19037	19038						
Dart	40793	40794	40795	41149	41384	41390	41392	41491
	42208	42212	42213	42214	42216	42412	42581	42582
	42583	42585	42586	42587	42588	42589	42591	42592
	42593	42595	42597	42598	42600	42601	42602	42603
	42604	42605	42606	42607	42608	42609	42610	42611
	42612	42614	42621	42622	42675	42679	42714	42716
	42865	42866	42867	42868	42870	43584		
Enviro 200	44500	44501	44552	44553	44554	44555	44556	44557
	44558	44559	44573	44574	44575	44576	44577	44578
	44579	44580	44581					
Optare Solo	50279	53003	53004	53005				
Volvo B7RLE	66716	66717	66718	69239	69253			
Enviro 300	67431	67432	67433	67434	67435	67436	67437	67438
	67439							

Ancillary / Reserve / Specials:

Javelin	21145	67501
Bristol VRT	39971	
Dart	42211	42596
BMC Schoolbus	68568	68569

Coaching Unit (Pentregethin Road, Ravenhill) - RAC

Volvo B7R	20321	20322						
Scania	23304	23311	23312	23313	23314	23315	23316	23317
	23318	23319	23325					

Ancillary / Reserve / Specials:

Scania	23020	23204	23302	23303	23310
Volvo B10M	60473				

Aircoach

Belfast (Great Northern Mall) - BT

Setra S415 HD	24030	24031	24032	24033	24034	24035

Dublin Airport - D

Mercedes-Benz Citaro	11073	11074	11075	11076	11077	11078	11079	11080
	11081	11082	11083					
Volvo B12BT	20651	20652	20653	20654	20655	20656	20657	20658
	20659	20660	20661	20662	20663	20664	20665	20666
	20667	20668	20669					
Volvo B11R	20901	20902	20903	20904	20905	20906	20907	20908
	20909	20910						
Scania	23016	23017	23018					
Setra S315 GT-HD	24000							
Setra S415 HD	24029	24036	24038	24041	24043	24044	24047	
Mercedes-Benz	64000							
Volvo B7RLE	66994							

Ancillary / Reserve / Specials:

Setra	20429					
Scania	23016	23017	23018	23501	23502	23503	23504

Vehicle index

Registration	Fleet No	Operator
02D78371	64000	Aircoach
04D22632	24029	Aircoach
04D22822	24036	Aircoach
04D22824	24038	Aircoach
04D22843	24041	Aircoach
04D22845	24043	Aircoach
04D22855	24044	Aircoach
04D34313	24047	Aircoach
04D72883	23017	Aircoach
04D74479	23018	Aircoach
04D74499	23016	Aircoach
05D62327	24000	Aircoach
06D85192	66994	Aircoach
06D120303	23502	Aircoach
06D120304	23503	Aircoach
06D120305	23501	Aircoach
06D120368	23504	Aircoach
08D67693	11073	Aircoach
08D67694	11074	Aircoach
08D67697	11075	Aircoach
08D69040	11076	Aircoach
08D69043	11077	Aircoach
08D69070	11078	Aircoach
08D69442	20651	Aircoach
08D69972	11079	Aircoach
08D69973	11080	Aircoach
08D69991	11081	Aircoach
08D70256	20652	Aircoach
08D70351	20653	Aircoach
08D70352	20654	Aircoach
08D70354	20655	Aircoach
08D70357	20656	Aircoach
08D70459	20657	Aircoach
08D70460	20658	Aircoach
08D70461	20659	Aircoach
08D70462	20660	Aircoach
09D2773	20661	Aircoach
09D2774	20662	Aircoach
09D2777	20663	Aircoach
09D3364	20664	Aircoach
09D3365	20665	Aircoach
09D3708	20666	Aircoach
09D4276	20669	Aircoach
09D4282	20667	Aircoach
09D4649	20668	Aircoach
09D5300	11082	Aircoach
09D5303	11083	Aircoach
141D24	20901	Aircoach
141D25	20903	Aircoach
141D26	20902	Aircoach
141D27	20904	Aircoach
141D28	20905	Aircoach
141D29	20906	Aircoach
141D30	20907	Aircoach
141D31	20908	Aircoach
141D32	20909	Aircoach
141D34	20910	Aircoach
260ERY	40583	South West
481FPO	34194	South West
510CLT	39810	Hampshire D&B
530OHU	34192	South West
3910WE	37229	South Yorkshire
AN02EDN	10178	West of England
AO02ODM	43801	Essex
AO02ODN	43802	Essex
AO02RBX	20500	Essex
AO02RBY	20501	Essex
AO02RBZ	20502	Glasgow
AO02RCF	20503	Glasgow
AO02RCU	20504	Glasgow
AO02RCV	20505	Aberdeen
AO02RCX	20506	Glasgow
AO02RCY	20507	Aberdeen
AO02RCZ	20508	Glasgow
AO02RDU	20509	Glasgow
AU05DME	69005	Eastern Counties
AU05DMF	69006	Eastern Counties
AU05DMO	69007	Eastern Counties
AU05DMV	69008	Eastern Counties
AU05DMX	69009	Eastern Counties
AU05DMY	69010	Eastern Counties
AU05DMZ	69011	Eastern Counties
AU05MUO	32651	Essex
AU05MUP	32652	Essex
AU05MUV	32653	Eastern Counties
AU05MUW	32654	Essex
AU05MUY	32655	Eastern Counties
AU05MVA	32656	Eastern Counties
AU07DXS	37156	Midlands
AU07DXT	37157	Midlands
AU07DXV	37158	Midlands
AU07DXW	37159	Midlands
AU07DXX	37160	Midlands
AU53HJJ	32475	Essex
AU53HJK	32476	Essex
AU53HJN	32477	Essex
AU53HJO	32478	Essex
AU53HJV	32479	Eastern Counties
AU53HJX	32480	Essex
AU53HJY	32481	Essex
AU53HJZ	32482	Essex
AU53HKA	32483	Essex
AU53HKB	32484	Essex
AU53HKC	32485	Essex
AU53HKD	32486	Eastern Counties
AU53HKE	32487	Eastern Counties
AU53HKF	32488	Eastern Counties
AU53HKG	32489	Eastern Counties
AU53HKH	32490	Eastern Counties
AU53HKJ	32491	Eastern Counties
AU53HKK	32492	Eastern Counties
AU53HKL	32493	Eastern Counties
AU53HKM	32494	Eastern Counties
AU58ECA	37563	Eastern Counties
AU58ECC	37564	Eastern Counties
AU58ECD	37565	Eastern Counties
AU58ECE	37566	Eastern Counties
AU58ECF	37567	Eastern Counties
AU58ECJ	37568	Eastern Counties
AU58ECN	37569	Eastern Counties
AU58ECT	37570	Eastern Counties
AU58ECV	37571	Eastern Counties
AU58ECW	37572	Eastern Counties
AU58ECX	37573	Eastern Counties
AU58ECY	37574	Eastern Counties
AU58ECZ	37575	Eastern Counties
AU58EDC	37576	Eastern Counties
AU58EDF	37577	Eastern Counties
AU58EDJ	37578	Eastern Counties
AU58EDK	37579	Eastern Counties
AU58FFH	69421	Essex
AU58FFJ	69422	Eastern Counties
AU58FFK	69423	Eastern Counties
AU58FFL	69424	Eastern Counties
AU58FFM	69425	Eastern Counties
AU58FFN	69426	Eastern Counties
AU58FFO	69427	Eastern Counties
AU58FFP	69428	Eastern Counties
AU58FFR	69429	Eastern Counties
AU58FFS	69430	Essex
AU58FFT	69431	Eastern Counties
AU58FFV	69432	Eastern Counties
AU58FFW	69433	Eastern Counties
AY08EKT	44900	Essex
B46PJA	30722	West Yorkshire
BD11CDX	36178	Eastern Counties
BD11CDY	36179	Eastern Counties
BD11CDZ	36180	Eastern Counties
BD11CEN	69521	Manchester
BD11CEO	69523	Manchester
BD11CEU	69522	Manchester
BD11CEV	69524	Manchester
BD11CEX	69527	Manchester
BD11CEY	69526	Manchester
BD11CFA	69525	Manchester
BD11CFE	69531	Manchester
BD11CFF	69530	Manchester
BD11CFG	69528	Manchester
BD11CFJ	69529	Manchester
BD11CFK	36166	Eastern Counties
BD11CFM	36167	Eastern Counties
BD11CFN	36168	Eastern Counties
BD11CFO	36169	Eastern Counties
BD11CFP	36170	Eastern Counties
BD11CFU	36171	Eastern Counties
BD11CFV	36172	Eastern Counties
BD11CFX	36173	Eastern Counties
BD11CFY	36174	Eastern Counties
BD11CFZ	36175	Eastern Counties
BD11CGE	36176	Eastern Counties
BD11CGF	36177	Eastern Counties
BD12SZY	36222	West Yorkshire
BD12SZZ	36223	West Yorkshire
BD12TAO	36224	West Yorkshire
BD12TAV	36225	West Yorkshire
BD12TBO	36226	West Yorkshire
BD12TBU	36227	West Yorkshire
BD12TBV	36228	West Yorkshire
BD12TBX	36229	West Yorkshire
BD12TBY	36230	West Yorkshire
BD12TBZ	36231	West Yorkshire
BD12TCJ	36280	Manchester
BD12TCK	36276	West Yorkshire
BD12TCO	36275	West Yorkshire
BD12TCU	36233	West Yorkshire
BD12TCV	36232	West Yorkshire
BD12TCX	36235	West Yorkshire
BD12TCY	36234	West Yorkshire
BD12TCZ	36278	West Yorkshire
BD12TDO	36277	West Yorkshire
BD12TDU	36279	Manchester
BD12TDV	36274	West Yorkshire
BD13NFK	69564	West Yorkshire
BD13NFL	69563	West Yorkshire
BD13NFM	69568	Manchester

Reg	No	Depot	Reg	No	Depot	Reg	No	Depot
BD13NFN	69567	Manchester	BG58OMB	11107	York	BN12JYP	36190	West Yorkshire
BD13NFO	69565	West Yorkshire	BG58OMC	11108	York	BN12JYR	36191	West Yorkshire
BD13NFP	69566	Manchester	BG58OMD	11109	York	BN12JYS	36192	West Yorkshire
BD13NFR	69569	Manchester	BG58OME	11110	York	BN12JYT	36193	West Yorkshire
BD13NFV	69570	Manchester	BG58OMF	11111	York	BN12JYU	36194	West Yorkshire
BD13OHK	69571	Manchester	BG58OMH	11112	York	BN12JYV	36195	West Yorkshire
BD13OHL	69572	Manchester	BG58OMJ	11113	York	BN12JYW	36196	West Yorkshire
BD13OHN	69573	Manchester	BG58OMK	11114	York	BN12KXU	36181	West Yorkshire
BD13OHO	69574	Manchester	BG58OML	11115	York	BN12KXV	36182	West Yorkshire
BD13OHP	69575	Manchester	BJ10VGA	69500	West of England	BN12WNX	36197	West Yorkshire
BD13OHR	69576	Manchester	BJ10VGC	69502	West of England	BN12WNY	36198	West Yorkshire
BD13OHS	69577	Manchester	BJ10VGD	69501	West of England	BN12WNZ	36199	West Yorkshire
BD13OHT	69578	West Yorkshire	BJ10VGE	69503	West of England	BN12WOA	36200	West Yorkshire
BF12KWC	69545	Hampshire D&B	BJ10VGF	69504	West of England	BN12WOB	36201	West Yorkshire
BF12KWD	69544	Hampshire D&B	BJ10VGG	69505	West of England	BN12WOC	36202	West Yorkshire
BF12KWE	69542	Hampshire D&B	BJ11EBU	69510	West of England	BN12WOD	36203	West Yorkshire
BF12KWG	69543	Hampshire D&B	BJ11EBV	69507	West of England	BN12WOH	36204	West Yorkshire
BF12KWH	69547	Hampshire D&B	BJ11EBX	69508	West of England	BN12WOJ	36205	West Yorkshire
BF12KWJ	69548	Hampshire D&B	BJ11EBZ	69511	West of England	BN12WOM	36206	West Yorkshire
BF12KWK	69549	Hampshire D&B	BJ11ECA	69512	Essex	BN12WOR	36236	West Yorkshire
BF12KWL	69546	Hampshire D&B	BJ11ECC	69513	Essex	BN12WOU	36237	West Yorkshire
BF12KWM	69553	Hampshire D&B	BJ11ECD	69517	Essex	BN12WOV	36238	West Yorkshire
BF12KWN	69551	Hampshire D&B	BJ11ECE	69516	Essex	BN12WOX	36239	West Yorkshire
BF12KWO	69550	Hampshire D&B	BJ11ECF	69514	Essex	BN12WOY	36240	West Yorkshire
BF12KWP	69552	Hampshire D&B	BJ11ECN	69515	Essex	BN12WPA	36241	West Yorkshire
BF12KWR	69555	Hampshire D&B	BJ11ECT	69518	Essex	BN12WPD	36242	West Yorkshire
BF12KWS	69554	Hampshire D&B	BJ11ECV	69519	Essex	BN12WPE	36243	West Yorkshire
BF12KWU	36249	West Yorkshire	BJ11ECW	69520	Essex	BN12WPF	36244	West Yorkshire
BF63HDN	69537	Hampshire D&B	BJ11ECY	37986	Hampshire D&B	BN12WPJ	36245	West Yorkshire
BF63HDO	69539	Hampshire D&B	BJ11ECZ	37987	Hampshire D&B	BN61MWE	39207	Manchester
BF63HDU	69538	Hampshire D&B	BJ11XGY	37985	Hampshire D&B	BN61MWF	39208	Manchester
BF63HDV	37997	Hampshire D&B	BJ11XHY	69506	West of England	BN61MWG	39209	Manchester
BF63HDX	37998	Hampshire D&B	BJ11XHZ	69509	West of England	BN61MWJ	39210	Manchester
BF63HDY	37999	Hampshire D&B	BJ12PNS	36247	West Yorkshire	BN61MWK	39211	Manchester
BG12UKM	36248	West Yorkshire	BJ12VNR	36246	West Yorkshire	BN61MWL	39212	Manchester
BG12YJF	36250	West Yorkshire	BJ12VWO	36207	West Yorkshire	BN61MWM	39213	Manchester
BG12YJH	36251	West Yorkshire	BJ12VWP	36208	West Yorkshire	BN61MWO	39214	Manchester
BG12YJJ	36252	West Yorkshire	BJ12VWR	36209	West Yorkshire	BN61MWP	39215	Manchester
BG12YJK	36253	West Yorkshire	BJ12VWS	36210	West Yorkshire	BN61MWU	39216	Manchester
BG12YJL	36254	West Yorkshire	BJ12VWT	36211	West Yorkshire	BN61MWV	39217	Manchester
BG12YJM	36255	West Yorkshire	BJ12VWU	36212	West Yorkshire	BN61MWW	39218	Manchester
BG12YJN	36256	West Yorkshire	BJ12VWV	36213	West Yorkshire	BN61MWX	39219	Manchester
BG12YJO	36257	West Yorkshire	BJ12VWW	36214	West Yorkshire	BN61MWY	39220	Manchester
BG12YJP	36258	West Yorkshire	BJ12VWX	36215	West Yorkshire	BP11JWA	39221	West Yorkshire
BG12YJR	36259	West Yorkshire	BJ12VWY	36216	West Yorkshire	BP11JWC	39223	West Yorkshire
BG12YJS	36260	West Yorkshire	BJ12VXA	36217	West Yorkshire	BP11JWD	39222	West Yorkshire
BG12YJT	36261	West Yorkshire	BJ12VXB	36218	West Yorkshire	BP11JWE	39224	West Yorkshire
BG12YJU	36262	West Yorkshire	BJ12VXC	36219	West Yorkshire	BP11JWF	39225	West Yorkshire
BG12YJV	36263	West Yorkshire	BJ12VXD	36220	West Yorkshire	BP11JWG	39226	West Yorkshire
BG12YJW	36264	West Yorkshire	BJ12VXE	36221	West Yorkshire	BP11JWJ	39230	West Yorkshire
BG12YJX	36265	West Yorkshire	BJ60BZA	39201	West Yorkshire	BP11JWK	39231	West Yorkshire
BG12YJY	36266	West Yorkshire	BJ60BZB	39202	West Yorkshire	BP11JWL	39227	West Yorkshire
BG12YJZ	36267	West Yorkshire	BJ60BZC	39203	West Yorkshire	BP11JWM	39228	West Yorkshire
BG12YKA	36268	West Yorkshire	BJ60BZD	39204	West Yorkshire	BP11JWN	39229	West Yorkshire
BG12YKB	36269	West Yorkshire	BJ60BZE	39205	West Yorkshire	BP11JWO	39232	West Yorkshire
BG12YKC	36270	West Yorkshire	BJ60BZF	39206	West Yorkshire	BP11JWU	39233	West Yorkshire
BG12YKD	36271	West Yorkshire	BJ63UHZ	69930	Hampshire D&B	BP11JWV	39234	West Yorkshire
BG12YKE	36272	West Yorkshire	BJ63UJV	69931	Hampshire D&B	BP11JWW	39236	West Yorkshire
BG12YKF	36273	West Yorkshire	BJ63UJW	69932	Hampshire D&B	BP11JWX	39235	West Yorkshire
BG13VUD	69560	West Yorkshire	BJ63UJX	69933	Hampshire D&B	BT13YVV	69579	West Yorkshire
BG13VUE	69562	West Yorkshire	BJ63UJZ	69934	Hampshire D&B	BT13YVW	69580	West Yorkshire
BG13VUG	69561	West Yorkshire	BN02EDN	10179	West of England	BT13YVX	69581	West Yorkshire
BG57ZGJ	68571	South West	BN12JYF	36183	West Yorkshire	BT13YVY	69582	West Yorkshire
BG58OLR	11101	York	BN12JYG	36184	West Yorkshire	BT13YVZ	69583	West Yorkshire
BG58OLT	11102	York	BN12JYH	36185	West Yorkshire	BT13YWA	69584	West Yorkshire
BG58OLU	11103	York	BN12JYJ	36186	West Yorkshire	BT13YWB	69585	West Yorkshire
BG58OLV	11104	York	BN12JYK	36187	West Yorkshire	BT13YWC	69586	West Yorkshire
BG58OLX	11105	York	BN12JYL	36188	West Yorkshire	BT13YWD	69587	West Yorkshire
BG58OMA	11106	York	BN12JYO	36189	West Yorkshire	BU04EZF	64020	Hampshire D&B

Reg	No	Region	Reg	No	Region	Reg	No	Region
BU04EZG	64021	Hampshire D&B	CU08AHN	69301	Cymru	CV55AMX	20371	Scotland East
BV13YZZ	69559	West Yorkshire	CU08AHO	69302	Cymru	CV55ANF	20372	Aberdeen
BV13ZBC	69901	Essex	CU08AHP	69303	Cymru	CV55ANP	20373	Aberdeen
BV13ZBD	69902	Essex	CU08AHV	69304	Cymru	CV55AOO	20374	Aberdeen
BV13ZBE	69903	Essex	CU08AHX	69305	Cymru	D700GHY	38000	South West
BV13ZBF	69904	Essex	CU53APO	42674	Cymru	D701GHY	38001	South West
BV13ZBG	69905	Essex	CU53APV	42675	Cymru	D702GHY	38002	South West
BV13ZBJ	69906	Essex	CU53APX	42676	Cymru	D704GHY	38004	South West
BV13ZBL	69907	Essex	CU53APY	42683	Cymru	D705GHY	38005	South West
BV13ZBN	69908	Essex	CU53APZ	42682	Cymru	D706GHY	38006	South West
BV13ZBO	69909	Essex	CU53ARF	42681	Cymru	DK57SPZ	44511	Midlands
BV13ZBP	69910	Essex	CU53ARO	42680	Cymru	DK57SXF	44512	Midlands
BV13ZBR	69911	Essex	CU53ARX	42679	Cymru	DK57SXG	44513	Eastern Counties
BV13ZBT	69912	Essex	CU53ARZ	42678	Cymru	EG52FFJ	43873	Midlands
BV13ZBU	69913	Essex	CU53ASO	42677	Cymru	EG52FFK	43863	Eastern Counties
BV13ZBW	69914	Essex	CU53AUO	42685	Cymru	EG52FFL	43869	Eastern Counties
BV13ZBX	69915	Essex	CU53AUP	42684	Cymru	EG52FFT	43870	Midlands
BV13ZBY	69916	Essex	CU53AUT	42686	Cymru	EG52FFU	43872	Midlands
BV13ZBZ	69917	Essex	CU53AUV	42687	Cymru	EG52FFV	43871	Midlands
BV13ZCA	69918	Essex	CU53AUW	42688	Cymru	EG52FFY	43874	Midlands
BV13ZCE	69919	Essex	CU53AUX	42690	Cymru	EG52FFZ	43854	Essex
BV13ZCF	69920	Hampshire D&B	CU53AUY	42691	Cymru	EG52FGA	43864	Eastern Counties
BV13ZCJ	69921	Hampshire D&B	CU53AVB	42692	Cymru	EG52FGC	43855	Essex
BV13ZCK	69922	Hampshire D&B	CU53AVJ	42861	Cymru	EG52FGD	43856	Essex
BV13ZCL	69923	Hampshire D&B	CU53AVK	42862	Cymru	EG52FGE	43857	Essex
BV13ZCN	69924	Hampshire D&B	CU53AVL	42863	Cymru	EG52FGF	43860	Eastern Counties
BV13ZCO	69925	Hampshire D&B	CU53AVM	42864	Cymru	EG52FGJ	43861	Eastern Counties
BV13ZCT	69926	Hampshire D&B	CU53AVN	42865	Cymru	EG52FGK	43862	Eastern Counties
BV13ZCU	69927	Hampshire D&B	CU53AVO	42866	Cymru	EG52FGU	43865	Eastern Counties
BV13ZCX	69928	Hampshire D&B	CU53AVP	42868	Cymru	EG52FGV	43866	Eastern Counties
BV13ZCY	69929	Hampshire D&B	CU53AVR	42867	Cymru	EG52FGX	43868	Eastern Counties
BV13ZDH	69556	West Yorkshire	CU53AVT	42870	Cymru	EG52FHC	43867	Eastern Counties
BV13ZDJ	69557	West Yorkshire	CU53AVV	42869	Cymru	EG52FHD	43859	Eastern Counties
BV13ZDK	69558	West Yorkshire	CU53AVW	42689	Cymru	EHO228	90557	Hampshire D&B
BV57MSO	68567	Cymru	CU54CYX	68504	Scotland East	EO02FKZ	53111	South West
BV57MSU	68568	Cymru	CU54CYY	68505	Cymru	EO02FLA	53101	West Yorkshire
BV57MSX	68569	Cymru	CU54CYZ	68506	Cymru	EO02FLB	53102	West of England
BV57MSY	68570	Cymru	CU54DCE	68513	Cymru	EO02FLC	53103	West of England
BX02CMK	64029	Manchester	CU54DCF	68514	Scotland East	EO02FLD	53104	West Yorkshire
BX06NZT	68302	Hampshire D&B	CU54HYK	42600	Cymru	EO02FLG	53107	South West
BX5VUN	68503	Cymru	CU54HYL	42601	Cymru	EO02FLH	53108	South West
BX55NZV	68301	Hampshire D&B	CU54HYM	42602	Cymru	EO02FLJ	53109	South West
CN06BXF	53830	Midlands	CU54HYN	42603	Cymru	EO02FLK	53110	South West
CN06BXH	53155	Midlands	CU54HYO	42604	Cymru	EO02NDX	53112	Essex
CN07HVG	66691	Midlands	CU54HYP	42605	Cymru	EO02NDY	53113	Essex
CN07HVH	66692	Midlands	CU54HYR	42606	Cymru	EO02NDZ	53114	Essex
CN07HVJ	66694	Midlands	CU54HYT	42607	Cymru	EO02NEF	53115	Essex
CN07HVK	66693	Midlands	CU54HYV	42608	Cymru	EO02NEJ	53116	Essex
CN07HVL	66698	Midlands	CU54HYW	42609	Cymru	EO02NEN	53117	Essex
CN07HVM	66699	Midlands	CU54HYX	42610	Cymru	EO02NEU	53118	Eastern Counties
CN07KZK	53207	Midlands	CU54HYY	42611	Cymru	EO02NEY	53119	Eastern Counties
CN07KZL	53208	Midlands	CU54HYZ	42612	Cymru	EO02NFA	53120	Eastern Counties
CN07KZM	53209	Midlands	CU54HZA	42613	Cymru	EO02NFC	53121	Essex
CN57EFB	66695	Midlands	CU54HZB	42614	Cymru	EO02NFD	53122	Eastern Counties
CN57EFE	66696	Midlands	CV55ABK	20357	Scotland East	EO02NFE	53123	Eastern Counties
CN57EFF	66697	Midlands	CV55ABN	20356	Scotland East	EO02NFF	53124	Eastern Counties
CRG325C	31529	Aberdeen	CV55ACO	20358	Scotland East	EO02NFG	53125	Essex
CU03BHV	42693	Cymru	CV55ACU	20359	Scotland East	EO02NFH	53126	Essex
CU03BHW	42694	Cymru	CV55ACX	20360	Scotland East	EO02NFJ	53127	Essex
CU04AYP	20550	Hampshire D&B	CV55ACY	20361	Scotland East	EO02NFK	53128	Essex
CU04AYS	20551	Hampshire D&B	CV55ACZ	20363	Scotland East	EO02NFL	53129	Essex
CU05LGJ	20354	Scotland East	CV55AFA	20362	Scotland East	EO02NFM	53130	Essex
CU05LGK	20355	Scotland East	CV55AFE	20364	Scotland East	EO02NFN	53131	Essex
CU08ACY	44501	Cymru	CV55AFF	20366	Scotland East	EO02NFP	53132	Essex
CU08ACZ	44502	Hampshire D&B	CV55AGX	20367	Aberdeen	EO02NFR	53133	Essex
CU08ADO	44503	Hampshire D&B	CV55AGY	20370	Scotland East	EO02NFT	53134	Essex
CU08ADV	44504	Hampshire D&B	CV55AGZ	20368	Scotland East	EO02NFU	53135	Essex
CU08ADX	44505	Hampshire D&B	CV55AHA	20365	Scotland East	EO02NFV	53136	Essex
CU08ADZ	44506	Hampshire D&B	CV55AMU	20369	Scotland East	EO02NFX	53137	Essex

Reg	No	Depot
EU05AUK	42918	Essex
EU05AUL	42919	Eastern Counties
EU05AUM	42920	Eastern Counties
EU05AUN	42921	Eastern Counties
EU05AUO	42922	Essex
EU05AUP	42923	Essex
EU05DXR	68535	Essex
EU05DXS	68551	Essex
EU05DXT	68552	Essex
EU06KDK	43877	Midlands
EU08FHB	44928	Eastern Counties
EU54BNJ	53139	Essex
EU54BNK	53138	Essex
EU58JWZ	69434	Essex
EU60LFS	44596	Essex
EY05FYP	42358	Eastern Counties
EY54BPX	56004	Scotland East
EY54BPZ	56005	Aberdeen
EY54BRF	56006	Aberdeen
EY54BRV	56007	Aberdeen
EY54BRX	56008	Aberdeen
EY54BRZ	56009	Aberdeen
FC52AFC	20021	Aberdeen
FJ08FYN	37562	Eastern Counties
FJ55KMO	68226	Manchester
FJ55KMY	68227	Manchester
FJ55KMZ	68228	Manchester
FJ55KNB	68225	Manchester
FJ58YLS	44597	Essex
FN08AZZ	67665	Midlands
FN55EDV	68229	Manchester
FSU 382	20207	Aberdeen
G601NWA	61256	Glasgow
G602NWA	60457	South Yorkshire
G603NWA	60458	South Yorkshire
G605NWA	60460	Midlands
G609NWA	60464	Glasgow
G613NWA	60466	Glasgow
G621NWA	61266	Glasgow
G622NWA	60467	West Yorkshire
G623NWA	60468	West Yorkshire
G627NWA	60472	South Yorkshire
G628NWA	60473	Cymru
G629NWA	60474	West of England
G641NWA	60486	West Yorkshire
G755XRE	30031	Midlands
G757XRE	30033	Midlands
G762XRE	30038	Midlands
H642RKU	60487	South Yorkshire
HIG1512	32853	South West
HIG1519	32851	South West
HIG1521	32872	West of England
HIG1523	32873	South West
HIG1524	32874	South West
HIG1526	32875	South West
HIG1527	32876	South West
HIG1528	32858	South West
HIG1531	32878	South West
HIG1533	32879	South West
HIG1538	32880	South West
HIG1540	32861	South West
HIG8433	53154	South West
HIG8434	53205	South West
HIG8790	40584	South West
HIG8791	40580	South West
HVJ716	34197	South West
HX05BUJ	68553	Hampshire D&B
HX05BUO	68550	Hampshire D&B
HX08DHE	37583	Hampshire D&B

Reg	No	Depot
HX08DHF	37581	Hampshire D&B
HX08DHG	37584	Hampshire D&B
HX08DHJ	37586	Hampshire D&B
HX08DHK	37582	Hampshire D&B
HX08DHL	37580	Hampshire D&B
HX08DHY	37585	Hampshire D&B
HX55AOH	68562	Hampshire D&B
HX55AOJ	68561	Scotland East
HX55AOK	68563	Hampshire D&B
HY07FSU	37164	Hampshire D&B
HY07FSV	37162	Hampshire D&B
HY07FSX	37165	Hampshire D&B
HY07FSZ	37163	Hampshire D&B
HY07FTA	37161	Hampshire D&B
HY09AJV	69385	Hampshire D&B
HY09AJX	69380	Cymru
HY09AKF	69384	Cymru
HY09AKG	69381	Cymru
HY09AOR	69392	Hampshire D&B
HY09AOS	69390	Hampshire D&B
HY09AOT	69388	Hampshire D&B
HY09AOU	69382	Cymru
HY09AUO	69389	Hampshire D&B
HY09AUV	69391	Hampshire D&B
HY09AUW	69387	Hampshire D&B
HY09AUX	69398	Hampshire D&B
HY09AZA	69383	Cymru
HY09AZB	69386	Hampshire D&B
HY09AZC	69394	Hampshire D&B
HY09AZD	69393	Hampshire D&B
HY09AZF	69395	Hampshire D&B
HY09AZG	69401	Hampshire D&B
HY09AZJ	69400	Hampshire D&B
HY09AZL	69397	Hampshire D&B
HY09AZN	69399	Hampshire D&B
HY09AZO	69396	Hampshire D&B
J461OVU	60374	Midlands
J732KBC	21032	South West
JDZ2339	61207	South Yorkshire
JDZ2340	61208	South Yorkshire
JDZ2391	61209	South Yorkshire
JJD480D	39480	Eastern Counties
K114PRV	66651	West Yorkshire
K125URP	38125	Midlands
K174EUX	30107	Glasgow
K615LAE	34615	South West
K626LAE	34626	South West
K629LAE	34629	South West
K803ORL	34003	South West
KDZ5104	32275	South Yorkshire
KFZ4361	24035	Aircoach
KFZ4362	24034	Aircoach
KFZ4563	24033	Aircoach
KFZ4652	24031	Aircoach
KFZ4653	24032	Aircoach
KFZ4654	24030	Aircoach
KP51VZO	32066	Midlands
KP51VZR	32067	Midlands
KP51VZS	32068	Midlands
KP51VZT	32069	Midlands
KP51VZW	32070	Midlands
KP51VZX	32071	Midlands
KP51VZY	32072	Midlands
KP51VZZ	32073	Midlands
KP51WAJ	32074	Midlands
KP51WAO	32075	Midlands
KP51WAU	32076	Midlands
KP51WBD	32077	Midlands
KP51WBG	32078	Midlands

Reg	No	Depot
KP51WBJ	32079	Midlands
KP51WBK	32080	Midlands
KP51WBL	32081	Midlands
KP51WBO	32082	Midlands
KP51WBT	32083	Midlands
KP51WBU	32084	Midlands
KP51WBV	32085	Midlands
KP51WBY	32086	Midlands
KP51WBZ	32087	Midlands
KP51WCA	32088	Unallocated
KP51WCF	32089	Midlands
KP51WCG	32090	Midlands
KP51WCJ	32091	Midlands
KP51WCN	32092	Midlands
KP51WCO	32093	Midlands
KP51WCR	32094	Midlands
KP51WCW	32095	Midlands
KP51WCX	32096	Midlands
KP51WCY	32097	Midlands
KP51WDD	32098	Midlands
KP51WDE	32099	Midlands
KP51WDF	32277	Midlands
KP54AZA	32639	Midlands
KP54AZB	32640	Essex
KP54AZC	32641	Essex
KP54AZD	32642	Essex
KP54AZF	32643	Midlands
KP54AZG	32644	Midlands
KP54AZJ	32645	Midlands
KP54AZL	32646	Midlands
KP54AZN	32647	Midlands
KP54AZU	68520	Essex
KP54AZV	68521	Essex
KP54KAO	32627	Midlands
KP54KAU	32628	Essex
KP54KAX	32629	Midlands
KP54KBE	32630	Midlands
KP54KBF	32631	Midlands
KP54KBJ	32632	Midlands
KP54KBK	32648	Midlands
KP54KBN	32649	Midlands
KP54KBO	32650	Midlands
KP54LAE	32633	Midlands
KP54LAO	32634	Midlands
KR52ZSW	11035	Unallocated
KU52RXJ	43810	South West
KV02VVC	66301	Eastern Counties
KV02VVD	66302	Midlands
KV02VVE	66303	Midlands
KV02VVF	66304	Midlands
KV02VVG	66305	Midlands
KV02VVH	66306	Midlands
KV02VVJ	66307	Midlands
KV02VVK	66308	Midlands
KV02VVL	66309	Midlands
KV02VVM	66310	Midlands
KV02VVN	66311	Midlands
KV02VVO	66312	Midlands
KV02VVP	66313	Midlands
KV02VVR	66314	Midlands
KV02VVS	66315	Midlands
KV02VVT	66316	Midlands
KV02VVU	66317	Midlands
KV02VVW	66318	Midlands
KV02VVX	66319	Midlands
KV02VVY	66320	Midlands
KV02VVZ	66321	Midlands
KV02VWA	66322	Midlands
KV02VWB	66323	Midlands

Reg	No.	Region	Reg	No.	Region	Reg	No.	Region
KX05AOC	66972	Midlands	LK03NHC	32303	Glasgow	LK51UZA	33023	Glasgow
KX05AOD	66973	Midlands	LK03NHD	32304	Glasgow	LK51UZB	33024	Glasgow
KX05AOE	66974	Midlands	LK03NHE	32305	Glasgow	LK51UZE	33007	Eastern Counties
KX05MGV	32635	Midlands	LK03NHH	32308	South Yorkshire	LK51UZF	33008	Glasgow
KX05MGY	66975	Midlands	LK03NHJ	32309	South Yorkshire	LK51UZG	33009	Glasgow
KX05MGZ	66976	Essex	LK03NHL	32310	South Yorkshire	LK51UZH	33010	Glasgow
KX05MHA	66977	Essex	LK03NHM	32311	South Yorkshire	LK51UZJ	33011	Glasgow
KX05MHE	66978	Essex	LK03NHN	32312	South Yorkshire	LK51UZL	33012	Glasgow
KX05MHF	66979	Essex	LK03NKN	42519	Essex	LK51UZM	33013	Glasgow
KX05MHJ	66980	Essex	LK03NLD	41502	Midlands	LK51UZN	33014	Glasgow
KX05MHK	66981	Eastern Counties	LK03NLN	41498	Midlands	LK51UZO	33001	Essex
KX05MHL	66982	Essex	LK03UEX	41520	Midlands	LK51UZP	33002	Essex
KX05MHM	66983	Essex	LK03UEY	41521	Midlands	LK51UZS	33003	Eastern Counties
KX05MHN	66984	Essex	LK03UEZ	41522	Midlands	LK51UZT	33004	Eastern Counties
KX05MHO	66985	Essex	LK03UFA	41523	Essex	LK53EXT	33355	Glasgow
KX05MHU	66986	Essex	LK03UFB	41524	Essex	LK53EXU	33356	Glasgow
KX05MHV	66987	Eastern Counties	LK03UFC	41525	Essex	LK53EXV	33357	Glasgow
KX05MHY	66962	Midlands	LK04HYP	32360	West of England	LK53EXW	33358	Glasgow
KX05MHZ	66963	Midlands	LK05DXP	53702	Scotland East	LK53EXX	33359	Glasgow
KX05MJE	66964	Midlands	LK05DXR	53703	Scotland East	LK53EXZ	33360	Glasgow
KX05MJF	66965	Midlands	LK05DXS	53704	Scotland East	LK53EYA	33361	Glasgow
KX05MJJ	66966	Midlands	LK05DXT	53705	Scotland East	LK53EYB	33362	Glasgow
KX05MJK	66967	Midlands	LK05DXU	53706	Scotland East	LK53EYC	33363	Glasgow
KX05MJO	66968	Midlands	LK05DYO	53701	Essex	LK53EYD	33364	Glasgow
KX05MJU	66969	Midlands	LK05FCE	68554	Hampshire D&B	LK53EYF	33365	Glasgow
KX05MJV	66970	Midlands	LK07CCA	64030	Hampshire D&B	LK53EYG	33366	Glasgow
KX05MJY	66971	Midlands	LK07CCD	64031	Hampshire D&B	LK53EYH	33367	Glasgow
KX54AHP	68507	Midlands	LK07CCE	64032	Hampshire D&B	LK53EYJ	33368	Glasgow
KX54AHU	68508	Essex	LK07CCF	64033	Hampshire D&B	LK53EYL	33369	Glasgow
KX54AHY	68509	Essex	LK07CCJ	64034	Hampshire D&B	LK53EYM	33370	Glasgow
KX54ANR	68510	Essex	LK07CCN	64035	Hampshire D&B	LK53EYO	33371	Glasgow
KX57BWF	44598	Essex	LK07CCO	64036	Hampshire D&B	LK53EYP	33372	Glasgow
L204KSX	61351	Manchester	LK07CCU	64037	Hampshire D&B	LK53EYR	33373	Essex
L209KSX	61356	Manchester	LK07CCV	64038	Hampshire D&B	LK53EYT	33374	Glasgow
L212KSX	61359	Manchester	LK07CCX	64039	Hampshire D&B	LK53EYU	33375	Glasgow
L225VHU	46225	West of England	LK07CDE	20611	Hampshire D&B	LK53EYV	33376	Essex
L304VSU	61363	West Yorkshire	LK07CDF	20612	Hampshire D&B	LK53EYW	33377	South West
L305PWR	34305	Essex	LK07CDN	20613	Hampshire D&B	LK53EYX	33378	South West
L306VSU	61365	Manchester	LK08FKY	33506	Midlands	LK53EYY	33379	South West
L307VSU	61366	Manchester	LK08FKZ	33507	Midlands	LK53EYZ	33380	South West
L311PWR	34311	Midlands	LK08FLA	33508	Midlands	LK53EZA	33381	South West
L503VHU	46603	West of England	LK08FLX	33504	Midlands	LK53EZB	33382	South West
L637SEU	34137	South West	LK08FMC	64043	Hampshire D&B	LK53EZC	33383	Essex
L638SEU	34138	South West	LK08FMD	64044	Hampshire D&B	LK53EZD	33384	Essex
L650SEU	39920	Hampshire D&B	LK08FME	64045	Hampshire D&B	LK53EZE	33385	Essex
L816CFJ	34116	South West	LK08FMF	64046	Hampshire D&B	LK53EZF	33386	Glasgow
LK03LLX	41493	Midlands	LK08FMG	64047	Hampshire D&B	LK53EZV	33343	Glasgow
LK03LLZ	41494	Midlands	LK08FMJ	64048	Hampshire D&B	LK53EZW	33344	Glasgow
LK03LME	41495	Midlands	LK08FNL	64042	Hampshire D&B	LK53EZX	33345	Glasgow
LK03LMF	41496	Midlands	LK51JYO	41414	Glasgow	LK53EZZ	33346	Glasgow
LK03LMJ	41492	Midlands	LK51UYD	33035	Glasgow	LK53FCF	33347	Glasgow
LK03LNE	64018	Hampshire D&B	LK51UYF	33025	Glasgow	LK53FCJ	33348	Glasgow
LK03LNF	64019	Hampshire D&B	LK51UYG	33026	Glasgow	LK53FCL	33349	Glasgow
LK03LNU	41497	Midlands	LK51UYH	33027	Glasgow	LK53FCX	33350	Glasgow
LK03LNV	41499	Midlands	LK51UYJ	33028	Glasgow	LK53FCY	33351	Glasgow
LK03LNW	41500	Midlands	LK51UYL	33029	South Yorkshire	LK53FCZ	33352	Glasgow
LK03LNX	41501	Midlands	LK51UYM	33030	South Yorkshire	LK53FDA	33353	Glasgow
LK03NGE	41512	Midlands	LK51UYN	33031	South Yorkshire	LK53FDD	33354	Glasgow
LK03NGF	41513	Essex	LK51UYO	33032	South Yorkshire	LK53FDX	41527	Essex
LK03NGG	41514	Midlands	LK51UYP	33033	Glasgow	LK53FDY	41538	Essex
LK03NGJ	32294	Scotland East	LK51UYR	33034	Glasgow	LK53FDZ	41540	Midlands
LK03NGN	32295	Scotland East	LK51UYS	33015	Glasgow	LK53FEF	41541	Essex
LK03NGU	32296	Scotland East	LK51UYT	33016	Glasgow	LK53FEG	41542	Essex
LK03NGV	32297	Scotland East	LK51UYU	33017	Glasgow	LK53FEH	41543	Essex
LK03NGX	32298	Scotland East	LK51UYV	33018	Glasgow	LK53FEJ	41544	Essex
LK03NGY	32299	Scotland East	LK51UYW	33019	Glasgow	LK53LYH	32328	West of England
LK03NGZ	32300	Glasgow	LK51UYX	33020	Glasgow	LK53LYJ	32329	West of England
LK03NHA	32301	Glasgow	LK51UYY	33021	Glasgow	LK53LYO	32330	West of England
LK03NHB	32302	Glasgow	LK51UYZ	33022	Glasgow			

Reg	No	Location	Reg	No	Location	Reg	No	Location
LK53LYP	32331	West of England	LN51DVG	33043	Midlands	LN51NRK	33094	Glasgow
LK53LYR	32332	West of England	LN51DVH	33044	Essex	LN51NRL	33095	Essex
LK53LYT	32333	West of England	LN51DVK	33045	Essex	LR02LWW	33141	Hampshire D&B
LK53LYU	32334	West of England	LN51DVL	33046	Glasgow	LR02LWX	33142	Hampshire D&B
LK53LYV	32335	West of England	LN51DVM	33047	Essex	LR02LWY	33143	Hampshire D&B
LK53LYW	32336	West of England	LN51DVR	41441	Unallocated	LR02LWZ	33144	Hampshire D&B
LK53LYX	32337	West of England	LN51DVW	41435	Unallocated	LR02LXA	33145	Hampshire D&B
LK53LYY	32338	West of England	LN51DVY	41437	Unallocated	LR02LXB	33146	Eastern Counties
LK53LYZ	32339	West of England	LN51DWA	33037	Scotland East	LR02LXC	33147	Hampshire D&B
LK53LZA	32340	West of England	LN51DWD	33039	Midlands	LR02LXG	33148	Hampshire D&B
LK53LZB	32341	West of England	LN51DWE	33040	Glasgow	LR02LXH	33149	Eastern Counties
LK53LZC	32342	West of England	LN51DWF	33041	South Yorkshire	LR02LXJ	33150	Eastern Counties
LK53LZD	32343	West of England	LN51DWG	33042	Midlands	LR02LXK	33151	Eastern Counties
LK53LZE	32344	West of England	LN51DWK	41426	Glasgow	LR02LXL	33152	Eastern Counties
LK53LZF	32345	West of England	LN51DWY	41415	Glasgow	LR02LXM	33153	Hampshire D&B
LK53LZG	32346	West of England	LN51DWZ	41416	Glasgow	LR02LXN	33154	Eastern Counties
LK53LZH	32347	West of England	LN51DXA	41417	Glasgow	LR02LXO	33155	Eastern Counties
LK53LZL	32348	Hampshire D&B	LN51DXB	41418	Glasgow	LR02LXP	33156	Eastern Counties
LK53LZM	32349	West of England	LN51DXC	41419	Unallocated	LR02LXS	33157	Eastern Counties
LK53LZN	32350	West of England	LN51DXD	41420	West of England	LR02LXT	33158	Eastern Counties
LK53LZO	32351	West of England	LN51DXE	41421	West of England	LR02LXU	33159	Eastern Counties
LK53LZP	32352	West of England	LN51DXF	41422	Glasgow	LR02LXV	33160	Eastern Counties
LK53LZR	32353	West of England	LN51DXG	41423	West of England	LR02LXW	33161	Eastern Counties
LK53LZT	32354	West of England	LN51GJJ	33057	Eastern Counties	LR02LXX	33162	Eastern Counties
LK53LZU	32355	West of England	LN51GJK	33058	Eastern Counties	LR02LXZ	33163	Eastern Counties
LK53LZV	32356	West of England	LN51GJO	33059	Scotland East	LR02LYA	33164	Eastern Counties
LK53LZW	32357	West of England	LN51GJU	33060	Eastern Counties	LR02LYC	33165	Eastern Counties
LK53LZX	32358	West of England	LN51GKA	33071	South Yorkshire	LR02LYD	33166	Eastern Counties
LK53MBF	32359	West of England	LN51GKF	33050	Scotland East	LR02LYF	33167	Eastern Counties
LK53MBX	53052	Hampshire D&B	LN51GKJ	33052	South Yorkshire	LR02LYG	33168	Eastern Counties
LK53MDE	53054	Hampshire D&B	LN51GKK	33053	Glasgow	LR02LYJ	33169	Eastern Counties
LK53MDF	53055	Hampshire D&B	LN51GKL	33054	Glasgow	LR02LYK	33170	Eastern Counties
LK53MDJ	53056	Hampshire D&B	LN51GKO	33055	Eastern Counties	LR02LYO	33171	Eastern Counties
LK53PNO	53057	Hampshire D&B	LN51GKP	33056	Eastern Counties	LR02LYP	33172	South West
LK54FNC	68531	Essex	LN51GKU	33061	South Yorkshire	LR02LYS	33173	South West
LK54FNE	68532	Essex	LN51GKV	33062	South Yorkshire	LR02LYT	33174	South West
LK54FNF	68536	Hampshire D&B	LN51GKX	33063	South Yorkshire	LR02LYU	33175	South West
LK54FNH	68537	Hampshire D&B	LN51GKY	33064	South Yorkshire	LR02LYV	33176	South West
LK54FNJ	68533	Hampshire D&B	LN51GKZ	33065	South Yorkshire	LR02LYW	33177	South West
LK54FNL	68534	Essex	LN51GLF	33066	South Yorkshire	LR02LYX	33178	Essex
LK55ABU	68558	Scotland East	LN51GLJ	33067	South Yorkshire	LR02LYY	33179	Hampshire D&B
LK55ABV	68559	Midlands	LN51GLK	33068	South Yorkshire	LR02LYZ	33180	Hampshire D&B
LK55ABX	68560	Scotland East	LN51GLV	33069	South Yorkshire	LR02LZA	33181	Hampshire D&B
LK55ABZ	65724	Hampshire D&B	LN51GLY	33070	South Yorkshire	LR02LZB	33182	Hampshire D&B
LK55ACF	65725	Hampshire D&B	LN51GLZ	33099	South Yorkshire	LR02LZC	33183	Hampshire D&B
LK55ACJ	65726	Hampshire D&B	LN51GME	33084	South Yorkshire	LR02LZD	33184	Essex
LK55ACO	32657	Glasgow	LN51GMF	33085	Unallocated	LSK570	23401	Aberdeen
LK57EJD	44001	Essex	LN51GMG	33086	Essex	LSK571	23402	Aberdeen
LK57EJE	44002	Essex	LN51GMO	33087	Essex	LT02NTV	64001	Hampshire D&B
LK57EJF	44003	Essex	LN51GMU	33088	Essex	LT02NTX	64002	Hampshire D&B
LK57EJG	44004	Essex	LN51GMV	33089	Glasgow	LT02NTY	64003	Scotland East
LK57EJJ	44005	Essex	LN51GMX	33090	Essex	LT02NUA	64004	Scotland East
LK57EJL	44006	Essex	LN51GMY	33091	Glasgow	LT02NUB	64005	Hampshire D&B
LK58ECV	39001	York	LN51GMZ	33092	Glasgow	LT02NUE	64007	Scotland East
LK58ECW	39002	York	LN51GNF	33077	Essex	LT02NUF	64008	Scotland East
LK58ECX	39003	York	LN51GNJ	33078	Essex	LT02NUJ	64010	Scotland East
LK58ECY	39004	York	LN51GNK	33079	South Yorkshire	LT02NVK	33123	South Yorkshire
LK58ECZ	39005	York	LN51GNP	33080	Essex	LT02NVL	33122	Glasgow
LK58EDF	37274	Hampshire D&B	LN51GNU	33081	Essex	LT02NVM	33124	South Yorkshire
LK58EDJ	37275	Hampshire D&B	LN51GNV	33082	South Yorkshire	LT02NVN	33125	South Yorkshire
LK58EDL	37276	Hampshire D&B	LN51GNX	33083	South Yorkshire	LT02NVO	33126	South Yorkshire
LK62FUJ	63039	South Yorkshire	LN51GNY	33096	Glasgow	LT02NVP	33127	South Yorkshire
LK62HJD	63038	South Yorkshire	LN51GNZ	33097	Glasgow	LT02NVR	33128	South Yorkshire
LK62HJX	63041	South Yorkshire	LN51GOA	33098	Essex	LT02NVS	33129	South Yorkshire
LK62HKG	63040	South Yorkshire	LN51GOC	33072	Essex	LT02NVU	33116	Glasgow
LN51DUJ	41446	Glasgow	LN51GOE	33073	Essex	LT02NVV	33115	Glasgow
LN51DUU	41447	Glasgow	LN51GOH	33074	Essex	LT02NVW	33114	Glasgow
LN51DUV	41448	Glasgow	LN51GOU	41795	South West	LT02NVX	33113	Eastern Counties
LN51DUY	41449	Glasgow	LN51NRJ	33093	Scotland East	LT02NVY	64011	Scotland East

Reg	No.	Location	Reg	No.	Location	Reg	No.	Location
LT02NVZ	33117	Glasgow	LT52WVG	33238	Eastern Counties	M967GDU	66652	West Yorkshire
LT02NWA	33118	Glasgow	LT52WVH	33239	Eastern Counties	MA51AET	40323	Manchester
LT02NWB	33119	Glasgow	LT52WVJ	33240	Eastern Counties	MA51AEU	40324	Manchester
LT02NWC	33120	Glasgow	LT52WVL	33242	Eastern Counties	MA51AEV	40325	Manchester
LT02NWD	33121	Glasgow	LT52WVM	32249	South Yorkshire	MA51AEW	40326	Manchester
LT02ZBX	33131	Scotland East	LT52WVN	32250	South Yorkshire	MH06ZSW	19004	West Yorkshire
LT02ZBY	33132	Essex	LT52WVO	32251	West of England	MH06ZSP	19006	West Yorkshire
LT02ZBZ	33133	Essex	LT52WVP	32252	West of England	ML02OFW	40327	Manchester
LT02ZCA	33134	Essex	LT52WVY	32253	West of England	ML02OFX	40328	Manchester
LT02ZCE	33135	Scotland East	LT52WVZ	32254	Hampshire D&B	ML02OFY	40329	Manchester
LT02ZCF	33136	Essex	LT52WWA	32255	Hampshire D&B	ML02OFZ	40330	Manchester
LT02ZCJ	32100	Eastern Counties	LT52WWB	32256	Hampshire D&B	ML02OGA	40331	Manchester
LT02ZCK	32101	Eastern Counties	LT52WWC	32257	Hampshire D&B	ML02OGB	40332	Manchester
LT02ZCL	32102	Eastern Counties	LT52WWD	32258	Hampshire D&B	ML02OGC	40333	Manchester
LT02ZCN	32103	Eastern Counties	LT52WWE	32259	Hampshire D&B	ML02OGD	40334	Manchester
LT02ZCO	32104	Eastern Counties	LT52WWF	32260	South Yorkshire	ML02OGE	40335	Manchester
LT02ZCU	32105	Eastern Counties	LT52WWG	32261	South Yorkshire	ML02OGF	40336	Manchester
LT02ZCV	32106	Eastern Counties	LT52WWH	32262	South Yorkshire	MOD571P	39971	Cymru
LT02ZCY	32107	Eastern Counties	LT52WWJ	32263	South Yorkshire	MV02VAA	60704	South Yorkshire
LT02ZCZ	32108	South Yorkshire	LT52WWK	32264	South Yorkshire	MV02VAD	60705	South Yorkshire
LT02ZDH	32109	South Yorkshire	LT52WWL	32265	South Yorkshire	MV02VAE	60706	South Yorkshire
LT02ZDJ	32110	South Yorkshire	LT52WWM	32266	South Yorkshire	MV02VAF	60707	South Yorkshire
LT02ZDK	32111	South Yorkshire	LT52WWN	32267	South Yorkshire	MV02VAH	60708	South Yorkshire
LT02ZDL	32112	Eastern Counties	LT52WWO	32268	South Yorkshire	MV02VAJ	60709	South Yorkshire
LT02ZDY	41487	Scotland East	LT52WWP	32269	South Yorkshire	MV02VAK	60710	South Yorkshire
LT02ZDZ	41488	Scotland East	LT52WWR	32270	South Yorkshire	MV02VAM	60711	South Yorkshire
LT02ZFA	41489	Cymru	LT52WWS	32271	South Yorkshire	MV02VAO	60712	South Yorkshire
LT02ZFB	41490	Cymru	LT52WWU	32272	South Yorkshire	MV02VAU	60713	South Yorkshire
LT02ZFC	41491	Cymru	LT52WWV	33233	Eastern Counties	MV02VAX	66324	Eastern Counties
LT02ZFJ	33137	Scotland East	LT52WWX	33234	Eastern Counties	MV02VAY	66325	Eastern Counties
LT02ZFK	33138	Scotland East	LT52WWY	33235	Eastern Counties	MV02VBA	66326	Eastern Counties
LT02ZFL	33139	Scotland East	LT52WWZ	33236	Eastern Counties	MV02VBB	66327	Eastern Counties
LT02ZFM	33140	Scotland East	LT52WXA	64012	Hampshire D&B	MV02VBC	66328	Eastern Counties
LT52WTE	32200	Eastern Counties	LT52WXB	64013	Hampshire D&B	MV02VBD	66329	Eastern Counties
LT52WTF	32201	Eastern Counties	LT52WXC	32273	South Yorkshire	MV02VBE	66330	Eastern Counties
LT52WTG	32202	Eastern Counties	LT52WXD	32274	South Yorkshire	MV02VBF	60714	South Yorkshire
LT52WTJ	32203	Eastern Counties	LT52WXF	32276	South Yorkshire	MV02VBG	60715	South Yorkshire
LT52WTK	32204	Eastern Counties	LT52WXG	33229	Essex	MV02VBJ	60716	South Yorkshire
LT52WTL	32205	Eastern Counties	LT52WXH	33230	South Yorkshire	MV02VBK	60717	South Yorkshire
LT52WTM	32206	Eastern Counties	LT52WXK	33232	Essex	MV02VBL	60718	South Yorkshire
LT52WTN	32207	Eastern Counties	LT52WXL	64014	Hampshire D&B	MV02VBM	60719	South Yorkshire
LT52WTO	32208	Eastern Counties	LT52WXN	64015	Hampshire D&B	MV02VBN	60720	South Yorkshire
LT52WTP	32209	Eastern Counties	LT52WXO	64016	Hampshire D&B	MV02VBO	60721	South Yorkshire
LT52WTR	32210	Eastern Counties	LT52WXP	64017	Hampshire D&B	MV02VBP	60722	South Yorkshire
LT52WTU	32211	Eastern Counties	LT52XAA	33190	Essex	MV02VBU	61148	Eastern Counties
LT52WTV	32212	Eastern Counties	LT52XAB	33191	Unallocated	MV02VBX	66332	Eastern Counties
LT52WTW	32213	Eastern Counties	LT52XAC	33192	Essex	MV02VBY	66333	Essex
LT52WTX	32214	Eastern Counties	LT52XAE	33194	Essex	MV02VBZ	66334	Eastern Counties
LT52WTY	32215	South Yorkshire	LT52XAF	33195	Essex	MV02VCA	66335	Eastern Counties
LT52WTZ	32216	South Yorkshire	LT52XAG	33196	Essex	MV02VCC	66336	Eastern Counties
LT52WUA	32217	South Yorkshire	LT52XAL	32227	Scotland East	MV02VCD	60724	South Yorkshire
LT52WUB	32218	South Yorkshire	LT52XAM	32228	Scotland East	MV02VCE	60725	South Yorkshire
LT52WUC	32219	South Yorkshire	M141FAE	67341	West of England	MV02VCF	60726	South Yorkshire
LT52WUD	32220	South Yorkshire	M406VWW	60944	West Yorkshire	MV02VCG	60727	South Yorkshire
LT52WUE	32221	Scotland East	M504PNA	60299	Hampshire D&B	MV02VCJ	60728	South Yorkshire
LT52WUG	32222	Scotland East	M506PNA	60301	Manchester	MV02VCK	60729	South Yorkshire
LT52WUH	32223	Scotland East	M507PNA	60302	Manchester	MV02VCL	60730	South Yorkshire
LT52WUJ	32224	Scotland East	M508PNA	60303	Manchester	MV02VCM	66337	Eastern Counties
LT52WUK	32225	Scotland East	M509DHU	46609	West of England	MV02VCN	66338	Eastern Counties
LT52WUL	32226	Scotland East	M509PNA	60304	Essex	MV02VCO	66339	Eastern Counties
LT52WUV	33244	Eastern Counties	M510PNA	60305	Essex	MV02VCP	66340	Eastern Counties
LT52WUW	33245	Eastern Counties	M513PNA	60308	Manchester	MV02VCT	66341	Eastern Counties
LT52WUX	33246	Eastern Counties	M516DHU	46616	West of England	MV02VCU	66342	Eastern Counties
LT52WUY	33247	Eastern Counties	M516PNA	60311	Midlands	MV02VCW	66343	Eastern Counties
LT52WVA	33248	Eastern Counties	M520FFB	46620	West of England	MV02VCX	66344	Eastern Counties
LT52WVB	33186	Essex	M523FFB	46623	West of England	MV02VCY	66345	Eastern Counties
LT52WVD	33188	Essex	M626XWS	67501	Cymru	MV02VCZ	66346	Eastern Counties
LT52WVE	33189	Unallocated	M818PGM	64818	Hampshire D&B	MV02VDA	66347	Eastern Counties
LT52WVF	33237	Eastern Counties	M847DUS	31518	Midlands	MV02VDC	66348	Eastern Counties

MV02VDD	60731	South Yorkshire	MX05CFN	66834	Manchester	MX06VOC	69150	Manchester
MV02VDF	60733	South Yorkshire	MX05CFO	66835	Manchester	MX06VOD	69151	Manchester
MV02VDG	60734	South Yorkshire	MX05CFP	66836	Manchester	MX06VOF	69152	Manchester
MV02VDJ	60735	South Yorkshire	MX05CFU	66837	Essex	MX06VOG	69153	Manchester
MV02VDK	60736	South Yorkshire	MX05CFV	66838	Midlands	MX06VOH	69154	Manchester
MV02VDL	60737	South Yorkshire	MX05CFY	66839	Midlands	MX06VOP	69139	Manchester
MV02VDM	60738	South Yorkshire	MX05CGE	66840	Midlands	MX06VOU	69141	Manchester
MV02VDN	60739	South Yorkshire	MX05CGF	66841	Midlands	MX06VOV	69142	Manchester
MV02VDO	60740	South Yorkshire	MX05CGG	66842	Midlands	MX06VOY	69143	Manchester
MV02VDP	60741	South Yorkshire	MX05CGK	66843	Midlands	MX06VPA	69144	Manchester
MV02VDR	60742	South Yorkshire	MX05CGO	66844	Manchester	MX06VPC	69203	Manchester
MV02VDT	60743	South Yorkshire	MX05CGU	66845	Midlands	MX06VPD	69204	Manchester
MV02VDX	60744	South Yorkshire	MX05CGV	66846	Manchester	MX06VPE	69205	Manchester
MV02VDY	60745	South Yorkshire	MX05CGY	66847	Midlands	MX06VPG	69207	South West
MV02VDZ	66349	Glasgow	MX05CGZ	66848	Manchester	MX06VPJ	69208	South West
MV02VEA	66350	South West	MX05CHC	66849	Midlands	MX06VPK	69209	South West
MV02VEB	66351	South West	MX05CHD	66850	Eastern Counties	MX06VPL	69210	Hampshire D&B
MV02VEF	66352	South West	MX05CHF	66851	Midlands	MX06VPM	69211	Hampshire D&B
MV02VEH	66353	South West	MX05CHG	66852	Midlands	MX06VPN	69212	Hampshire D&B
MV02VEK	66354	South West	MX05CHH	66853	Manchester	MX06VPO	69175	Manchester
MV02VEL	66355	South West	MX05CHJ	66854	Manchester	MX06VPP	69176	Manchester
MV02VEM	66356	South West	MX05CHK	66855	Manchester	MX06VPR	69195	Manchester
MV06CXB	69138	Manchester	MX05CHL	66856	Manchester	MX06VPT	69196	Manchester
MV06CZG	69136	Manchester	MX05CHN	66857	Manchester	MX06VPU	69197	Manchester
MV06CZJ	69172	Manchester	MX05CHO	66858	Manchester	MX06VPV	69198	Manchester
MV06CZS	69135	Manchester	MX05CHV	66859	Manchester	MX06VPW	69199	Manchester
MV06CZT	69137	Manchester	MX05CHY	66860	Manchester	MX06VPY	69200	Manchester
MV06DWZ	69173	Manchester	MX05CHZ	66861	Manchester	MX06VPZ	69201	Manchester
MV06DYU	69206	South West	MX05CJE	66862	Manchester	MX06VRC	69202	Manchester
MX05CBF	66794	Essex	MX05CJF	66863	Manchester	MX06YXJ	69177	Manchester
MX05CBU	66795	Essex	MX05CJJ	66864	Manchester	MX06YXK	69178	Manchester
MX05CBV	66796	Essex	MX05CJO	66865	Manchester	MX06YXL	69179	Manchester
MX05CBY	66797	Essex	MX05CJU	66866	Manchester	MX06YXM	69180	Manchester
MX05CCA	66798	Essex	MX05CJV	66867	Manchester	MX06YXN	69181	Glasgow
MX05CCD	66799	Essex	MX05CJY	66868	Manchester	MX06YXO	69182	Glasgow
MX05CCF	66800	Essex	MX05CJZ	66869	Manchester	MX06YXP	69183	Glasgow
MX05CCJ	66801	Essex	MX05CKA	66870	Manchester	MX06YXR	69184	Glasgow
MX05CCK	66802	Essex	MX05CKC	66871	Manchester	MX06YXS	69213	Hampshire D&B
MX05CCN	66803	Essex	MX05CKD	66872	Manchester	MX06YXT	69214	Hampshire D&B
MX05CCO	66804	Essex	MX05CKE	66873	Manchester	MX07BPY	37279	Manchester
MX05CCU	66805	Essex	MX05CKF	66874	Manchester	MX07BPZ	37280	Manchester
MX05CCV	66806	Essex	MX05CKJ	66876	Manchester	MX07BRF	37281	Manchester
MX05CCY	66807	Essex	MX05CKO	66880	Manchester	MX07BRV	37282	Manchester
MX05CCZ	66808	Essex	MX05CKP	66881	Hampshire D&B	MX07BRZ	37283	Manchester
MX05CDE	66809	Essex	MX05CLF	66885	Hampshire D&B	MX07BSO	37284	Manchester
MX05CDF	66810	Essex	MX06AEB	57000	West of England	MX07BSU	37285	Manchester
MX05CDK	66811	Essex	MX06VMW	69165	Manchester	MX07BSV	37286	Manchester
MX05CDN	66812	Essex	MX06VMZ	69166	Manchester	MX07BSY	37287	Manchester
MX05CDO	66813	Essex	MX06VNB	69167	Manchester	MX07BSZ	37288	Manchester
MX05CDU	66814	Essex	MX06VNC	69168	Manchester	MX07BTE	37289	Manchester
MX05CDV	66815	Essex	MX06VND	69169	Manchester	MX07BTF	37290	Manchester
MX05CDY	66816	Essex	MX06VNE	69170	Manchester	MX07BTO	37291	Manchester
MX05CDZ	66817	Essex	MX06VNF	69171	Manchester	MX07BTU	37292	Manchester
MX05CEA	66818	Essex	MX06VNK	69174	Manchester	MX07BTV	37293	Manchester
MX05CEF	66819	Essex	MX06VNL	69155	Manchester	MX07BTY	37294	Manchester
MX05CEJ	66820	Essex	MX06VNM	69156	Manchester	MX07BTZ	37295	Manchester
MX05CEK	66821	Essex	MX06VNN	69157	Manchester	MX07BUA	37296	Manchester
MX05CEO	66822	Essex	MX06VNO	69158	Manchester	MX07BUE	37297	Manchester
MX05CEU	66823	Essex	MX06VNP	69159	Manchester	MX07BUF	37298	Manchester
MX05CEV	66824	Essex	MX06VNR	69160	Manchester	MX07BUH	37299	Manchester
MX05CEY	66825	Essex	MX06VNS	69161	Manchester	MX07BUJ	37300	Manchester
MX05CFA	66826	Essex	MX06VNT	69162	Manchester	MX07BUU	37303	Manchester
MX05CFD	66827	Essex	MX06VNU	69163	Manchester	MX07BUV	37304	Manchester
MX05CFE	66828	Essex	MX06VNV	69164	Manchester	MX07OZD	44514	Midlands
MX05CFG	66829	Essex	MX06VNW	69145	Manchester	MX09GXY	37469	Manchester
MX05CFJ	66830	Essex	MX06VNY	69146	Manchester	MX09GXZ	37470	Manchester
MX05CFK	66831	Manchester	MX06VNZ	69147	Manchester	MX09GYA	37549	Manchester
MX05CFL	66832	Manchester	MX06VOA	69148	Manchester	MX09GYB	37552	Manchester
MX05CFM	66833	Manchester	MX06VOB	69149	Manchester	MX09GYC	37548	Manchester

Reg	Fleet	Depot	Reg	Fleet	Depot	Reg	Fleet	Depot
MX09GYD	37550	Manchester	MX55UAA	66891	Manchester	MX58DWY	37388	Manchester
MX09GYE	37545	Manchester	MX56ACV	69185	Manchester	MX58DWZ	37389	Manchester
MX09GYF	37553	Manchester	MX56ACY	69186	Manchester	MX58DXA	37390	Manchester
MX09GYG	37471	Manchester	MX56ACZ	69187	Glasgow	MX58DXB	37391	Manchester
MX09GYH	37554	Manchester	MX56ADO	69188	Glasgow	MX58DXC	37392	Manchester
MX09GYJ	37546	Manchester	MX56ADU	69189	Glasgow	MX58DXD	37393	Manchester
MX09GYK	37547	Manchester	MX56ADV	69190	Glasgow	MX58DXE	37394	Manchester
MX09HUK	37551	Manchester	MX56ADZ	69191	Glasgow	MX58DXF	37395	Manchester
MX09HUO	37557	Manchester	MX56AEA	69192	Glasgow	MX58DXG	37396	Manchester
MX09HUP	37559	Manchester	MX56AEB	69193	Glasgow	MX58DXH	37397	Manchester
MX09HUU	37558	Manchester	MX56AEC	69194	Glasgow	MX58DXJ	37398	Manchester
MX09LMF	37560	Manchester	MX56AED	69215	Hampshire D&B	MX58DXK	37399	Manchester
MX09LMJ	37561	Manchester	MX56AEE	69216	Hampshire D&B	MX58DXL	37400	Manchester
MX09LMK	37555	Manchester	MX56AEF	69217	Hampshire D&B	MX58DXM	37401	Manchester
MX09LML	37556	Manchester	MX56AEG	69218	South West	MX58DXO	37402	Manchester
MX10DXU	44515	Midlands	MX56AEJ	69219	South West	MX58DXP	37403	Manchester
MX54GZA	53143	Manchester	MX56AEK	69220	South West	MX58DXR	37404	Manchester
MX54GZB	53144	Manchester	MX56AEL	69221	South West	MX58DXS	37405	Manchester
MX54GZC	53145	Manchester	MX56AEM	69222	South West	MX58DXT	37406	Manchester
MX54GZD	53146	Manchester	MX56AEN	69223	South West	MX58DXU	37407	Manchester
MX54GZE	53147	Manchester	MX56AEO	69224	South West	MX58DXV	37408	Manchester
MX54GZF	53148	Manchester	MX56AEP	69225	South West	MX58DXW	37409	Manchester
MX54GZG	53149	Manchester	MX56AET	69226	South West	MX58DXZ	37410	Manchester
MX54GZH	53150	Manchester	MX56AEU	69227	South West	MX58DYA	37411	Manchester
MX55FFD	66894	Manchester	MX56AEV	69228	South West	MX58DYC	37412	Manchester
MX55FFE	66895	Manchester	MX56AEW	69229	South West	MX58DYD	37413	Manchester
MX55FFG	66896	Manchester	MX56AEY	69230	South West	MX58DYF	37414	Manchester
MX55FFH	66897	Manchester	MX56AEZ	69231	Cymru	MX58DYG	37415	Manchester
MX55FFJ	66898	Manchester	MX56AFA	69232	Cymru	MX58DYH	37416	Manchester
MX55FFK	66899	Manchester	MX56AFE	69233	Cymru	MX58DYJ	37417	Manchester
MX55FFL	66900	Manchester	MX56AFF	69234	Cymru	MX58DYM	37418	Manchester
MX55FFM	66901	Manchester	MX56AFJ	69235	Cymru	MX58DYN	37419	Manchester
MX55FFO	66902	Manchester	MX56AFK	69236	Cymru	MX58DYO	37420	Manchester
MX55FFP	66903	Manchester	MX56AFN	69237	Cymru	MX58DYP	37421	Manchester
MX55FFR	66904	Manchester	MX56AFO	69238	Cymru	MX58DYS	37422	Manchester
MX55FFS	66905	Manchester	MX56AFU	69239	Cymru	MX58DYT	37423	Manchester
MX55FFT	66906	Manchester	MX56AFV	69240	Cymru	MX58DYU	37424	Manchester
MX55FFU	66907	Manchester	MX56AFY	69241	Cymru	MX58DYV	37425	Manchester
MX55FFV	66908	Manchester	MX56AFZ	69242	Cymru	MX58DYW	37426	Manchester
MX55FFW	66909	Manchester	MX56AGO	69243	Cymru	MX58DYY	37427	Manchester
MX55FFY	66910	Manchester	MX56AGU	69244	Cymru	MX58DZA	37428	Manchester
MX55FFZ	66911	Manchester	MX56HXZ	42940	Manchester	MX58DZB	37429	Manchester
MX55FGA	66912	Manchester	MX56HYO	43875	Midlands	MX58DZC	37430	Manchester
MX55FGC	66913	Manchester	MX56HYP	43876	Midlands	MX58DZD	37431	Manchester
MX55FGE	66914	Manchester	MX56NLJ	53828	Midlands	MX58DZE	37432	Manchester
MX55FGF	66915	Manchester	MX56NLK	53829	Midlands	MX58DZF	37433	Manchester
MX55FGG	66916	Manchester	MX57HDZ	37301	Manchester	MX58DZG	37434	Manchester
MX55FGJ	66917	Manchester	MX57HEJ	37302	Manchester	MX58DZH	37435	Manchester
MX55FGK	66918	Manchester	MX58DVU	37367	Manchester	MX58DZJ	37436	Manchester
MX55FGM	66919	Manchester	MX58DVV	37368	Manchester	MX58DZK	37437	Manchester
MX55FGN	66920	Manchester	MX58DVW	37369	Manchester	MX58DZL	37438	Manchester
MX55FGP	66922	Manchester	MX58DVY	37370	Manchester	MX58DZN	37439	Manchester
MX55FGU	66923	Manchester	MX58DVZ	37371	Manchester	MX58DZO	37440	Manchester
MX55FHC	66928	Manchester	MX58DWA	37372	Manchester	MX58DZP	37441	Manchester
MX55FHD	66929	Manchester	MX58DWC	37373	Manchester	MX58DZR	37442	Manchester
MX55FHE	66930	Manchester	MX58DWD	37374	Manchester	MX58DZS	37443	Manchester
MX55FHF	66931	Manchester	MX58DWE	37375	Manchester	MX58DZT	37444	Manchester
MX55FHH	66933	Manchester	MX58DWF	37376	Manchester	MX58DZU	37445	Manchester
MX55HHO	66884	Hampshire D&B	MX58DWG	37377	Manchester	MX58DZV	37446	Manchester
MX55HHP	66883	Hampshire D&B	MX58DWJ	37378	Manchester	MX58DZW	37447	Manchester
MX55HHR	66882	Hampshire D&B	MX58DWK	37379	Manchester	MX58DZY	37448	Manchester
MX55LDJ	66892	Manchester	MX58DWL	37380	Manchester	MX58DZZ	37449	Manchester
MX55LDK	66893	Manchester	MX58DWM	37381	Manchester	MX58EAA	37450	Manchester
MX55LHL	66886	Hampshire D&B	MX58DWN	37382	Manchester	MX58EAC	37451	Manchester
MX55NWC	68556	Scotland East	MX58DWO	37383	Manchester	MX58EAF	37452	Manchester
MX55NWD	68557	Hampshire D&B	MX58DWP	37384	Manchester	MX58EAG	37453	Manchester
MX55NWE	66875	Manchester	MX58DWU	37385	Manchester	MX58EAJ	37454	Manchester
MX55NWH	66890	Manchester	MX58DWV	37386	Manchester	MX58EAK	37455	Manchester
MX55NWS	68555	Essex	MX58DWW	37387	Manchester	MX58EAM	37456	Manchester

Reg	No.	Location	Reg	No.	Location	Reg	No.	Location
MX58EAO	37457	Manchester	P132NLW	41132	South West	P579EFL	34079	Hampshire D&B
MX58EAP	37458	Manchester	P134NLW	41134	South West	P588WSU	31684	Scotland East
MX58EAY	37459	Manchester	P143NLW	41143	South West	P592WSU	31687	Scotland East
MX58EBA	37460	Manchester	P144NLW	41144	West of England	P593WSU	31688	Scotland East
MX58EBC	37461	Manchester	P149NLW	41149	Cymru	P594WSU	31572	Scotland East
MX58EBD	37462	Manchester	P156NLW	41156	South West	P596WSU	31469	Glasgow
MX58EBF	37463	Manchester	P176NAK	20418	Hampshire D&B	P605WSU	31477	Glasgow
MX58EBG	37464	Manchester	P177NAK	20417	Hampshire D&B	P606WSU	31478	Glasgow
MX58EBK	37465	Manchester	P185TGD	34285	Midlands	P613WSU	31677	West Yorkshire
MX58EBL	37466	Manchester	P186TGD	34286	Midlands	P617WSU	31481	Glasgow
MX58EBM	37467	Manchester	P188TGD	34288	Midlands	P619WSU	31483	Glasgow
MX58EBN	37468	Manchester	P190TGD	30560	Scotland East	P627CGM	46727	Hampshire D&B
MX58KZA	53707	Cymru	P191TGD	34290	Scotland East	P632CGM	40911	Scotland East
MX58KZB	53708	Cymru	P192TGD	30740	Scotland East	P655UFB	34155	Eastern Counties
N123OGG	61391	Glasgow	P193TGD	30741	Scotland East	P656UFB	34156	Eastern Counties
N212WRD	42412	Cymru	P195TGD	30743	Scotland East	P658UFB	34158	Midlands
N235KAE	46235	South West	P196TGD	30744	Scotland East	P732NVG	20122	Eastern Counties
N239KAE	46239	West of England	P197TGD	30745	Scotland East	P768XHS	20128	Essex
N240KAE	46240	West of England	P198TGD	30746	Scotland East	P829FEF	34129	Hampshire D&B
N244LHT	46244	West of England	P201TGD	30748	Scotland East	P834YUM	42634	South West
N324ECR	46324	Hampshire D&B	P202TGD	30749	Scotland East	P908RYO	31828	South West
N325ECR	46325	Hampshire D&B	P203TGD	30750	Scotland East	P920RYO	31820	South West
N345CJA	48045	Glasgow	P204TGD	30751	Scotland East	P921RYO	31821	South West
N414ENW	60133	West Yorkshire	P206NSC	40915	Scotland East	P926RYO	31826	South West
N465ETR	46365	Hampshire D&B	P241UCW	34041	South West	P930RYO	31830	South West
N466ETR	46366	Hampshire D&B	P243UCW	34043	Hampshire D&B	PL05UBR	69533	Eastern Counties
N467ETR	46367	Hampshire D&B	P244UCW	34044	Hampshire D&B	PL05UBS	69532	Eastern Counties
N521WVR	60316	Midlands	P247OEW	41147	Hampshire D&B	PSU 628	23305	Aberdeen
N522WVR	60317	Midlands	P248UCW	34048	Scotland East	PSU 629	23306	Aberdeen
N527WVR	60322	Manchester	P249UCW	34049	South West	PT59JPT	67699	Midlands
N533LHG	34259	South West	P250UCW	34050	South West	Q275LBA	68000	Essex
N542LHG	34261	South West	P251UCW	34051	South West	R110GSF	61524	Glasgow
N542WVR	60337	Hampshire D&B	P252PAE	46252	West of England	R117GSF	61529	Midlands
N545WVR	60340	Midlands	P252UCW	34052	South West	R119GSF	61531	Midlands
N547HAE	46647	South West	P255RFL	41155	Cymru	R120FUP	42620	Cymru
N551LHU	46651	West of England	P259PAE	46259	West of England	R121FUP	42621	Cymru
N553LHU	46653	West of England	P262PAE	46262	West of England	R121GSF	61533	Essex
N557LHU	46657	West of England	P264PAE	46264	West of England	R122FUP	42622	Cymru
N583WND	51685	South West	P295KPX	34295	Hampshire D&B	R122GSF	61534	Glasgow
N609APU	20109	Eastern Counties	P404KOW	42504	Hampshire D&B	R124GSF	61244	Midlands
N615DWY	47015	Hampshire D&B	P405KOW	42505	Hampshire D&B	R126GSF	61243	Midlands
N763CKY	60600	West of England	P406KOW	42506	Hampshire D&B	R127GSF	61245	Midlands
N802FLW	46902	West of England	P407KOW	42507	Hampshire D&B	R128GSF	61537	Glasgow
N890HWS	51590	South West	P425PVW	31925	Manchester	R131FUP	42631	Cymru
N946SOS	31435	Glasgow	P430ORL	42430	South West	R131GSF	61540	Glasgow
N949SOS	31438	Glasgow	P436YSH	61056	West Yorkshire	R131JYG	60798	South Yorkshire
N951SOS	31440	Scotland East	P439ORL	42439	Essex	R132JYG	60799	South Yorkshire
N952SOS	31441	Scotland East	P448NEX	43448	Essex	R133JYG	60800	South Yorkshire
N953SOS	31442	Glasgow	P452SCV	42252	South West	R134JYG	60801	South Yorkshire
N954SOS	31443	Scotland East	P455SCV	42255	South West	R135GSF	65535	Glasgow
N955SOS	31444	Glasgow	P510LND	40416	Manchester	R135JYG	60802	South Yorkshire
N956SOS	31445	Scotland East	P529TYS	61499	Glasgow	R136JYG	65536	Glasgow
N957SOS	31446	Scotland East	P535EFL	34015	Scotland East	R136JYG	60803	South Yorkshire
N958SOS	31447	Scotland East	P536EFL	34016	Hampshire D&B	R137JYG	60804	South Yorkshire
N959SOS	31448	Glasgow	P540EFL	34017	Hampshire D&B	R138GSF	65538	Essex
N960SOS	31449	Glasgow	P542HMP	34022	Hampshire D&B	R138JYG	60805	South Yorkshire
N968SOS	31457	South West	P554EFL	34014	Essex	R139JYG	60806	South Yorkshire
N969SOS	31458	South West	P559EFL	34059	Hampshire D&B	R140GSF	65540	Eastern Counties
N972SOS	31461	South West	P564EFL	34064	South West	R143EHS	31486	Glasgow
NDZ3162	61210	South Yorkshire	P566EFL	34066	Scotland East	R146EHS	31489	Glasgow
NDZ3164	61211	South Yorkshire	P567EFL	34067	Scotland East	R147GSF	65527	Essex
NER621	34199	South West	P568EFL	34068	South West	R148EHS	31491	Glasgow
NML623E	39623	Eastern Counties	P569BTH	42569	Cymru	R148GSF	65528	Eastern Counties
OWB243	34196	South West	P573BTH	42573	Cymru	R149EHS	31492	Glasgow
OWJ782A	90092	South Yorkshire	P574BTH	42574	Cymru	R149GSF	65529	Eastern Counties
P106MFS	61478	Glasgow	P575BTH	42575	Cymru	R150GSF	65530	Glasgow
P117NLW	40161	Cymru	P575EFL	34075	Scotland East	R152 EHS	31200	Glasgow
P126NLW	40173	Midlands	P576EFL	34076	Scotland East	R152GSF	65532	Essex
P129NLW	41129	South West	P578DMS	62345	Scotland East	R154GSF	62359	Scotland East

Reg	No.	Location	Reg	No.	Location	Reg	No.	Location
R158GSF	61543	Glasgow	R290GHS	40786	South West	R454JFS	61068	West Yorkshire
R160GSF	61545	Glasgow	R292GHS	40788	South West	R455JFS	61069	West Yorkshire
R162TLM	41162	Cymru	R294GHS	40790	Hampshire D&B	R456CCV	42456	Cymru
R163GSF	61548	Glasgow	R296GHS	40792	Hampshire D&B	R456JFS	61070	West Yorkshire
R165TLM	41165	Hampshire D&B	R297GHS	40793	Cymru	R457JFS	61071	West Yorkshire
R166TLM	41166	Hampshire D&B	R298GHS	40794	Cymru	R458JFS	61072	West Yorkshire
R167TLM	41167	Cymru	R299GHS	40795	Cymru	R459CCV	42459	South West
R168GSF	61553	Midlands	R305JAF	20405	Scotland East	R459JFS	61073	West Yorkshire
R171TLM	41171	Cymru	R308GHS	40722	Glasgow	R460JFS	61074	West Yorkshire
R172GSX	61557	Glasgow	R308JAF	20408	South West	R460VOP	66100	West of England
R174TLM	41174	Cymru	R310GHS	40803	Glasgow	R462CCV	42462	Cymru
R175GSX	61158	Glasgow	R312GHS	40805	Midlands	R462JFS	61076	West Yorkshire
R175VWN	21145	Cymru	R317GHS	40809	Glasgow	R463CCV	42463	South West
R176HUG	30808	West Yorkshire	R322TLM	41222	Cymru	R463JFS	61077	West Yorkshire
R177GSX	60135	Midlands	R324HYG	40703	Scotland East	R464JFS	61078	West Yorkshire
R178GSX	60131	West Yorkshire	R326GHS	62146	West Yorkshire	R466CAH	43466	Eastern Counties
R179GSX	60136	Midlands	R329GHS	62148	West Yorkshire	R474CAH	43474	Essex
R183TLM	41183	Cymru	R330GHS	62156	Scotland East	R524BMS	62310	Scotland East
R185TLM	41185	Cymru	R330HYG	40179	Midlands	R551CNG	65551	Essex
R186TLM	41186	Cymru	R331GHS	62157	Scotland East	R554CNG	65554	Essex
R188TLM	41188	Cymru	R332GHS	62158	Scotland East	R556CNG	65556	Essex
R190TLM	41190	Cymru	R334GHS	62159	Glasgow	R571YNC	60361	South Yorkshire
R191VLD	41191	Cymru	R336LGH	31836	South West	R576SBA	60366	South Yorkshire
R192VLD	41192	Cymru	R339GHS	61241	Manchester	R577SBA	60367	South Yorkshire
R193VLD	41193	Cymru	R340GHS	61240	Manchester	R578SBA	60368	South Yorkshire
R194VLD	41194	Cymru	R342SUT	61562	Glasgow	R579SBA	60369	Manchester
R195GSX	61558	Glasgow	R344SUT	61564	Glasgow	R580SBA	60370	Manchester
R207MSA	42207	South West	R345SUT	61565	Glasgow	R581SBA	60371	Manchester
R208MSA	42208	Cymru	R346SUT	60011	Midlands	R581SWN	42581	Cymru
R211GSF	61559	Glasgow	R408WPX	42508	Hampshire D&B	R582SWN	42582	Cymru
R211MSA	42211	Cymru	R409WPX	42509	Hampshire D&B	R583SBA	60373	Manchester
R212MSA	42212	Cymru	R410WPX	42510	Hampshire D&B	R583SWN	42583	Cymru
R213MSA	42213	Cymru	R411WPX	42511	Hampshire D&B	R583YMS	62394	Scotland East
R214MSA	42214	Cymru	R412WPX	42512	Hampshire D&B	R584SBA	62215	Manchester
R215MSA	42215	Cymru	R413WPX	42513	Hampshire D&B	R584SWN	43584	Cymru
R216MSA	42216	Cymru	R414WPX	42514	Hampshire D&B	R585SBA	62216	Manchester
R216TLM	41216	Glasgow	R415WPX	41515	Hampshire D&B	R585SWN	42585	Cymru
R217TLM	41217	Glasgow	R416WPX	41516	Hampshire D&B	R586SBA	62217	Manchester
R218MSA	42218	Cymru	R417WPX	41517	Hampshire D&B	R586SWN	42586	Cymru
R221MSA	42221	Hampshire D&B	R418WPX	41518	Cymru	R587SBA	62218	Manchester
R221TLM	41221	Glasgow	R419WPX	41519	Cymru	R587SWN	42587	Cymru
R224GFS	40891	Cymru	R420WPX	42520	Cymru	R588SBA	62142	South Yorkshire
R230TLM	41230	Cymru	R421WPX	42521	Hampshire D&B	R588SWN	42588	Cymru
R233SBA	40946	Scotland East	R422WPX	42522	Hampshire D&B	R589SBA	62143	West Yorkshire
R233TLM	41233	Cymru	R423WPX	42523	Hampshire D&B	R589SWN	42589	Cymru
R234TLM	41234	Cymru	R424WPX	42524	Hampshire D&B	R591SWN	42591	Cymru
R235SBA	40361	Manchester	R425WPX	42525	Hampshire D&B	R592SWN	42592	Cymru
R238SBA	40364	Manchester	R426WPX	42526	Hampshire D&B	R593SWN	42593	Cymru
R241LGH	31841	South West	R427WPX	42527	Hampshire D&B	R595SWN	42595	Cymru
R241SBA	40367	Midlands	R429ULE	31929	Manchester	R596SWN	42596	Cymru
R243SBA	40369	Manchester	R430PSH	40935	Cymru	R597SWN	42597	Cymru
R246LGH	31846	South West	R434GSF	61054	Essex	R598SWN	42598	Cymru
R247SBA	40373	Midlands	R437GSF	61057	Essex	R599SWN	42599	Cymru
R249SBA	40375	Midlands	R438ALS	60075	Midlands	R609YCR	42109	Hampshire D&B
R250SBA	40376	Midlands	R439ALS	60076	Manchester	R610JUB	30790	West Yorkshire
R252SBA	40378	Midlands	R441ALS	60078	Midlands	R611JUB	30791	West Yorkshire
R257DVF	65557	Unallocated	R442ALS	60079	Midlands	R611YCR	42111	Hampshire D&B
R257SBA	40383	Midlands	R443ULE	31943	Manchester	R612YCR	42112	Hampshire D&B
R258DVF	65558	Unallocated	R445ALS	62302	Scotland East	R613YCR	42113	Hampshire D&B
R259DVF	65559	Unallocated	R446ALS	62303	Scotland East	R614YCR	42114	Hampshire D&B
R260DVF	65560	Unallocated	R447ALS	62304	Scotland East	R615YCR	42115	Hampshire D&B
R261DVF	65561	Midlands	R447CCV	42447	Essex	R616JUB	30796	West Yorkshire
R262DVF	65562	Midlands	R448ALS	62305	Scotland East	R616YCR	42116	Hampshire D&B
R263DVF	65563	Unallocated	R449CCV	42449	Cymru	R617YCR	42117	Hampshire D&B
R264DVF	65564	Midlands	R451JSG	61065	West Yorkshire	R618YCR	42118	Hampshire D&B
R277LGH	31877	South West	R452JSG	61066	West Yorkshire	R619YCR	42119	Hampshire D&B
R277SBA	40403	Manchester	R453CCV	42453	Cymru	R620JUB	30800	West Yorkshire
R278LGH	31878	South West	R453JFS	61067	West Yorkshire	R620YCR	42120	Hampshire D&B
R280SBA	40406	Manchester	R454CCV	42454	Hampshire D&B	R621CVR	60376	Manchester

Reg	No.	Location	Reg	No.	Location	Reg	No.	Location
R621YCR	42121	Hampshire D&B	R688DPW	43488	Eastern Counties	R931WOE	31767	West Yorkshire
R622CVR	60377	Manchester	R689DPW	43489	Eastern Counties	R932YOV	31768	West Yorkshire
R622JUB	30802	West Yorkshire	R701BAE	42701	West of England	R933YOV	31769	West Yorkshire
R622YCR	42122	Hampshire D&B	R702BAE	42702	West of England	R934YOV	31770	West Yorkshire
R623YCR	42123	Hampshire D&B	R703BAE	42703	West of England	R935YOV	31771	West Yorkshire
R624CVR	60379	Manchester	R704BAE	42704	West of England	R936YOV	31808	West Yorkshire
R625CVR	60380	Manchester	R705BAE	42705	West of England	R938YOV	31773	West Yorkshire
R625JUB	30805	West Yorkshire	R706BAE	42706	West of England	R939YOV	31774	West Yorkshire
R626CVR	60381	Manchester	R707BAE	42707	West of England	R940YOV	31775	West Yorkshire
R626JUB	30806	West Yorkshire	R708BAE	42708	West of England	R979NVT	40137	Midlands
R629JUB	30809	West Yorkshire	R709BAE	42709	West of England	RA04YGX	54601	West of England
R630CVR	60385	Manchester	R710BAE	42710	West of England	RA04YHS	54602	South West
R630JUB	30810	West Yorkshire	R711BAE	42711	West of England	RD51FKV	68001	Hampshire D&B
R631CVR	60386	Manchester	R711VLA	41011	Essex	RD51FKW	68002	Hampshire D&B
R631JUB	30811	West Yorkshire	R712BAE	42712	West of England	RD51FKZ	68003	Hampshire D&B
R632JUB	30812	West Yorkshire	R712DJN	43712	Essex	RD51FLA	68004	Hampshire D&B
R633JUB	30813	West Yorkshire	R713BAE	42713	Cymru	RG1173	62121	Aberdeen
R633VLX	41633	Hampshire D&B	R713DJN	43713	Essex	RG51FWZ	41403	Hampshire D&B
R634CVR	60856	South Yorkshire	R714BAE	42714	Cymru	RG51FXA	41404	West of England
R634JUB	30814	West Yorkshire	R714DJN	43714	Essex	RG51FXB	41405	Glasgow
R634VLX	41634	Hampshire D&B	R715BAE	42715	Cymru	RG51FXC	41406	Glasgow
R635CVR	60857	South Yorkshire	R715DJN	43715	Essex	RG51FXD	41407	Glasgow
R636CVR	60858	South Yorkshire	R716BAE	42716	Cymru	RG51FXE	41408	Glasgow
R636HYG	30816	West Yorkshire	R717BAE	42717	Hampshire D&B	RG51FXF	41409	Glasgow
R636JUB	30815	West Yorkshire	R717DJN	43717	Essex	RG51FXH	41410	Glasgow
R636VLX	41636	Hampshire D&B	R718BAE	42718	West of England	RKZ4760	66993	West of England
R637CVR	60859	South Yorkshire	R719DJN	43719	Essex	RKZ4761	66992	West of England
R637DUS	40819	Glasgow	R719RAD	42719	South West	RL02FYX	90489	West Yorkshire
R637HYG	30817	West Yorkshire	R720DJN	43720	Essex	RT09JPT	45119	Eastern Counties
R638CVR	60860	South Yorkshire	R721DJN	43721	Essex	RX54AOV	68511	Hampshire D&B
R638DUS	40820	Glasgow	R781WKW	60618	South Yorkshire	RX54AOY	68512	Hampshire D&B
R638HYG	30818	West Yorkshire	R782WKW	60619	South Yorkshire	RX54OGZ	68513	Hampshire D&B
R639CVR	60861	South Yorkshire	R783WKW	60620	South Yorkshire	S10FTR	19030	Cymru
R640CVR	60862	South Yorkshire	R784WKW	60621	West Yorkshire	S20FTR	19032	Cymru
R641CVR	60863	Essex	R785WKW	60622	South Yorkshire	S30FTR	19034	Cymru
R641HYG	30821	West Yorkshire	R787WKW	60624	South Yorkshire	S40FTR	19035	Cymru
R642DUS	40822	Hampshire D&B	R789WKW	60626	South Yorkshire	S50FTR	19036	Cymru
R642HYG	30822	West Yorkshire	R790WKW	60627	South Yorkshire	S60FTR	19037	Cymru
R643CVR	60865	Essex	R813HWS	20457	Hampshire D&B	S70FTR	19038	Cymru
R643DUS	40823	Hampshire D&B	R878ERE	60112	Manchester	S80FTR	19033	Cymru
R643HYG	30823	West Yorkshire	R879HRF	60113	West Yorkshire	S90FTR	19000	Cymru
R643TLM	41643	Hampshire D&B	R881HRF	60115	Manchester	S100FTR	19029	Cymru
R644CVR	60766	Essex	R901BOU	66101	West Yorkshire	S101CSG	61137	Manchester
R644DUS	40824	Hampshire D&B	R902BOU	66102	West of England	S101TNB	60081	Midlands
R644TLM	41644	Essex	R904BOU	66104	West of England	S102CSG	65602	Hampshire D&B
R645DUS	40825	Hampshire D&B	R905BOU	66105	West of England	S103TNB	60013	Midlands
R646DUS	40826	Hampshire D&B	R906BOU	66106	West of England	S105CSG	61140	Manchester
R646HYG	30826	Scotland East	R907BOU	66107	West of England	S105TNB	60128	Midlands
R646TLM	41646	Hampshire D&B	R908BOU	66108	West of England	S106CSG	61291	Glasgow
R647DUS	40827	Hampshire D&B	R909BOU	66109	West of England	S106TNB	60015	Midlands
R647HYG	30827	Scotland East	R910BOU	66110	West of England	S107CSG	61292	Glasgow
R648HYG	30828	Scotland East	R912BOU	66112	West Yorkshire	S108CSG	61293	Glasgow
R649HYG	30829	Scotland East	R913BOU	66113	South Yorkshire	S108TNB	60161	Manchester
R652HYG	30832	Scotland East	R914BOU	66114	South Yorkshire	S109CSG	61294	Glasgow
R655DUS	31497	Scotland East	R915BOU	66115	West of England	S110CSG	61295	Glasgow
R661NHY	34161	Cymru	R916BOU	66116	West of England	S110TNB	60163	Scotland East
R662NHY	34162	Cymru	R917BOU	66117	West of England	S112TNB	60165	Scotland East
R663NHY	34163	Cymru	R918BOU	66118	West of England	S113CSG	61298	Glasgow
R664DUS	40828	Glasgow	R919BOU	66119	South Yorkshire	S113TNB	60166	Scotland East
R664NHY	34164	Cymru	R920COU	66120	West of England	S114CSG	61299	Glasgow
R667DUS	40830	Glasgow	R921WOE	31760	West Yorkshire	S114TNB	60167	Scotland East
R672DUS	40835	West of England	R922WOE	31761	West Yorkshire	S115CSG	61300	Glasgow
R677MEW	43677	Cymru	R923WOE	31762	West Yorkshire	S115TNB	60168	Scotland East
R679MEW	43679	Essex	R924WOE	31763	West Yorkshire	S116CSG	61017	Glasgow
R680DPW	43480	Essex	R925WOE	31764	West Yorkshire	S116JTP	66126	Eastern Counties
R680MEW	43680	Cymru	R926WOE	31765	West Yorkshire	S117CSG	61018	Glasgow
R681DPW	43481	Essex	R928WOE	31806	West Yorkshire	S117JTP	66127	Hampshire D&B
R683DPW	43483	Essex	R929WOE	31807	West Yorkshire	S118CSG	61019	Glasgow
R685DPW	43485	Essex	R930WOE	31766	West Yorkshire	S118JTP	66128	Hampshire D&B

Reg	Fleet	Region	Reg	Fleet	Region	Reg	Fleet	Region
S119CSG	61020	Glasgow	S445BSG	61059	West Yorkshire	S657RNA	60767	Essex
S120JTP	66130	Hampshire D&B	S446BSG	61060	West Yorkshire	S658RNA	60807	Eastern Counties
S121JTP	66121	Hampshire D&B	S447BSG	61061	West Yorkshire	S658SNG	42758	South West
S122UOT	66122	Hampshire D&B	S448BSG	61062	West Yorkshire	S659RNA	60808	Eastern Counties
S197KLM	41197	Cymru	S474TJX	40961	Hampshire D&B	S659SNG	42759	Hampshire D&B
S198KLM	41198	Cymru	S512UAK	40517	West of England	S660RNA	60809	Essex
S206LLO	34206	Manchester	S513RWP	52513	Hampshire D&B	S661RNA	60810	Essex
S209LLO	34209	Manchester	S517RWP	52517	Hampshire D&B	S662RNA	60811	Essex
S210LLO	34210	Manchester	S520UAK	40525	West of England	S664RNA	60813	Eastern Counties
S211CSG	61296	Glasgow	S520UMS	62383	Scotland East	S664SNG	42764	South West
S211LLO	34211	West Yorkshire	S523UMS	62309	Scotland East	S665AAE	34165	Hampshire D&B
S214LLO	34214	West Yorkshire	S524UAK	40529	West of England	S665RNA	60814	Eastern Counties
S215LLO	34215	Hampshire D&B	S526RWP	52526	South West	S667AAE	34167	Hampshire D&B
S216LLO	34216	Hampshire D&B	S526UMS	62312	Scotland East	S667RNA	60815	West Yorkshire
S218LLO	34218	Hampshire D&B	S529UAK	40534	West of England	S668AAE	34168	Hampshire D&B
S219LLO	34219	Manchester	S530UAK	40535	West of England	S668RNA	60816	West Yorkshire
S220GKS	61021	Glasgow	S533RWP	52533	Hampshire D&B	S670AAE	34170	Hampshire D&B
S220KLM	41200	Cymru	S536UAK	40541	West of England	S671AAE	34171	South West
S236KLM	41236	Glasgow	S537UAK	40542	West of England	S672AAE	34172	South West
S238KLM	41238	Essex	S540RWP	52540	Hampshire D&B	S672SVU	62118	West Yorkshire
S239KLM	41239	Essex	S549SCV	43809	South West	S673AAE	34173	South West
S240KLM	41240	Essex	S550JSE	61567	Glasgow	S673SNG	42773	Hampshire D&B
S241CSF	40892	Cymru	S551JSE	61568	Glasgow	S673SVU	62214	Manchester
S241KLM	41241	Essex	S551WAT	42551	Essex	S674AAE	34174	South West
S242KLM	41242	Glasgow	S554RWP	52554	South West	S675AAE	34175	Hampshire D&B
S243KLM	41243	Glasgow	S555JSE	61572	Glasgow	S675SVU	60818	West Yorkshire
S244CSF	40938	Scotland East	S556JSE	61573	Glasgow	S676AAE	34176	South West
S244KLM	41244	Glasgow	S557JSE	61574	Glasgow	S676SVU	60819	West Yorkshire
S245KLM	41245	Glasgow	S558JSE	61575	Glasgow	S677AAE	34177	South West
S246KLM	41246	Glasgow	S558RWP	52558	Hampshire D&B	S677SNG	42777	South West
S247CSF	40175	Midlands	S559JSE	61576	Glasgow	S677SVU	60820	West Yorkshire
S251CSF	40899	Scotland East	S559RWP	52559	Hampshire D&B	S678AAE	34178	South West
S301EWU	50270	Hampshire D&B	S560JSE	60222	West Yorkshire	S678SNG	42778	Hampshire D&B
S303EWU	50272	Hampshire D&B	S560RWP	52560	Hampshire D&B	S679AAE	34179	South West
S306EWU	50275	Scotland East	S561JSE	60215	Midlands	S679SNG	42779	South West
S312SCV	20412	South West	S565TPW	65565	Essex	S680BFS	61235	Midlands
S334TJX	40958	South West	S566TPW	65566	Essex	S681AAE	34181	South West
S335TJX	40959	Hampshire D&B	S567TPW	65567	Unallocated	S681BFS	61237	Midlands
S338TJX	40960	South West	S568TPW	65568	Unallocated	S682AAE	34182	South West
S342EWU	42642	Cymru	S569TPW	65569	Essex	S683AAE	34183	South West
S343EWU	42643	West of England	S570TPW	65570	Essex	S683BFS	61238	Midlands
S343SUX	40033	South West	S571TPW	65571	Unallocated	S683SNG	42783	Hampshire D&B
S344SUX	40956	Hampshire D&B	S572TPW	65572	Midlands	S684AAE	34184	South West
S348MFP	60012	Midlands	S573TPW	65573	Essex	S684BFS	61160	Midlands
S350MFP	60006	Midlands	S574TPW	65574	Essex	S684SNG	42784	South West
S351NPO	66151	Hampshire D&B	S624KTP	42124	Hampshire D&B	S685AAE	34185	South West
S352NPO	66152	Hampshire D&B	S625KTP	42125	Hampshire D&B	S686AAE	34186	Eastern Counties
S353MFP	60083	Midlands	S626KTP	42126	Hampshire D&B	S686BFS	61246	Midlands
S353NPO	66153	Hampshire D&B	S627KTP	42127	Hampshire D&B	S687AAE	34187	Eastern Counties
S354NPO	66154	Hampshire D&B	S628KTP	42128	Hampshire D&B	S688AAE	34188	South West
S356MFP	60004	Midlands	S629KTP	42129	Hampshire D&B	S689AAE	34189	South West
S356XCR	66156	Hampshire D&B	S630KTP	42130	Hampshire D&B	S689BFS	61239	Midlands
S357XCR	66157	Hampshire D&B	S631KTP	42131	Hampshire D&B	S690AAE	34190	South West
S358XCR	66158	Hampshire D&B	S632KTP	42132	Hampshire D&B	S690BFS	61145	Midlands
S359MFP	61141	Manchester	S633KTP	42133	Hampshire D&B	S691AAE	34191	South West
S359XCR	66159	West of England	S634KTP	42134	Hampshire D&B	S692BFS	61579	Glasgow
S360MFP	61142	Manchester	S636XCR	42136	Hampshire D&B	S693BFS	61580	Glasgow
S360XCR	66160	West of England	S637XCR	42137	Hampshire D&B	S694BFS	61581	Glasgow
S361MFP	61143	Midlands	S638XCR	42138	Hampshire D&B	S696BFS	61582	Glasgow
S361XCR	66161	West of England	S639XCR	42139	Hampshire D&B	S698BFS	61584	Glasgow
S362XCR	66162	West of England	S640XCR	42140	Hampshire D&B	S701BFS	61586	Glasgow
S363XCR	66163	West of England	S641XCR	42141	Hampshire D&B	S720AFB	42720	South West
S372SUX	40957	Hampshire D&B	S642XCR	42142	Hampshire D&B	S721AFB	42721	Cymru
S374SUX	40034	South West	S644BSG	61058	West Yorkshire	S722AFB	42722	Cymru
S375SUX	40035	South West	S652SNG	42752	South West	S723AFB	42723	West of England
S376SUX	40036	South West	S653SNG	42754	Hampshire D&B	S724AFB	42724	South West
S377SUX	40037	South West	S654FWY	30834	West Yorkshire	S725AFB	42725	South West
S378SUX	40038	South West	S655NUG	30239	West Yorkshire	S729TWC	43729	Essex
S389SUX	40039	South West	S657SNG	42757	South West	S731TWC	43731	Essex

Reg	No	Depot	Reg	No	Depot	Reg	No	Depot
S732TWC	43732	Essex	SF05KUJ	53202	Glasgow	SF06GZT	69108	Glasgow
S733TWC	43733	Essex	SF05KUK	53203	Glasgow	SF06GZV	69109	Glasgow
S734TWC	43734	Essex	SF05KWY	42877	Cymru	SF06GZX	69111	Glasgow
S735TWC	43735	Essex	SF05KWZ	42878	Cymru	SF06GZY	69112	Glasgow
S736TWC	43736	Essex	SF05KXA	42879	Cymru	SF06GZZ	69113	Glasgow
S738TWC	43738	Essex	SF05KXB	42880	Cymru	SF06HAA	69114	Glasgow
S753SNG	42753	South West	SF05KXC	42881	Cymru	SF06HAE	69115	Glasgow
S764RNE	40002	South West	SF05KXD	42882	Cymru	SF06HAO	69116	Glasgow
S766RNE	40003	Midlands	SF05KXE	42883	Cymru	SF06HAU	69117	Glasgow
S791RWG	66191	Manchester	SF05KXH	42884	Cymru	SF06HAX	69118	Glasgow
S792RWG	66192	Manchester	SF05KXJ	42885	Glasgow	SF06HBA	69119	Glasgow
S793RWG	66193	Manchester	SF05KXK	42886	Glasgow	SF06HBB	69120	Glasgow
S794RWG	66194	Manchester	SF05KXL	42887	Glasgow	SF06HBC	69121	Glasgow
S795RWG	66195	Manchester	SF05KXM	42888	Glasgow	SF07FCC	37188	Glasgow
S796RWG	66196	Hampshire D&B	SF06GXG	69039	Glasgow	SF07FCD	37189	Glasgow
S797RWG	66197	Hampshire D&B	SF06GXH	69059	Glasgow	SF07FCE	37190	Glasgow
S798RWG	66198	Hampshire D&B	SF06GXJ	69038	Glasgow	SF07FCG	37191	Glasgow
S799RWG	66199	Hampshire D&B	SF06GXK	69040	Glasgow	SF07FCJ	37192	Glasgow
S801RWG	66201	Hampshire D&B	SF06GXL	69041	Glasgow	SF07FCL	37199	Glasgow
S802RWG	66202	Hampshire D&B	SF06GXM	69057	Glasgow	SF07FCM	37201	Glasgow
S803RWG	66203	Hampshire D&B	SF06GXN	69058	Glasgow	SF07FCO	37202	Glasgow
S804RWG	66204	Hampshire D&B	SF06GXO	69060	Glasgow	SF07FCP	37166	Glasgow
S805RWG	66205	Hampshire D&B	SF06GXP	69061	Glasgow	SF07FCV	37167	Glasgow
S806RWG	66206	West of England	SF06GXR	69062	Glasgow	SF07FCX	37168	Glasgow
S807RWG	66207	West of England	SF06GXS	69063	Glasgow	SF07FCY	37169	Glasgow
S808RWG	61288	West Yorkshire	SF06GXT	69064	Glasgow	SF07FCZ	37170	Glasgow
S809RWG	61289	West Yorkshire	SF06GXU	69065	Glasgow	SF07FDA	37171	Glasgow
S810RWG	60628	West Yorkshire	SF06GXV	69072	Glasgow	SF07FDC	37172	Glasgow
S811RWG	60629	South Yorkshire	SF06GXW	69073	Glasgow	SF07FDD	37173	Glasgow
S812RWG	60630	South Yorkshire	SF06GXX	69074	Glasgow	SF07FDE	37174	Glasgow
S813RWG	60631	South Yorkshire	SF06GXY	69075	Glasgow	SF07FDG	37175	Glasgow
S814RWG	60632	South Yorkshire	SF06GXZ	69076	Glasgow	SF07FDJ	37176	Glasgow
S815AEH	60057	Midlands	SF06GYA	69077	Glasgow	SF07FDK	37177	Glasgow
S816AEH	60058	Midlands	SF06GYB	69066	Glasgow	SF07FDL	37178	Glasgow
S817AEH	60059	Midlands	SF06GYC	69067	Glasgow	SF07FDM	37179	Glasgow
S817KPR	42817	Hampshire D&B	SF06GYD	69068	Glasgow	SF07FDN	37180	Glasgow
S818AEH	60060	Midlands	SF06GYE	69069	Glasgow	SF07FDO	37181	Glasgow
S818KPR	42818	Hampshire D&B	SF06GYG	69070	Glasgow	SF07FDP	37182	Glasgow
S819AEH	60061	Midlands	SF06GYH	69071	Glasgow	SF07FDU	37183	Glasgow
S819KPR	42819	Hampshire D&B	SF06GYJ	69078	Glasgow	SF07FDV	37184	Glasgow
S820AEH	60062	Midlands	SF06GYK	69079	Glasgow	SF07FDX	37185	Glasgow
S820KPR	42820	Hampshire D&B	SF06GYN	69080	Glasgow	SF07FDY	37186	Glasgow
S821AEH	60063	Midlands	SF06GYO	69081	Glasgow	SF07FDZ	37187	Glasgow
S821KPR	42821	Hampshire D&B	SF06GYP	69082	Glasgow	SF07FEG	37193	Glasgow
S822KPR	42822	Hampshire D&B	SF06GYR	69083	Glasgow	SF07FEH	37194	Glasgow
S823KPR	42823	Hampshire D&B	SF06GYS	69084	Glasgow	SF07FEJ	37195	Glasgow
S824WYD	42824	West of England	SF06GYT	69085	Glasgow	SF07FEK	37196	Glasgow
S825WYD	42825	South West	SF06GYU	69086	Glasgow	SF07FEM	37197	Glasgow
S925AKS	31656	Scotland East	SF06GYV	69087	Glasgow	SF07FEO	37198	Glasgow
S929AKS	31660	Scotland East	SF06GYW	69088	Glasgow	SF07FEP	37200	Glasgow
S932AKS	31663	Scotland East	SF06GYX	69089	Glasgow	SF07FET	37203	Glasgow
S935AKS	31666	Scotland East	SF06GYY	69090	Glasgow	SF07FEU	37204	Glasgow
S936AKS	31667	Scotland East	SF06GYZ	69091	Glasgow	SF08SMU	37530	Glasgow
S938AKS	31669	Scotland East	SF06GZA	69092	Glasgow	SF08SMV	37531	Glasgow
SA02BZD	61587	Glasgow	SF06GZB	69093	Glasgow	SF08SMX	37532	Glasgow
SA02BZE	61588	Glasgow	SF06GZC	69094	Glasgow	SF08SNJ	37533	Glasgow
SA02BZF	61589	Glasgow	SF06GZD	69095	Glasgow	SF08SNK	37534	Glasgow
SA02BZG	61590	Glasgow	SF06GZE	69096	Glasgow	SF08SNN	37535	Glasgow
SA02BZH	61591	Glasgow	SF06GZG	69097	Glasgow	SF08SNU	37536	Glasgow
SA02BZJ	61592	Glasgow	SF06GZH	69098	Glasgow	SF08SNV	37537	Glasgow
SA02BZK	61593	Glasgow	SF06GZJ	69099	Glasgow	SF08SNX	37538	Glasgow
SA02BZL	61594	Glasgow	SF06GZK	69100	Glasgow	SF08SNY	37539	Glasgow
SA02BZM	61595	Glasgow	SF06GZL	69101	Glasgow	SF08SNZ	37540	Glasgow
SA02BZN	61596	Glasgow	SF06GZM	69102	Glasgow	SF09LDD	37736	Glasgow
SF04HXW	69295	Glasgow	SF06GZN	69103	Glasgow	SF09LDE	37737	Glasgow
SF04HXX	69296	Glasgow	SF06GZO	69104	Glasgow	SF09LDJ	37738	Glasgow
SF04ZPE	69297	Glasgow	SF06GZP	69105	Glasgow	SF09LDK	37739	Glasgow
SF04ZPG	69298	Glasgow	SF06GZR	69106	Glasgow	SF09LDL	37740	Glasgow
SF05KUH	10183	Aberdeen	SF06GZS	69107	Glasgow	SF09LDN	37741	Glasgow

Reg	No	Location	Reg	No	Location	Reg	No	Location
SF09LDO	37742	Glasgow	SF54OTP	32572	Glasgow	SF55UAR	69023	South Yorkshire
SF09LDU	37743	Glasgow	SF54OTR	32573	Glasgow	SF55UAS	69024	South Yorkshire
SF09LDV	37744	Glasgow	SF54OTT	32574	Glasgow	SF55UAT	69025	South Yorkshire
SF09LDX	37745	Glasgow	SF54OTU	32575	Glasgow	SF55UAU	69026	South Yorkshire
SF09LDY	37746	Glasgow	SF54OTV	32576	Glasgow	SF55UAV	69027	Glasgow
SF09LDZ	37747	Glasgow	SF54OTW	32577	Glasgow	SF55UAW	69028	South Yorkshire
SF09LEJ	37748	Glasgow	SF54OTX	32578	Glasgow	SF55UAX	69029	South Yorkshire
SF09LEU	37749	Glasgow	SF54OTY	32579	Glasgow	SF55UAY	69030	South Yorkshire
SF09LFA	37750	Glasgow	SF54OTZ	32580	Glasgow	SF55UAZ	69031	South Yorkshire
SF09LFB	37751	Glasgow	SF54OUA	32581	Glasgow	SF55UBA	69032	South Yorkshire
SF51YAA	61597	Glasgow	SF54OUB	32582	Glasgow	SF55UBB	69042	Glasgow
SF51YAD	61598	Glasgow	SF54OUC	32583	Glasgow	SF55UBC	69043	South Yorkshire
SF51YAE	61599	Glasgow	SF54OUD	32584	Glasgow	SF55UBD	69044	South Yorkshire
SF51YAG	61600	Glasgow	SF54OUE	32585	Glasgow	SF55UBE	69045	South Yorkshire
SF51YAH	61601	Glasgow	SF54OUG	32586	Glasgow	SF55UBG	69046	South Yorkshire
SF51YAJ	61602	Glasgow	SF54OUH	32587	Glasgow	SF55UBH	69047	South Yorkshire
SF51YAK	61603	Glasgow	SF54OUJ	32588	Glasgow	SF55UBJ	69048	South Yorkshire
SF51YAO	61604	Glasgow	SF54OUK	32589	Glasgow	SF55UBK	69049	South Yorkshire
SF51YAU	61605	Glasgow	SF54OUL	32590	Glasgow	SF55UBL	69050	South Yorkshire
SF51YAV	61606	Glasgow	SF54OUM	32591	Glasgow	SF55UBM	69051	South Yorkshire
SF51YAW	61607	Glasgow	SF54OUN	32592	Glasgow	SF55UBN	69052	South Yorkshire
SF51YAX	61608	Glasgow	SF54THV	32593	Glasgow	SF55UBO	69053	South Yorkshire
SF51YAY	61609	Glasgow	SF54THX	32594	Glasgow	SF55UBP	69054	South Yorkshire
SF51YBA	61610	Glasgow	SF54THZ	32595	Glasgow	SF55UBR	69055	South Yorkshire
SF51YBB	61611	Glasgow	SF54TJO	32596	Glasgow	SF55UBS	69056	South Yorkshire
SF51YBC	61612	Glasgow	SF54TJU	32597	Glasgow	SF55UBT	69033	South Yorkshire
SF51YBD	61613	Glasgow	SF54TJV	32598	Glasgow	SF55UBU	69034	Glasgow
SF51YBE	61614	Glasgow	SF54TJX	32599	Glasgow	SF55UBV	69035	Glasgow
SF51YBG	61615	Glasgow	SF54TJY	32600	Glasgow	SF55UBW	69036	Glasgow
SF51YBH	61616	Glasgow	SF54TJZ	32601	Glasgow	SF55UBX	69037	Glasgow
SF51YBJ	61617	Glasgow	SF54TKA	32602	Glasgow	SF56GYP	66988	Glasgow
SF51YBK	61618	Glasgow	SF54TKC	32603	Glasgow	SF56GYR	66989	Glasgow
SF51YBL	61619	Glasgow	SF54TKD	32604	Glasgow	SF56GYS	66990	Glasgow
SF51YBM	61620	Glasgow	SF54TKE	32605	Glasgow	SF56GYT	66991	Glasgow
SF51YBN	61621	Glasgow	SF54TKJ	32606	Glasgow	SF57MKA	37205	Glasgow
SF51YBO	61622	Glasgow	SF54TKK	32607	Glasgow	SF57MKC	37206	Glasgow
SF51YBP	61623	Glasgow	SF54TKN	32609	Glasgow	SF57MKD	37207	Glasgow
SF51YBR	61624	Glasgow	SF54TKO	32608	Glasgow	SF57MKG	37208	Glasgow
SF51YBS	61625	Glasgow	SF54TKT	32610	Glasgow	SF57MKJ	37209	Glasgow
SF51YBT	61626	Glasgow	SF54TKU	32611	Glasgow	SF57MKK	37210	Glasgow
SF54OSD	32543	Glasgow	SF54TKV	32612	Glasgow	SF57MKL	37211	Glasgow
SF54OSE	32544	Glasgow	SF54TKX	32613	Glasgow	SF57MKM	37212	Glasgow
SF54OSG	32545	Glasgow	SF54TKY	32614	Glasgow	SF57MKN	37213	Glasgow
SF54OSJ	32546	Glasgow	SF54TKZ	32615	Glasgow	SF57MKO	37214	Glasgow
SF54OSK	32547	Glasgow	SF54TLJ	32616	Glasgow	SF57MKP	37215	Glasgow
SF54OSL	32548	Glasgow	SF54TLK	32617	Glasgow	SF57MKU	37216	Glasgow
SF54OSM	32549	Glasgow	SF54TLN	32618	Glasgow	SF57MKV	37217	Glasgow
SF54OSN	32550	Glasgow	SF54TLO	32619	Glasgow	SF57MKX	37218	Glasgow
SF54OSO	32551	Glasgow	SF54TLU	32620	Glasgow	SF57MKZ	37219	Glasgow
SF54OSP	32552	Glasgow	SF54TLX	32621	Glasgow	SF57MLE	37220	Glasgow
SF54OSR	32553	Glasgow	SF54TLY	32622	Glasgow	SF57MLJ	37221	Glasgow
SF54OSU	32554	Glasgow	SF54TLZ	32623	Glasgow	SF57MLK	37222	Glasgow
SF54OSV	32555	Glasgow	SF54TMO	32624	Glasgow	SF57MLL	37223	Glasgow
SF54OSW	32556	Glasgow	SF54TMU	32625	Glasgow	SF57MLN	37224	Glasgow
SF54OSX	32557	Glasgow	SF54TMV	32626	Glasgow	SF57MLO	37225	Glasgow
SF54OSY	32558	Glasgow	SF55TXA	68564	Hampshire D&B	SF57MLU	37226	Glasgow
SF54OSZ	32559	Glasgow	SF55TXB	68565	Hampshire D&B	SF57MLV	37227	Glasgow
SF54OTA	32560	Glasgow	SF55TXC	68566	Scotland East	SF58ATY	37541	Glasgow
SF54OTB	32561	Glasgow	SF55UAD	69012	South Yorkshire	SF58ATZ	37542	Glasgow
SF54OTC	32562	Glasgow	SF55UAE	69013	South Yorkshire	SF58AUA	37543	Glasgow
SF54OTD	32563	Glasgow	SF55UAG	69014	Glasgow	SF58AUC	37544	Glasgow
SF54OTE	32564	Glasgow	SF55UAH	69015	Glasgow	SH51MHY	61627	Glasgow
SF54OTG	32565	Glasgow	SF55UAJ	69016	Glasgow	SH51MHZ	61628	Glasgow
SF54OTH	32566	Glasgow	SF55UAK	69017	South Yorkshire	SH51MJE	61629	Glasgow
SF54OTJ	32567	Glasgow	SF55UAL	69018	South Yorkshire	SH51MJF	61630	Glasgow
SF54OTK	32568	Glasgow	SF55UAM	69019	Glasgow	SH51MKF	61631	South Yorkshire
SF54OTL	32569	Glasgow	SF55UAN	69020	South Yorkshire	SH51MKG	61632	Glasgow
SF54OTM	32570	Glasgow	SF55UAO	69021	Glasgow	SH51MKJ	61633	South Yorkshire
SF54OTN	32571	Glasgow	SF55UAP	69022	South Yorkshire	SH51MKK	61634	Glasgow

SH51MKL	61635	Glasgow	SK63KGF	63115	Manchester	SK63KLF	47406	Hampshire D&B
SJ03DNY	40965	Glasgow	SK63KGG	63116	Manchester	SK63KLJ	47407	Hampshire D&B
SJ03DOA	40966	Glasgow	SK63KGJ	63117	Manchester	SK63KLL	47408	Hampshire D&B
SJ03DOH	50460	Scotland East	SK63KGN	63118	Manchester	SK63KLM	47409	Hampshire D&B
SJ03DPE	50461	Glasgow	SK63KGO	63017	South Yorkshire	SK63KLO	47410	Hampshire D&B
SJ03DPF	50462	Glasgow	SK63KGP	63018	South Yorkshire	SK63KLP	47411	Hampshire D&B
SJ03DPN	50463	Glasgow	SK63KGU	63019	South Yorkshire	SK63KLS	47412	Hampshire D&B
SJ03DPU	50464	Glasgow	SK63KGV	63020	South Yorkshire	SK63KLU	47413	Hampshire D&B
SJ03DPV	50465	Glasgow	SK63KGX	63021	South Yorkshire	SK63KLV	47414	Hampshire D&B
SJ03DPX	50466	South West	SK63KGY	63022	South Yorkshire	SK63KLX	47415	Hampshire D&B
SJ03DPY	50467	South West	SK63KGZ	63023	South Yorkshire	SK63KLZ	47416	Hampshire D&B
SJ03DPZ	50468	Scotland East	SK63KHA	63024	South Yorkshire	SK63KMA	47417	Hampshire D&B
SJ51DHD	61636	South Yorkshire	SK63KHB	63025	South Yorkshire	SK63KME	47418	Hampshire D&B
SJ51DHE	61637	South Yorkshire	SK63KHC	63026	South Yorkshire	SK63KMF	47419	Hampshire D&B
SJ51DHF	61638	South Yorkshire	SK63KHD	63027	South Yorkshire	SK63KMG	47420	Hampshire D&B
SJ51DHG	61639	South Yorkshire	SK63KHE	63028	South Yorkshire	SK63KMJ	47421	Hampshire D&B
SJ51DHK	61640	Glasgow	SK63KHF	63029	South Yorkshire	SK63KMM	47422	Hampshire D&B
SJ51DHL	61641	Glasgow	SK63KHG	63030	South Yorkshire	SK63KMO	47423	Hampshire D&B
SJ51DHM	61642	Glasgow	SK63KHH	63031	South Yorkshire	SK63KMU	47424	Hampshire D&B
SJ51DHN	61643	Glasgow	SK63KHJ	63032	South Yorkshire	SK63KMV	47425	Hampshire D&B
SJ51DHO	61644	Glasgow	SK63KHL	63033	South Yorkshire	SK63KMX	47426	Hampshire D&B
SJ51DHP	61645	Glasgow	SK63KHM	63034	South Yorkshire	SK63KMY	47427	Hampshire D&B
SJ51DHV	61646	Glasgow	SK63KHO	63035	South Yorkshire	SK63KMZ	47428	Hampshire D&B
SJ51DHX	61647	Glasgow	SK63KHP	63036	South Yorkshire	SK63KNA	47429	Hampshire D&B
SJ51DHZ	61648	Glasgow	SK63KHR	63037	South Yorkshire	SK63KNB	47430	Hampshire D&B
SJ51DJD	61649	Glasgow	SK63KHT	63042	Hampshire D&B	SK63KNC	47431	Hampshire D&B
SJ51DJE	61650	Glasgow	SK63KHU	63043	Hampshire D&B	SK63KND	47432	Hampshire D&B
SJ51DJF	61651	Glasgow	SK63KHV	63044	Hampshire D&B	SK63KNE	47433	Hampshire D&B
SJ51DJK	61652	Glasgow	SK63KHW	63045	Hampshire D&B	SK63KNF	47434	Hampshire D&B
SJ51DJO	61653	Glasgow	SK63KHX	63046	Hampshire D&B	SK63KNG	47435	West of England
SJ51DJU	61654	Glasgow	SK63KHY	63047	Hampshire D&B	SK63KNH	47436	West of England
SJ51DJX	61656	Glasgow	SK63KHZ	63048	Hampshire D&B	SK63KNJ	47437	West of England
SJ51DJY	61657	Glasgow	SK63KJA	63049	Hampshire D&B	SK63KNK	47438	West of England
SJ51DJZ	61306	Glasgow	SK63KJE	63050	Hampshire D&B	SK63KNL	47439	West of England
SJ51DKA	61658	Glasgow	SK63KJF	63051	Hampshire D&B	SK63KNN	47440	West of England
SJ51DKD	61659	Glasgow	SK63KJJ	63052	Hampshire D&B	SK63KNO	47441	West of England
SJ51DKE	61660	Glasgow	SK63KJN	63053	Hampshire D&B	SK63KNP	47442	West of England
SJ51DKF	61661	Glasgow	SK63KJO	63054	Hampshire D&B	SK63KNR	47443	West of England
SJ51DKK	61662	South Yorkshire	SK63KJU	63055	Hampshire D&B	SK63KNS	47444	West of England
SJ51DKL	61663	Glasgow	SK63KJV	63056	Hampshire D&B	SK63KNU	47445	West of England
SJ51DKN	61664	Glasgow	SK63KJX	63057	Hampshire D&B	SK63KNV	47446	West of England
SK02ZYG	65755	Glasgow	SK63KJY	63058	Hampshire D&B	SK63KNX	47447	West of England
SK02ZYH	65756	Glasgow	SK63KJZ	63059	Hampshire D&B	SK63KNY	47448	West of England
SK07JVN	69254	Scotland East	SK63KKA	63060	Hampshire D&B	SL63GBF	67431	Cymru
SK07JVO	69255	Scotland East	SK63KKB	63061	Hampshire D&B	SL63GBO	67432	Cymru
SK07JVP	69256	Scotland East	SK63KKC	63062	Hampshire D&B	SL63GBU	67433	Cymru
SK57ADO	69257	Scotland East	SK63KKD	63063	Hampshire D&B	SL63GBV	67434	Cymru
SK57ADU	69258	Scotland East	SK63KKE	63064	Hampshire D&B	SL63GBX	67435	Cymru
SK57ADV	69259	Scotland East	SK63KKF	63065	Hampshire D&B	SL63GBY	67436	Cymru
SK57ADX	69260	Scotland East	SK63KKG	63066	Hampshire D&B	SL63GBZ	67437	Cymru
SK57ADZ	69261	Scotland East	SK63KKH	63067	Hampshire D&B	SL63GCF	67438	Cymru
SK57AEA	69262	Scotland East	SK63KKJ	47449	West of England	SL63GCK	67439	Cymru
SK57AEB	69263	Scotland East	SK63KKL	47450	West of England	SM13NAE	63068	West of England
SK57AEC	69264	Scotland East	SK63KKM	47451	West of England	SM13NAO	63069	West of England
SK63ATY	67884	Glasgow	SK63KKN	47452	West of England	SM13NBA	63070	West of England
SK63ATZ	67885	Glasgow	SK63KKO	47453	West of England	SM13NBB	63071	West of England
SK63AUA	67886	Glasgow	SK63KKP	47454	West of England	SM13NBD	63072	West of England
SK63AUC	67887	Glasgow	SK63KKR	47455	West of England	SM13NBE	63073	West of England
SK63AUE	67888	Glasgow	SK63KKS	47456	West of England	SM13NBF	63074	West of England
SK63AUF	67889	Glasgow	SK63KKU	47457	West of England	SM13NBG	63075	West of England
SK63AUH	67890	Glasgow	SK63KKV	47458	West of England	SM13NBJ	63076	West of England
SK63AUJ	67891	Glasgow	SK63KKW	47459	West of England	SM13NBK	63077	West of England
SK63AUL	67892	Glasgow	SK63KKX	47460	West of England	SM13NBL	63078	West of England
SK63AUM	67893	Glasgow	SK63KKY	47461	West of England	SM13NBN	63096	Manchester
SK63AUN	67894	Glasgow	SK63KKZ	47462	West of England	SM13NBO	63097	Manchester
SK63KFY	63111	Manchester	SK63KLA	47463	West of England	SM13NBX	63098	Manchester
SK63KFZ	63112	Manchester	SK63KLC	47464	West of England	SM13NBY	63099	Manchester
SK63KGA	63113	Manchester	SK63KLD	47465	West of England	SM13NBZ	63100	Manchester
SK63KGE	63114	Manchester	SK63KLE	47405	Hampshire D&B	SM13NCA	63101	Manchester

The 2014 First Bus Handbook

Reg	Fleet	Area	Reg	Fleet	Area	Reg	Fleet	Area
SM13NCC	63102	Manchester	SN05HWD	36023	Scotland East	SN12ADX	33658	South West
SM13NCD	63103	Manchester	SN05HWE	36022	Scotland East	SN12ADZ	33659	South West
SM13NCE	63104	Manchester	SN05HWF	36020	Scotland East	SN12AEA	33660	South West
SM13NCF	63105	Manchester	SN05HWG	36018	Scotland East	SN12AEB	33661	South West
SM13NCJ	63106	Manchester	SN05HWH	36019	Scotland East	SN12AED	33662	South West
SM13NCN	63107	Manchester	SN05HWJ	36017	Scotland East	SN12AEE	33663	Manchester
SM13NCO	63108	Manchester	SN05HWK	36014	Scotland East	SN12AEF	33664	South West
SM13NCU	63109	Manchester	SN05HWL	36013	Scotland East	SN12AEG	33665	South West
SM13NCV	63110	Manchester	SN05HWM	36016	Scotland East	SN12AEJ	33666	South West
SM13NDJ	63001	South Yorkshire	SN05HWO	36015	Scotland East	SN12AEK	33667	South West
SM13NDK	63002	South Yorkshire	SN05HWP	36021	Scotland East	SN12AEL	33668	Manchester
SM13NDL	63003	South Yorkshire	SN05HWR	36024	Scotland East	SN12AEM	33669	Manchester
SM13NDN	63004	South Yorkshire	SN05HWS	36025	Scotland East	SN12AEO	33670	Manchester
SM13NDO	63005	South Yorkshire	SN05HWT	36028	Scotland East	SN12AEP	33671	Manchester
SM13NDU	63006	South Yorkshire	SN05HWU	36026	Scotland East	SN12AET	33672	Manchester
SM13NDV	63007	South Yorkshire	SN05HWV	36027	Scotland East	SN12AEU	33673	Manchester
SM13NDX	63008	South Yorkshire	SN05HWW	36007	Scotland East	SN12AEV	33674	Manchester
SM13NDY	63009	South Yorkshire	SN05HWX	36008	Scotland East	SN12AEW	33675	Manchester
SM13NDZ	63010	South Yorkshire	SN05HWY	36009	Scotland East	SN12AEX	33676	Manchester
SM13NEF	63011	South Yorkshire	SN05HWZ	36010	Scotland East	SN12AEY	33677	Manchester
SM13NEJ	63012	South Yorkshire	SN05HXA	36011	Scotland East	SN12AEZ	33678	Manchester
SM13NEN	63013	South Yorkshire	SN05HXB	36012	Scotland East	SN12AFA	33679	Manchester
SM13NEO	63014	South Yorkshire	SN06AHK	65754	Scotland East	SN12AFE	33680	Manchester
SM13NEU	63015	South Yorkshire	SN09CAU	38201	Glasgow	SN12AFF	33681	Manchester
SM13NEY	63016	South Yorkshire	SN09CAV	38202	Glasgow	SN12AFJ	33682	Manchester
SMK735F	39735	Hampshire D&B	SN09CAX	38203	Glasgow	SN12AFK	33683	Manchester
SN03CLX	65757	Glasgow	SN09CBF	38204	Glasgow	SN12AFO	33684	Manchester
SN03CLY	65758	Glasgow	SN09CBO	38205	Glasgow	SN12AFU	33685	Manchester
SN03LGG	43901	Cymru	SN09CBU	38206	Glasgow	SN12AFV	33686	Manchester
SN03LGJ	43902	Cymru	SN09CBV	38207	Glasgow	SN12AFX	33687	Manchester
SN03LGK	43903	Cymru	SN09CBX	38208	Glasgow	SN12AFY	33688	Manchester
SN03WLD	42482	Essex	SN09CBY	38209	Glasgow	SN12AFZ	33689	Manchester
SN03WLK	42483	Essex	SN09CCA	38210	Glasgow	SN12AGO	33690	Manchester
SN03WLW	42484	Essex	SN09CCD	38211	Glasgow	SN12AGU	33691	Manchester
SN03WME	42487	Essex	SN09CCE	38212	Glasgow	SN12AGV	33692	Manchester
SN03WMJ	62411	Scotland East	SN09CCF	38213	Glasgow	SN12AGX	33693	Manchester
SN03WMM	42485	Essex	SN09CCJ	38214	Glasgow	SN12AGY	33694	Manchester
SN03WMU	62412	Scotland East	SN09CCK	38215	Glasgow	SN12AGZ	33695	Manchester
SN03WMX	42486	Essex	SN09CCO	38216	Glasgow	SN12AHA	33696	Manchester
SN04CKX	65701	Scotland East	SN09CCU	38217	Glasgow	SN12AHC	33697	Manchester
SN04CKY	65700	Scotland East	SN09CCV	38218	Glasgow	SN12AHD	33698	Manchester
SN04CLF	65702	Scotland East	SN09CCX	38219	Glasgow	SN12AHE	33699	Manchester
SN04CNK	65703	Scotland East	SN09CCY	38220	Glasgow	SN12AHF	33700	Manchester
SN04EFX	43842	Scotland East	SN09CCZ	38221	Glasgow	SN12AHG	33701	Manchester
SN04EFZ	43844	Scotland East	SN09CDE	38222	Glasgow	SN12AHJ	33702	Manchester
SN04XXY	11037	South West	SN09CDF	38223	Glasgow	SN12AHK	33703	Manchester
SN04XXZ	11038	South West	SN09CDK	38224	Glasgow	SN12AHL	33704	Manchester
SN04XYA	11036	South West	SN09CDO	38225	Glasgow	SN12AHO	33705	Manchester
SN05DZO	42933	Essex	SN09EZW	69402	Scotland East	SN12AHP	33706	Manchester
SN05DZP	42934	Essex	SN09EZX	69403	Scotland East	SN12AHU	33707	Manchester
SN05DZR	42935	Essex	SN09FAU	69404	Scotland East	SN12AHV	33708	Manchester
SN05DZS	42936	Essex	SN09FBA	69405	Scotland East	SN12AHX	33709	Manchester
SN05DZT	42937	Essex	SN09FBB	69406	Scotland East	SN12AHY	33710	Manchester
SN05DZU	42558	South West	SN09FBC	69407	Scotland East	SN12AHZ	33711	Manchester
SN05DZV	42559	South West	SN09FBD	69408	Scotland East	SN12AJO	33712	Manchester
SN05DZW	42560	South West	SN09FBE	69409	Scotland East	SN12AJU	33714	Manchester
SN05DZX	42561	West of England	SN09FBF	69410	Scotland East	SN12AJV	33713	Manchester
SN05DZY	42562	South West	SN11FOJ	33901	Glasgow	SN12AJX	33715	Manchester
SN05DZZ	42563	South West	SN11FOK	33902	Glasgow	SN12AJY	33716	Manchester
SN05EAA	42924	South West	SN11FOM	33903	Glasgow	SN12AKF	33717	Manchester
SN05EAC	42925	West of England	SN11FOP	33904	Glasgow	SN12AKG	33718	Manchester
SN05EAE	42926	West of England	SN11FOT	33905	Glasgow	SN12AKJ	33719	Manchester
SN05EAF	42927	Essex	SN11FOU	33906	Glasgow	SN12AKK	33720	Manchester
SN05EAG	42928	Essex	SN11FOV	33907	Glasgow	SN12AKO	33721	Manchester
SN05EAJ	42929	Eastern Counties	SN11FPA	33908	Glasgow	SN12AKP	33722	Manchester
SN05EAM	42930	Essex	SN11FPC	33909	Glasgow	SN12AKU	33723	Manchester
SN05EAO	42931	Essex	SN11FPD	33910	Glasgow	SN12AKV	33724	Manchester
SN05EAP	42932	Essex	SN12ADU	33656	Manchester	SN12AKX	33725	Manchester
SN05HEJ	43849	West of England	SN12ADV	33657	Manchester	SN12AKY	33726	Manchester

SN12AKZ	33727	Manchester	SN13CMF	67429	Manchester	SN13EEP	67850	Glasgow
SN12ALO	33728	Manchester	SN13CMK	67430	Manchester	SN13EES	67851	Glasgow
SN12ALU	33729	Manchester	SN13CMO	67783	Aberdeen	SN13EET	67852	Glasgow
SN12AMK	33730	Manchester	SN13CMU	67784	Aberdeen	SN13EEU	67853	Glasgow
SN12AMO	33731	Manchester	SN13CMV	67785	Aberdeen	SN13EEV	67854	Glasgow
SN12AMU	33732	Manchester	SN13CMX	67786	Aberdeen	SN13EEW	67855	Glasgow
SN12AMV	33733	Manchester	SN13CMY	67787	Aberdeen	SN13EEX	67856	Glasgow
SN12AMX	33734	Manchester	SN13CMZ	67788	Aberdeen	SN13EEY	67857	Glasgow
SN12ANF	33735	Manchester	SN13CNA	67789	Aberdeen	SN13EEZ	67858	Glasgow
SN12ANP	33736	Manchester	SN13CNC	67790	Aberdeen	SN13EFA	67859	Glasgow
SN12ANR	33737	Manchester	SN13CNE	67791	Aberdeen	SN13EFB	67860	Glasgow
SN12ANU	33738	Manchester	SN13CNF	67792	Aberdeen	SN13EFC	67861	Glasgow
SN12ANV	33739	Manchester	SN13CNJ	67793	Aberdeen	SN13EFD	67862	Glasgow
SN12ANX	33740	Manchester	SN13CNK	67794	Aberdeen	SN13EFE	67863	Glasgow
SN12AOA	33741	Manchester	SN13CNO	67795	Aberdeen	SN13EFF	67864	Glasgow
SN12AOB	33742	Manchester	SN13CNU	67796	Aberdeen	SN13EFG	67865	Glasgow
SN12AOC	33743	Manchester	SN13CNV	67797	Aberdeen	SN13EFH	67866	Glasgow
SN12AOD	33744	Manchester	SN13CNX	67798	Aberdeen	SN13EFJ	67867	Glasgow
SN12AOE	33745	Manchester	SN13CNY	67799	Aberdeen	SN13EFK	67868	Glasgow
SN12AOF	33746	Manchester	SN13CNZ	67800	Aberdeen	SN13EFL	67869	Glasgow
SN12AOG	33747	Manchester	SN13COA	67801	Aberdeen	SN14DTX	63079	Cymru
SN12AOH	33748	Manchester	SN13COH	67802	Aberdeen	SN14DTY	63080	Cymru
SN12AOJ	33749	Manchester	SN13COJ	67803	Aberdeen	SN14DTZ	63081	Cymru
SN12AOK	33750	Manchester	SN13COU	67804	Aberdeen	SN14DUA	63082	Cymru
SN12AOL	33751	Manchester	SN13CPE	67805	Aberdeen	SN14DUJ	63083	Cymru
SN12AOM	33752	Manchester	SN13EAY	67806	Glasgow	SN14DUU	63084	Cymru
SN12AOO	33753	Manchester	SN13EBA	67807	Glasgow	SN14DUV	63085	Cymru
SN12AOP	33754	Manchester	SN13EBC	67808	Glasgow	SN51MSU	62356	Scotland East
SN12AOR	33755	Manchester	SN13EBD	67809	Glasgow	SN51MSV	62355	Scotland East
SN13CGF	67766	Glasgow	SN13EBF	67810	Glasgow	SN51MSX	62358	Scotland East
SN13CGG	67767	Glasgow	SN13EBG	67811	Glasgow	SN51MSY	62357	Scotland East
SN13CGK	67768	Glasgow	SN13EBJ	67812	Glasgow	SN51UXX	65665	Essex
SN13CGO	67769	Glasgow	SN13EBK	67813	Glasgow	SN51UXY	65666	Essex
SN13CGU	67770	Glasgow	SN13EBL	67814	Glasgow	SN51UXZ	65667	Essex
SN13CGV	67771	Glasgow	SN13EBM	67815	Glasgow	SN51UYA	65668	Essex
SN13CGX	67772	Glasgow	SN13EBO	67816	Glasgow	SN51UYB	65669	Essex
SN13CHO	67901	Essex	SN13EBP	67817	Glasgow	SN51UYC	65670	Eastern Counties
SN13CHV	67902	Essex	SN13EBU	67818	Glasgow	SN51UYD	65671	Essex
SN13CHX	67903	Essex	SN13EBV	67819	Glasgow	SN51UYE	65672	Eastern Counties
SN13CHY	67904	Essex	SN13EBX	67820	Glasgow	SN51UYG	65673	Eastern Counties
SN13CHZ	33788	Manchester	SN13EBZ	67821	Glasgow	SN51UYH	65674	Eastern Counties
SN13CJV	67401	Manchester	SN13ECA	67822	Glasgow	SN51UYJ	65675	Eastern Counties
SN13CJX	67402	Manchester	SN13ECC	67823	Glasgow	SN51UYK	65676	Essex
SN13CJY	67403	Manchester	SN13ECD	67824	Glasgow	SN51UYL	65677	Essex
SN13CJZ	67404	Manchester	SN13ECF	67825	Glasgow	SN53ESU	43837	Cymru
SN13CKA	67405	Manchester	SN13ECJ	67826	Glasgow	SN53ESV	43836	Cymru
SN13CKC	67406	Manchester	SN13ECT	67827	Glasgow	SN53ESY	43838	Cymru
SN13CKD	67407	Manchester	SN13ECV	67828	Glasgow	SN53ETD	43839	Cymru
SN13CKE	67408	Manchester	SN13ECW	67829	Glasgow	SN53ETE	43840	Cymru
SN13CKF	67409	Manchester	SN13ECX	67830	Glasgow	SN53ETF	43841	Cymru
SN13CKG	67410	Manchester	SN13ECY	67831	Glasgow	SN53KHH	65693	Glasgow
SN13CKJ	67411	Manchester	SN13ECZ	67832	Glasgow	SN53KHJ	65694	Scotland East
SN13CKK	67412	Manchester	SN13EDC	67833	Glasgow	SN53KHK	65695	Scotland East
SN13CKL	67413	Manchester	SN13EDF	67834	Glasgow	SN53KHL	65696	Glasgow
SN13CKO	67414	Manchester	SN13EDJ	67835	Glasgow	SN53KHM	65697	Glasgow
SN13CKP	67415	Manchester	SN13EDK	67836	Glasgow	SN53KHO	65698	Scotland East
SN13CKU	67416	Manchester	SN13EDL	67837	Glasgow	SN53KHP	65699	Scotland East
SN13CKV	67417	Manchester	SN13EDO	67838	Glasgow	SN53KJX	42488	Essex
SN13CKX	67418	Manchester	SN13EDP	67839	Glasgow	SN53KJY	42489	Essex
SN13CKY	67419	Manchester	SN13EDR	67840	Glasgow	SN53KJZ	42876	South West
SN13CLF	67420	Manchester	SN13EDU	67841	Glasgow	SN53KKA	42871	South West
SN13CLJ	67421	Manchester	SN13EDV	67842	Glasgow	SN53KKB	42872	South West
SN13CLO	67422	Manchester	SN13EDX	67843	Glasgow	SN53KKC	42873	South West
SN13CLU	67423	Manchester	SN13EEF	67844	Glasgow	SN53KKD	42874	South West
SN13CLV	67424	Manchester	SN13EEG	67845	Glasgow	SN53KKE	42875	South West
SN13CLX	67425	Manchester	SN13EEH	67846	Glasgow	SN53KKY	67600	Midlands
SN13CLY	67426	Manchester	SN13EEJ	67847	Glasgow	SN54KDF	65708	Scotland East
SN13CLZ	67427	Manchester	SN13EEM	67848	Glasgow	SN54KDJ	65709	Scotland East
SN13CME	67428	Manchester	SN13EEO	67849	Glasgow	SN54KDK	65710	Scotland East

Reg	No	Depot	Reg	No	Depot	Reg	No	Depot
SN54KDO	65711	Scotland East	SN57JBX	37273	Scotland East	SN61BFK	39101	Glasgow
SN54KDU	65712	Scotland East	SN57JBZ	69281	Scotland East	SN61BFL	39102	Glasgow
SN54KDV	65713	Scotland East	SN57JCJ	69282	Scotland East	SN61BFM	39103	Glasgow
SN54KDX	65714	Scotland East	SN57JCO	69283	Scotland East	SN61BFO	39104	Glasgow
SN54KDZ	65715	Scotland East	SN57JCU	69284	Scotland East	SN61BFP	39105	Glasgow
SN54KEJ	65716	Scotland East	SN57JCV	69285	Scotland East	SN61BFU	39106	Glasgow
SN54KEK	65717	Scotland East	SN57JCX	69286	Scotland East	SN61BFV	39107	Glasgow
SN54KEU	65718	Scotland East	SN57JCY	69287	Scotland East	SN61BFX	39108	Glasgow
SN54KFA	65719	Scotland East	SN57JCZ	69288	Scotland East	SN61BFY	39109	Glasgow
SN54KFC	65720	Scotland East	SN57JDF	69289	Scotland East	SN61BFZ	39110	Glasgow
SN54KFD	65721	Scotland East	SN57JDJ	69290	Scotland East	SN62ABU	67711	Glasgow
SN54KFE	65722	Scotland East	SN57JDK	69291	Scotland East	SN62ABV	67712	Glasgow
SN54KFF	65723	Scotland East	SN57MSU	69280	Scotland East	SN62ABX	67713	Glasgow
SN55CXE	43848	Essex	SN58CFK	33544	Midlands	SN62ABZ	67714	Glasgow
SN55CXF	43846	Essex	SN58CFL	33545	Midlands	SN62ACX	67715	Glasgow
SN55CXH	43845	Essex	SN58CFM	33546	Midlands	SN62ACZ	67716	Glasgow
SN55CXJ	43847	Essex	SN58CFO	33547	Midlands	SN62ADU	67717	Glasgow
SN55HDZ	32669	Scotland East	SN58CFP	33548	Midlands	SN62ADV	67718	Glasgow
SN55HEJ	32670	Scotland East	SN58CFU	33549	Midlands	SN62AEA	67719	Glasgow
SN55HEU	32671	Scotland East	SN58CFV	33550	Midlands	SN62AEF	67720	Glasgow
SN55HEV	32672	Scotland East	SN58CFX	33551	Midlands	SN62AEK	67721	Glasgow
SN55HFA	32673	Scotland East	SN58CFY	33552	Midlands	SN62AET	67722	Glasgow
SN55HFB	32674	Scotland East	SN58CFZ	33553	Midlands	SN62AEU	67723	Glasgow
SN55HFC	32675	Scotland East	SN58CGE	33554	Midlands	SN62AEY	67724	Glasgow
SN55HFD	32676	Scotland East	SN58CGF	33555	Midlands	SN62AFE	67725	Glasgow
SN55HFE	32677	Scotland East	SN58CGG	33556	Midlands	SN62AFJ	67726	Glasgow
SN55HFF	32678	Scotland East	SN58CGK	33557	Midlands	SN62AFK	67727	Glasgow
SN55HFG	32679	Scotland East	SN58CGO	33558	Midlands	SN62AFU	67728	Glasgow
SN55HFH	32680	Scotland East	SN58CGU	33559	Midlands	SN62AFY	67729	Glasgow
SN55HFJ	32681	Scotland East	SN58CGV	33560	Midlands	SN62AFZ	67730	Glasgow
SN55HFK	32682	Scotland East	SN58CGX	33561	Midlands	SN62AGV	67731	Glasgow
SN55HFL	32683	Scotland East	SN58CGY	33562	Midlands	SN62AGY	67732	Glasgow
SN55JVA	65750	Scotland East	SN58CGZ	33563	Midlands	SN62AHD	67733	Glasgow
SN55JVC	65751	Scotland East	SN58CHC	33564	Midlands	SN62AHF	67734	Glasgow
SN55JVD	65752	Scotland East	SN58CHD	33565	Midlands	SN62AHL	67735	Glasgow
SN55JVE	65753	Scotland East	SN58CHF	33566	Midlands	SN62AHV	67736	Glasgow
SN55JVG	65742	Scotland East	SN58CHG	33567	Midlands	SN62AHX	67737	Glasgow
SN55JVH	65743	Scotland East	SN58CHH	33568	Midlands	SN62AJU	67738	Glasgow
SN55JVJ	65744	Scotland East	SN58CHJ	33569	Midlands	SN62AJV	67739	Glasgow
SN55JVK	65745	Scotland East	SN58CHK	33570	Midlands	SN62AKG	67740	Glasgow
SN55JVL	65746	Scotland East	SN58CHL	33571	Midlands	SN62AKJ	67741	Glasgow
SN55JVM	65747	Scotland East	SN58CHO	33572	Midlands	SN62AKO	67742	Glasgow
SN55JVO	65748	Scotland East	SN58ENR	33573	Midlands	SN62AKP	67743	Glasgow
SN55JVP	65749	Scotland East	SN58ENT	33574	Midlands	SN62AMV	67744	Glasgow
SN55KKE	36029	Scotland East	SN59AWV	33425	Essex	SN62ANR	67745	Glasgow
SN55KKF	36030	Scotland East	SN60CAA	33423	Eastern Counties	SN62ANU	67746	Glasgow
SN57HCP	37135	Scotland East	SN60EAA	67701	Glasgow	SN62AOA	67747	Glasgow
SN57HCU	37136	Scotland East	SN60EAC	67702	Glasgow	SN62AOC	67748	Glasgow
SN57HCV	37137	Scotland East	SN60EAE	67703	Glasgow	SN62AOF	67749	Glasgow
SN57HCX	37138	Scotland East	SN60EAF	67704	Glasgow	SN62AOG	67750	Glasgow
SN57HCY	37139	Scotland East	SN60EAG	67705	Glasgow	SN62AOZ	67751	Glasgow
SN57HCZ	37140	Scotland East	SN60EAJ	67706	Glasgow	SN62APO	67753	Glasgow
SN57HDA	37141	Scotland East	SN60EAM	67707	Glasgow	SN62APF	67752	Glasgow
SN57HDC	37142	Scotland East	SN60EAO	67708	Glasgow	SN62APZ	67754	Glasgow
SN57HDD	37143	Scotland East	SN60EAP	67709	Glasgow	SN62ASO	67755	Glasgow
SN57HDE	37144	Scotland East	SN60EAW	67710	Glasgow	SN62ASU	67756	Glasgow
SN57HDF	37145	Scotland East	SN61BDU	33911	Glasgow	SN62ASX	67757	Glasgow
SN57HDG	37266	Scotland East	SN61BDV	33912	Glasgow	SN62ASZ	67758	Glasgow
SN57HDH	37133	Scotland East	SN61BDX	33913	Glasgow	SN62ATZ	67759	Glasgow
SN57HDJ	37134	Scotland East	SN61BDY	33914	Glasgow	SN62AUC	67760	Glasgow
SN57HZX	69292	Scotland East	SN61BDZ	33915	Glasgow	SN62AUH	67761	Glasgow
SN57HZY	69293	Scotland East	SN61BEJ	33916	Glasgow	SN62AUJ	67763	Glasgow
SN57HZZ	69294	Scotland East	SN61BEO	33917	Glasgow	SN62AUK	67762	Glasgow
SN57JAO	37267	Scotland East	SN61BEU	33918	Glasgow	SN62AUU	67764	Glasgow
SN57JAU	37268	Scotland East	SN61BEY	33919	Glasgow	SN62AUW	67765	Glasgow
SN57JBE	37269	Scotland East	SN61BFA	33920	Glasgow	SN62AWA	39133	West of England
SN57JBO	37270	Scotland East	SN61BFE	33921	Glasgow	SN62AWF	39134	West of England
SN57JBU	37271	Scotland East	SN61BFF	33922	Glasgow	SN62AWG	39135	West of England
SN57JBV	37272	Scotland East	SN61BFJ	33923	Glasgow	SN62AWO	39137	West of England

Reg	No	Area	Reg	No	Area	Reg	No	Area
SN62AWR	39138	West of England	SV06GRX	69124	Aberdeen	T301JLD	41301	Glasgow
SN62AWY	39139	West of England	SV07EHB	69125	Aberdeen	T302JLD	41302	Glasgow
SN62AXB	39140	West of England	SV07EHC	69126	Aberdeen	T303JLD	41303	Glasgow
SN62AXC	39141	West of England	SV07EHD	69127	Aberdeen	T304JLD	41304	Glasgow
SN62AXH	67773	Scotland East	SV07EHE	69128	Aberdeen	T306JLD	41306	Glasgow
SN62AXK	67774	Scotland East	SV07EHF	69129	Aberdeen	T309VYG	40560	Glasgow
SN62AXO	67775	Scotland East	SV07EHG	69130	Aberdeen	T310AHY	20460	West of England
SN62AXU	67776	Scotland East	SV07EHH	69131	Aberdeen	T311VYG	40562	Glasgow
SN62AXW	67777	Scotland East	SV07EHJ	69132	Aberdeen	T314VYG	40565	West Yorkshire
SN62AXY	67778	Scotland East	SV07EHK	69133	Aberdeen	T315VYG	40566	West Yorkshire
SN62AXZ	67779	Scotland East	SV07EHL	69134	Aberdeen	T336ALR	41336	Hampshire D&B
SN62AYA	67780	Scotland East	SV08FHA	69351	Aberdeen	T337ALR	41337	Scotland East
SN62AYB	67781	Scotland East	SV08FHB	69352	Aberdeen	T338ALR	41338	Cymru
SN62AYJ	67782	Scotland East	SV08FHC	69353	Aberdeen	T340ALR	41340	Cymru
SN62AYV	44527	Hampshire D&B	SV08FHD	69354	Aberdeen	T341ALR	41341	Cymru
SN62AYZ	44528	Hampshire D&B	SV08FHE	69355	Aberdeen	T343ALR	41343	Cymru
SN62AZA	44529	Hampshire D&B	SV08FHF	69356	Aberdeen	T344ALR	41344	Cymru
SN62AZB	44530	Hampshire D&B	SV08FHG	69357	Aberdeen	T356VWU	42656	Hampshire D&B
SN62AZW	44531	Hampshire D&B	SV08FXP	37633	Aberdeen	T359VWU	42659	Hampshire D&B
SN62DBO	44532	Hampshire D&B	SV08FXR	37634	Aberdeen	T364NUA	40153	Midlands
SN62DBV	44533	Hampshire D&B	SV08FXS	37635	Aberdeen	T365NUA	40154	Midlands
SN62DCX	44534	Hampshire D&B	SV08FXT	37636	Aberdeen	T366NUA	42841	South West
SN62DCY	44535	Hampshire D&B	SV08FXU	37637	Aberdeen	T367NUA	42842	South West
SN62DCZ	44536	Hampshire D&B	SV08FXW	37638	Aberdeen	T368NUA	42843	South West
SN63MYH	33825	West of England	SV08FXX	37639	Aberdeen	T369NUA	42844	South West
SN63MYJ	33826	West of England	SV08FXY	37640	Aberdeen	T370NUA	42845	Cymru
SN63MYK	33827	West of England	SV08FXZ	37641	Aberdeen	T371NUA	40030	Midlands
SN63MYL	33828	West of England	SV08FYA	37642	Aberdeen	T372NUA	40155	Midlands
SN63MYM	33829	West of England	SV08FYB	37643	Aberdeen	T373NUA	42673	Hampshire D&B
SN63MYO	33830	West of England	SV08FYC	37644	Aberdeen	T375NUA	40721	Hampshire D&B
SN63MYP	67870	Glasgow	SV54CFY	68518	Aberdeen	T421GUG	61022	Glasgow
SN63MYR	67871	Glasgow	SV54CFZ	68519	Aberdeen	T423GUG	61024	Glasgow
SN63MYS	67872	Glasgow	SV57EYH	69265	Aberdeen	T424GUG	61025	Glasgow
SN63MYT	67873	Glasgow	SV57EYJ	69266	Aberdeen	T425GUG	61026	Glasgow
SN63MYU	67874	Glasgow	SV57EYK	69267	Aberdeen	T426GUG	61027	Glasgow
SN63MYV	67875	Glasgow	SV58ASZ	23330	Aberdeen	T427GUG	61028	Glasgow
SN63MYW	67876	Glasgow	T3FCC	10180	Scotland East	T428GUG	61029	West Yorkshire
SN63MYX	67877	Glasgow	T4FCC	10181	Scotland East	T429GUG	61030	West Yorkshire
SN63MYY	67878	Glasgow	T5FCC	10182	Scotland East	T430GUG	61031	West Yorkshire
SN63MYZ	67879	Glasgow	T6FCC	19031	Scotland East	T431GUG	61032	West Yorkshire
SN63MZD	67880	Glasgow	T12TRU	43812	South West	T465JDT	40502	South Yorkshire
SN63MZE	67881	Glasgow	T20TVL	53402	South West	T469JCV	42469	South West
SN63MZF	67882	Glasgow	T32JCV	42232	Hampshire D&B	T470JCV	42470	South West
SN63MZG	67883	Glasgow	T34JCV	42234	Hampshire D&B	T471JCV	42471	South West
ST09JPT	45118	Eastern Counties	T35JCV	42235	South West	T472YTT	42472	South West
ST58JPT	45117	Eastern Counties	T77TRU	53206	Hampshire D&B	T473YTT	42473	South West
SV05DXA	10154	Aberdeen	T801LLC	32801	Essex	T563BSS	60217	West Yorkshire
SV05DXC	10155	Aberdeen	T154OUB	60821	West Yorkshire	T566BSS	60220	Scotland East
SV05DXD	10156	Aberdeen	T156OUB	60823	West Yorkshire	T567BSS	60221	Scotland East
SV05DXE	10157	Aberdeen	T157OUB	60824	West Yorkshire	T575JNG	65575	Unallocated
SV05DXF	10158	Aberdeen	T158OUB	60825	West Yorkshire	T576JNG	65576	Essex
SV05DXG	10159	Aberdeen	T159BBF	40006	Hampshire D&B	T577JNG	65577	Unallocated
SV05DXH	10160	Aberdeen	T160BBF	40007	Midlands	T578JNG	65578	Unallocated
SV05DXJ	10161	Aberdeen	T161BBF	40008	Essex	T579JNG	65579	Eastern Counties
SV05DXK	10162	Aberdeen	T162BBF	40009	Midlands	T580JNG	65580	Unallocated
SV05DXL	10163	Aberdeen	T163BBF	40010	Midlands	T622SEJ	42322	Cymru
SV05DXM	10164	Aberdeen	T164BBF	40011	Midlands	T623SEJ	42323	Cymru
SV05DXO	10165	Aberdeen	T165BBF	40012	Hampshire D&B	T625SEJ	42325	Cymru
SV05DXP	10166	Aberdeen	T167BBF	40683	Manchester	T626SEJ	42326	Cymru
SV05DXR	10167	Aberdeen	T255GUG	60822	West Yorkshire	T627SEJ	42327	Cymru
SV05DXS	10168	Aberdeen	T265JLD	41265	Cymru	T628SEJ	42328	Cymru
SV05DXT	10169	Aberdeen	T278JLD	41278	Glasgow	T629SEJ	42329	Cymru
SV05DXU	10170	Aberdeen	T279JLD	41279	Glasgow	T630SEJ	42330	Cymru
SV05DXW	10171	Aberdeen	T281JLD	41281	West Yorkshire	T631SEJ	42331	Cymru
SV05DXX	10172	Aberdeen	T282JLD	41282	West Yorkshire	T632SEJ	42332	Cymru
SV05DXY	10173	Aberdeen	T283JLD	41283	West Yorkshire	T633SEJ	42333	Cymru
SV06GRF	69110	Aberdeen	T288JLD	41288	Glasgow	T634SEJ	42334	Cymru
SV06GRK	69122	Aberdeen	T291JLD	41291	South West	T635SEJ	42335	Cymru
SV06GRU	69123	Aberdeen	T295JLD	41295	South West	T636SEJ	42336	Cymru

Reg	No	Region	Reg	No	Region	Reg	No	Region
T637SEJ	42337	Cymru	T827AFX	42827	Hampshire D&B	T865ODT	60683	South Yorkshire
T650SSF	65650	Essex	T827LLC	32827	Glasgow	T866KLF	32866	Glasgow
T651SSF	65651	Essex	T827SFS	60069	Midlands	T866ODT	60684	South Yorkshire
T652SSF	65652	Essex	T828AFX	42828	Hampshire D&B	T867ODT	60685	South Yorkshire
T653SSF	65653	Essex	T828LLC	32828	Glasgow	T868KLF	32868	Glasgow
T654SSF	65654	Essex	T828MAK	60646	South Yorkshire	T868ODT	60686	South Yorkshire
T660VWU	30840	West Yorkshire	T829AFX	42829	Hampshire D&B	T869ODT	60687	South Yorkshire
T661VWU	30841	West Yorkshire	T829LLC	32829	Glasgow	T870KLF	32870	Scotland East
T663VWU	30843	West Yorkshire	T829MAK	60647	South Yorkshire	T870ODT	60688	South Yorkshire
T664VWU	30844	West Yorkshire	T830LLC	32830	Scotland East	T871KLF	32871	Glasgow
T665VWU	30845	West Yorkshire	T830MAK	60648	South Yorkshire	T871ODT	60689	South Yorkshire
T701JLD	20201	Midlands	T830RYC	42830	South West	T872ODT	60690	South Yorkshire
T701PND	40437	Manchester	T831LLC	32831	Scotland East	T873ODT	60691	South Yorkshire
T702JLD	20202	Midlands	T831MAK	60649	South Yorkshire	T874ODT	60692	South Yorkshire
T702PND	40438	Manchester	T831RYC	42831	South West	T875ODT	60693	South Yorkshire
T703PND	40439	Manchester	T832LLC	32832	Glasgow	T876ODT	60694	South Yorkshire
T704PND	40440	Manchester	T832MAK	60650	South Yorkshire	T877ODT	60695	South Yorkshire
T705PND	40441	Manchester	T833LLC	32833	Glasgow	T878ODT	60696	South Yorkshire
T707PND	40443	Manchester	T833MAK	60651	South Yorkshire	T879ODT	60697	South Yorkshire
T708PND	40444	Manchester	T834LLC	32834	Scotland East	T880ODT	60698	South Yorkshire
T726REU	42726	Midlands	T835LLC	32835	Glasgow	T881ODT	60699	South Yorkshire
T727REU	42727	Midlands	T835MAK	60653	South Yorkshire	T882ODT	60700	South Yorkshire
T728REU	42728	Hampshire D&B	T836LLC	32836	Glasgow	T883KLF	32883	Essex
T730REU	42730	West of England	T836MAK	60654	South Yorkshire	T883ODT	60701	South Yorkshire
T731REU	42731	West of England	T837LLC	32837	Scotland East	T884ODT	60702	South Yorkshire
T801RHW	48201	South West	T837MAK	60655	South Yorkshire	T889KLF	34089	Manchester
T802LLC	32802	South West	T838LLC	32838	Scotland East	T890KLF	34090	South Yorkshire
T803LLC	32803	South West	T838MAK	60656	South Yorkshire	T891KLF	34091	Manchester
T804LLC	32804	Essex	T839LLC	32839	Glasgow	T892KLF	34092	Manchester
T805LLC	32805	Glasgow	T839MAK	60657	South Yorkshire	T893KLF	34093	Manchester
T806LLC	32806	Essex	T840LLC	32840	Glasgow	T894KLF	34094	Manchester
T807LLC	32807	Essex	T840MAK	60658	South Yorkshire	T895KLF	34095	Manchester
T808LLC	32808	South West	T841LLC	32841	Scotland East	T896KLF	34096	Manchester
T809LLC	32809	Essex	T841MAK	60659	South Yorkshire	T897KLF	34097	Manchester
T810LLC	32810	Essex	T842LLC	32842	Scotland East	T898KLF	34098	Manchester
T811LLC	32811	Scotland East	T842MAK	60660	South Yorkshire	T899KLF	34099	South Yorkshire
T813LLC	32813	Scotland East	T843LLC	32843	Glasgow	T902KLF	34102	Manchester
T814LLC	32814	Scotland East	T843MAK	60661	South Yorkshire	T904KLF	34104	Manchester
T815LLC	32815	Glasgow	T844LLC	32844	Glasgow	T905KLF	34105	Manchester
T815MAK	60633	South Yorkshire	T844MAK	60662	South Yorkshire	T907KLF	34107	West Yorkshire
T816LLC	32816	Glasgow	T845LLC	32845	Glasgow	T917SSF	60170	Midlands
T816MAK	60634	South Yorkshire	T845MAK	60663	Manchester	T918SSF	60171	Midlands
T817LLC	32817	South West	T846LLC	32846	South West	T919SSF	60172	West Yorkshire
T817MAK	60635	South Yorkshire	T846MAK	60664	South Yorkshire	T982LBF	40140	Midlands
T818LLC	32818	Essex	T847LLC	32847	Essex	T988KLF	34088	Manchester
T818MAK	60636	South Yorkshire	T847MAK	60665	South Yorkshire	T990KLF	34100	Manchester
T819LLC	32819	South West	T848LLC	32848	Glasgow	TJI4838	34195	South West
T819MAK	60637	South Yorkshire	T848MAK	60666	South Yorkshire	TL54TVL	53403	South West
T820LLC	32820	Glasgow	T849LLC	32849	Essex	TO54TRU	53401	West of England
T820MAK	60638	South Yorkshire	T850LLC	32850	Essex	TT03TRU	42860	South West
T821JBL	65621	Hampshire D&B	T850MAK	60668	South Yorkshire	TT04TRU	20556	South West
T821LLC	32821	Scotland East	T851MAK	60669	South Yorkshire	TT05TRU	20557	South West
T821MAK	60639	South Yorkshire	T852LLC	32852	Midlands	TT06NEX	20559	South West
T822JBL	65622	Hampshire D&B	T852MAK	60670	South Yorkshire	TT07TRU	20561	South West
T822MAK	60640	South Yorkshire	T853MAK	60671	South Yorkshire	TT54TVL	53404	South West
T823LLC	32823	Glasgow	T854KLF	32854	Midlands	TT55TRU	20558	South West
T823MAK	60641	South Yorkshire	T854MAK	60672	South Yorkshire	TU04TRU	53204	West of England
T823SFS	60065	West Yorkshire	T855MAK	60673	South Yorkshire	TX06NEX	20560	South West
T824JBL	65624	Hampshire D&B	T856MAK	60674	South Yorkshire	UHW661	40582	South West
T824LLC	32824	Scotland East	T857MAK	60675	South Yorkshire	UKT552	34198	South West
T824MAK	60642	South Yorkshire	T858MAK	60676	South Yorkshire	URS318X	31528	Aberdeen
T824SFS	60066	West Yorkshire	T859MAK	60677	South Yorkshire	V35ESC	62392	Scotland East
T825LLC	32825	Glasgow	T860MAK	60678	South Yorkshire	V41DTE	40180	Midlands
T825MAK	60643	South Yorkshire	T861MAK	60679	South Yorkshire	V42DTE	40181	Manchester
T825SFS	60067	West Yorkshire	T862MAK	60680	South Yorkshire	V71GEH	40304	Midlands
T826AFX	42826	Hampshire D&B	T863MAK	60681	South Yorkshire	V116FSF	61667	Glasgow
T826LLC	32826	Glasgow	T864KLF	32864	Essex	V117DLH	50019	Midlands
T826MAK	60644	South Yorkshire	T864MAK	60682	South Yorkshire	V117FSF	61668	Glasgow
T826SFS	60068	Midlands	T865KLF	32865	Glasgow	V118FSF	61669	Glasgow

Reg	Code	Location	Reg	Code	Location	Reg	Code	Location
V119FSF	61670	Glasgow	V589DVF	65589	Eastern Counties	V890HLH	32890	Glasgow
V120FSF	61671	Glasgow	V590DVF	65590	Eastern Counties	V891HLH	32891	Glasgow
V122DND	60174	Midlands	V601GGB	10044	Aberdeen	V892HLH	32892	Scotland East
V122FSF	61672	Glasgow	V602GGB	10045	Aberdeen	V893HLH	32893	Scotland East
V124DND	60176	Midlands	V603GGB	10103	Glasgow	V895HLH	32895	Scotland East
V124LGC	32027	West of England	V604GGB	10104	Glasgow	V896HLH	32896	Scotland East
V126DND	60178	Scotland East	V605GGB	10105	Glasgow	V897HLH	32897	Aberdeen
V128DND	60180	Scotland East	V606GGB	10106	Glasgow	V898HLH	32898	Aberdeen
V129DND	60181	Scotland East	V607GGB	10107	Glasgow	V899HLH	32899	Manchester
V130DND	60182	Scotland East	V608GGB	10108	Aberdeen	V900HLH	32900	Unallocated
V132DND	60184	Manchester	V609GGB	10109	Glasgow	V988HLH	32888	Glasgow
V133ESC	61034	West Yorkshire	V610GGB	10110	Glasgow	V989GBF	40147	Midlands
V134ESC	61035	West Yorkshire	V676FPO	42376	Glasgow	VJT738	34193	South West
V135DND	60187	Scotland East	V701FFB	32701	Hampshire D&B	VOO273	34200	South West
V135ESC	61036	West Yorkshire	V721UVY	60828	West Yorkshire	VT09JPT	45116	Eastern Counties
V136DND	60188	Scotland East	V732FAE	42732	West of England	VT59JPT	33424	Essex
V136ESC	61037	West Yorkshire	V733FAE	42733	West of England	VU02PKX	53040	Midlands
V137DND	60189	Midlands	V734FAE	42734	West of England	VU02PKY	53041	Midlands
V137ESC	61038	West Yorkshire	V735FAE	42735	West of England	VU03YJT	53042	Midlands
V138ESC	61039	West Yorkshire	V736FAE	42736	West of England	VU03YJV	53043	Midlands
V139ESC	61040	West Yorkshire	V737FAE	42737	West of England	VU03YJW	53044	Midlands
V140DND	60192	Scotland East	V738FAE	42738	West of England	VU03YJX	53045	Midlands
V140ESC	61041	West Yorkshire	V741GPU	43741	Essex	VU03YJY	53046	Midlands
V141DND	60193	Midlands	V742GPU	43742	Essex	VU03YJZ	53047	Midlands
V141ESC	61042	West Yorkshire	V743GPU	43743	Essex	VU03YKB	53048	Midlands
V142DND	60173	Midlands	V759UVY	60826	West Yorkshire	VU03YKC	53049	Midlands
V142ESC	61043	Glasgow	V760UVY	60827	West Yorkshire	VU03YKD	53050	Midlands
V143ESC	61044	Glasgow	V762UVY	60829	West Yorkshire	VU03YKE	53051	Midlands
V154LUA	42654	Hampshire D&B	V763UVY	60830	West Yorkshire	VX05JWW	42894	Midlands
V221GLS	61673	Glasgow	V764UVY	60831	West Yorkshire	VX05LVS	67652	Midlands
V307GBY	41307	Glasgow	V765UVY	60832	West Yorkshire	VX05LVT	67653	Midlands
V308GBY	41308	Glasgow	V767UVY	60834	West Yorkshire	VX05LVU	67654	Midlands
V309GBY	41309	Glasgow	V768UVY	60835	West Yorkshire	VX05LVV	67655	Midlands
V310GBY	41310	Glasgow	V769UVY	60836	West Yorkshire	VX05LVW	67656	Midlands
V311GBY	41311	Glasgow	V770UVY	60837	West Yorkshire	VX05LVY	67657	Midlands
V312GBY	41312	Glasgow	V771UVY	60838	West Yorkshire	VX05LVZ	67658	Midlands
V313GBY	41313	Glasgow	V772UVY	60839	West Yorkshire	VX05LWC	67659	Midlands
V314GBY	41314	Glasgow	V773UVY	60840	West Yorkshire	VX05LWD	67660	Midlands
V315GBY	41315	West Yorkshire	V801KAF	53001	South West	VX05LWE	67661	Midlands
V316GBY	41316	West Yorkshire	V802EFB	48202	Hampshire D&B	VX05LWF	67662	Midlands
V317GBY	41317	West Yorkshire	V802KAF	53002	Hampshire D&B	VX05LWG	67663	Midlands
V330DBU	60175	Midlands	V803KAF	53003	West of England	VX05LWH	67664	Midlands
V330GBY	41330	Cymru	V804EFB	48204	Hampshire D&B	VX53OEN	53059	Midlands
V331GBY	41331	Cymru	V805EFB	48205	Hampshire D&B	VX53OEO	53060	Midlands
V332GBY	41332	Cymru	V807EFB	48207	Hampshire D&B	VX53OEP	53061	Midlands
V334GBY	41334	Cymru	V808EFB	48208	Hampshire D&B	VX53OER	53062	Midlands
V335GBY	41335	Cymru	V809EFB	48209	Hampshire D&B	VX53OET	53063	Midlands
V345DLH	41345	Cymru	V810EFB	48210	West of England	VX53OEU	53064	Midlands
V346DLH	41346	Hampshire D&B	V826FSC	65626	Essex	VX53OEV	53058	Midlands
V347DLH	41347	Cymru	V827FSC	65627	Essex	VX53VJV	67601	Midlands
V348DLH	41348	Hampshire D&B	V828FSC	65628	Eastern Counties	VX53VJZ	67602	Midlands
V356DVG	43356	Essex	V830FSC	65630	Eastern Counties	VX53VKA	67603	Midlands
V357DVG	43357	Essex	V830GBF	60072	Midlands	VX53VKB	67604	Midlands
V359DVG	43359	Essex	V831FSC	65631	Eastern Counties	VX54MOV	67631	Midlands
V360DVG	43360	Essex	V831GBF	60073	Midlands	VX54MPE	67632	Midlands
V362CNH	65662	Scotland East	V832DYD	42832	South West	VX54MPF	67633	Midlands
V363CNH	65663	Scotland East	V832FSC	65632	Eastern Counties	VX54MPO	67634	Midlands
V364CNH	65664	Scotland East	V832GBF	60074	Midlands	VX54MPU	67635	Midlands
V370KLG	41070	Midlands	V833DYD	42833	South West	VX54MPV	67636	Midlands
V433GBY	41333	Cymru	V834DYD	42834	South West	VX54MPY	67637	Midlands
V527ESH	62385	Scotland East	V835DYD	42835	South West	VX54MPZ	67638	Midlands
V528ESH	62386	Scotland East	V855HBY	32855	Essex	VX54MRO	67639	Midlands
V529ESH	62387	Scotland East	V856HBY	32856	Essex	VX54MRU	67640	Midlands
V530ESH	62388	Scotland East	V859HBY	32859	Essex	VX54MRV	67641	Aberdeen
V531ESH	62389	Scotland East	V863HBY	32863	Essex	VX54MRY	67642	Midlands
V532ESH	62390	Scotland East	V867HBY	32867	Manchester	VX54MSO	67643	Midlands
V586DVF	65586	Essex	V869HBY	32869	Manchester	VX54MTF	67647	Midlands
V587DVF	65587	Essex	V887HBY	32887	Essex	VX54MTJ	67648	Midlands
V588DVF	65588	Eastern Counties	V889HLH	32889	Scotland East	VX54MTK	67649	Midlands

Reg	No.	Area	Reg	No.	Area	Reg	No.	Area
VX54MTO	67650	Midlands	W329DWX	50279	Cymru	W476SVT	40017	Midlands
VX54MTU	67651	Midlands	W329JND	60251	Manchester	W477SVT	40018	Midlands
VX54MTV	33401	Midlands	W331DWX	50290	West Yorkshire	W478SVT	40019	Midlands
VX54MTY	33402	Midlands	W331JND	60252	Manchester	W577RFS	62170	Aberdeen
VX54MTZ	33403	Midlands	W331RJA	60253	Manchester	W578RFS	62171	Aberdeen
VX54MUA	33404	Midlands	W332RJA	60254	Manchester	W579RFS	62172	Aberdeen
VX54MUB	33405	Midlands	W334JND	60238	Manchester	W581RFS	62173	Aberdeen
VX54MUU	42892	Midlands	W334RJA	60256	Manchester	W582RFS	62174	Aberdeen
VX54MUV	42893	Midlands	W335DWX	50294	West Yorkshire	W583RFS	62175	Aberdeen
VX57CYO	53405	Midlands	W335JND	60227	Manchester	W584RFS	62176	Aberdeen
W2FAL	10047	Aberdeen	W335RJA	60257	Manchester	W585RFS	62184	Scotland East
W3FAL	10048	Aberdeen	W336DWX	50285	South West	W586RFS	62185	Scotland East
W4FAL	10049	Aberdeen	W336JND	60228	Manchester	W587RFS	62186	Scotland East
W4TRU	56000	South West	W336RJA	60258	Manchester	W588RFS	62187	Scotland East
W5FAL	10050	Aberdeen	W337DWX	50292	West Yorkshire	W589RFS	62188	Scotland East
W6FAL	10051	Aberdeen	W337JND	60242	Manchester	W591RFS	62189	Scotland East
W7FAL	10052	Aberdeen	W337RJA	60259	Manchester	W591SNG	65591	Glasgow
W118CWR	10035	West of England	W338DWX	53028	Hampshire D&B	W592RFS	62190	Scotland East
W119CWR	10036	West of England	W338JND	60240	Manchester	W592SNG	65592	Glasgow
W122CWR	10037	West of England	W338RJA	60260	Manchester	W593RFS	62205	Scotland East
W122DWX	10039	West Yorkshire	W339JND	60245	Manchester	W593SNG	65593	Glasgow
W124DWX	10041	West Yorkshire	W339RJA	60261	Manchester	W594RFS	62206	Scotland East
W126DWX	10043	West Yorkshire	W341JND	60243	Manchester	W594SNG	65594	Scotland East
W127DWX	10038	West Yorkshire	W342RJA	60264	Manchester	W595RFS	62207	Scotland East
W128DWX	10040	West Yorkshire	W346RJA	60268	Manchester	W595SNG	65595	Scotland East
W129DWX	10042	West Yorkshire	W347RJA	60269	Manchester	W596RFS	62208	Aberdeen
W132VLO	32950	Glasgow	W348RJA	60270	Manchester	W596SNG	65596	Glasgow
W133VLO	41720	Cymru	W349RJA	60271	Manchester	W597RFS	62209	Scotland East
W133WPO	10133	Glasgow	W351RJA	60273	Manchester	W597SNG	65597	Scotland East
W142PSH	60194	Midlands	W352RJA	60274	Manchester	W598RFS	62210	Scotland East
W179BVP	60283	Manchester	W353RJA	60275	Manchester	W598SNG	65598	Scotland East
W213XBD	32053	Midlands	W354RJA	60276	Manchester	W599RFS	62211	Scotland East
W214XBD	32054	Midlands	W356RJA	60278	Manchester	W599SNG	65599	Scotland East
W215XBD	32055	Midlands	W357RJA	60279	Manchester	W601PAF	48261	South West
W216XBD	32056	Midlands	W358RJA	60280	Manchester	W601RFS	62219	Scotland East
W217XBD	32057	Midlands	W359RJA	60281	Manchester	W601SNG	65601	Scotland East
W218XBD	32058	Midlands	W361RJA	60262	Manchester	W602PAF	48262	South West
W219XBD	32059	Midlands	W362RJA	60272	Manchester	W602RFS	62220	Scotland East
W221XBD	32061	Midlands	W363RJA	60255	Manchester	W603PAF	48263	South West
W223XBD	32063	Midlands	W364EOW	66164	Hampshire D&B	W603RFS	62221	Scotland East
W224XBD	32064	Midlands	W364RJA	60282	Manchester	W604PAF	48264	South West
W301JND	60223	Manchester	W365EOW	66165	Essex	W604RFS	62222	Scotland East
W302JND	60224	Manchester	W365RJA	60267	Manchester	W605PAF	48265	South West
W303JND	60225	Manchester	W366EOW	66166	West of England	W605RFS	62223	Scotland East
W304JND	60226	Manchester	W366RJA	60277	Manchester	W606PAF	48266	South West
W307DWX	50276	South West	W367EOW	66167	West of England	W607PAF	48267	South West
W307JND	60229	Manchester	W368EOW	66168	Essex	W607RFS	62225	Scotland East
W308DWX	50277	Hampshire D&B	W369EOW	66169	Essex	W608RFS	62226	Scotland East
W308JND	60230	Manchester	W371EOW	66171	West of England	W609PAF	48269	South West
W309DWX	50278	Hampshire D&B	W373EOW	66173	West of England	W609RFS	62227	Scotland East
W311JND	60233	Manchester	W374EOW	66174	West of England	W667CWT	30855	West Yorkshire
W312DWX	50281	Midlands	W376EOW	66176	Hampshire D&B	W668CWT	30865	West Yorkshire
W312JND	60234	Manchester	W377EOW	66177	Essex	W681RNA	62204	Aberdeen
W313DWX	50282	Midlands	W378EOW	66178	West of England	W681ULL	41681	Glasgow
W313JND	60235	Manchester	W378JNE	60247	Manchester	W682RNA	62212	Scotland East
W314DWX	50283	Scotland East	W379EOW	66179	Essex	W682ULL	41682	Glasgow
W314JND	60236	Manchester	W379JNE	60250	Manchester	W683RNA	62213	Scotland East
W315DWX	50284	South West	W381EOW	66181	Hampshire D&B	W683ULL	41683	Glasgow
W315JND	60237	Manchester	W422SRP	32062	Midlands	W684ULL	41684	Glasgow
W317DWX	50286	West Yorkshire	W425SRP	32065	Midlands	W685ULL	41685	Glasgow
W317JND	60239	Manchester	W431CWX	34111	Eastern Counties	W686ULL	41686	West of England
W319JND	60241	Manchester	W432CWX	34112	Eastern Counties	W687ULL	41687	West of England
W322DWX	50291	West Yorkshire	W433CWX	34113	Eastern Counties	W701CWR	30846	South Yorkshire
W322JND	60244	Manchester	W434CWX	34114	Eastern Counties	W702CWR	30847	West Yorkshire
W324DWX	50293	Hampshire D&B	W435CWX	34108	Eastern Counties	W702PHT	32702	Hampshire D&B
W326DWX	50295	West Yorkshire	W436CWX	34109	Eastern Counties	W703CWR	30848	West Yorkshire
W326JND	60248	Manchester	W437CWX	34110	Eastern Counties	W703PHT	32703	Hampshire D&B
W327DWX	50296	Midlands	W474SVT	40015	Midlands	W704CWR	30849	West Yorkshire
W327JND	60249	Manchester	W475SVT	40016	Midlands	W704PHT	32704	Hampshire D&B

Reg	Fleet	Location	Reg	Fleet	Location	Reg	Fleet	Location
W705CWR	30850	West Yorkshire	W768DWX	30913	West Yorkshire	W815EOW	32045	Hampshire D&B
W705PHT	32705	Hampshire D&B	W769DWX	30914	West Yorkshire	W815PAE	32015	West of England
W706CWR	30851	West Yorkshire	W771DWX	30875	Manchester	W815PAF	53015	South West
W706PHT	32706	Hampshire D&B	W771KBT	30916	West Yorkshire	W815PFB	48215	West of England
W707CWR	30852	West Yorkshire	W772DWX	30885	South Yorkshire	W816DWX	60855	West Yorkshire
W707PHT	32707	Hampshire D&B	W772KBT	30917	West Yorkshire	W816EOW	32046	Hampshire D&B
W708CWR	30853	West Yorkshire	W773DWX	30895	West Yorkshire	W816PAE	32016	West of England
W708PHT	32708	Hampshire D&B	W773KBT	30918	West Yorkshire	W816PFB	48216	West of England
W709CWR	30854	West Yorkshire	W774DWX	30900	Eastern Counties	W817PAE	32017	West of England
W709RHT	32709	South West	W774KBT	30919	West Yorkshire	W817PFB	48217	West of England
W711CWR	30856	West Yorkshire	W776DWX	30905	South Yorkshire	W818PAE	32018	West of England
W711RHT	32711	South West	W776KBT	30921	West Yorkshire	W818PFB	48218	West of England
W712CWR	30857	West Yorkshire	W778DWX	30910	West Yorkshire	W819PAE	32019	West of England
W712RHT	32712	South West	W787KBT	30920	West Yorkshire	W819PFB	48219	West of England
W713CWR	30858	West Yorkshire	W788KBT	30922	West Yorkshire	W821PAE	32021	West of England
W713RHT	32713	South West	W801DWX	60841	West Yorkshire	W821PFB	48221	West of England
W714CWR	30859	West Yorkshire	W801EOW	32031	Hampshire D&B	W822PAE	32022	West of England
W714RHT	32714	South West	W801PAE	32001	West of England	W822PFB	48222	West of England
W715CWR	30860	West Yorkshire	W802DWX	60842	West Yorkshire	W823PAE	32023	West of England
W715RHT	32715	South West	W802EOW	32032	Hampshire D&B	W823PFB	48223	West of England
W716CWR	30861	South Yorkshire	W802PAE	32002	West of England	W824PAE	32024	West of England
W716RHT	32716	South West	W803DWX	60843	West Yorkshire	W824PFB	48224	West of England
W717CWR	30862	South Yorkshire	W803EOW	32033	Hampshire D&B	W825PFB	48225	South West
W717RHT	32717	South West	W803PAE	32003	West of England	W826PFB	48226	South West
W718CWR	30863	West Yorkshire	W804DWX	60844	West Yorkshire	W827PFB	48227	South West
W718ULL	41718	Cymru	W804EOW	32034	Hampshire D&B	W828PFB	48228	South West
W719CWR	30864	West Yorkshire	W804PAE	32004	West of England	W829PFB	48229	South West
W719ULL	41719	Cymru	W805DWX	60845	West Yorkshire	W831PFB	48231	South West
W721CWR	30866	West Yorkshire	W805EOW	32035	Hampshire D&B	W832PFB	48232	South West
W721ULL	41721	Cymru	W805PAE	32005	West of England	W833PFB	48233	South West
W722CWR	30867	West Yorkshire	W805PAF	53005	Cymru	W834PFB	48234	South West
W723CWR	30868	West Yorkshire	W806DWX	60846	West Yorkshire	W840VLO	32940	Glasgow
W724CWR	30869	West Yorkshire	W806EOW	32036	Hampshire D&B	W895VLN	32910	Scotland East
W726CWR	30870	West Yorkshire	W806PAE	32006	West of England	W896VLN	32911	Manchester
W726DWX	30871	Manchester	W806PAF	53006	Hampshire D&B	W897VLN	32920	Glasgow
W726ULL	41726	Cymru	W807DWX	60847	West Yorkshire	W898VLN	32925	Glasgow
W727DWX	30872	Manchester	W807EOW	32037	Cymru	W899VLN	32930	Glasgow
W727ULL	41727	Cymru	W807PAE	32007	West of England	W901VLN	32901	Unallocated
W728DWX	30873	Manchester	W807PAF	53007	South West	W902VLN	32902	Unallocated
W728VLO	41728	Cymru	W808DWX	60848	West Yorkshire	W903VLN	32903	Unallocated
W729DWX	30874	Manchester	W808EOW	32038	Hampshire D&B	W904VLN	32904	Scotland East
W731DWX	30876	Manchester	W808PAE	32008	West of England	W905VLN	32905	Essex
W732DWX	30877	Manchester	W808PAF	53008	Hampshire D&B	W906VLN	32906	Manchester
W733DWX	30878	Manchester	W809DWX	60849	West Yorkshire	W907VLN	32907	Scotland East
W734DWX	30879	Manchester	W809EOW	32039	Hampshire D&B	W908VLN	32908	Manchester
W735DWX	30880	Manchester	W809PAE	32009	West of England	W909VLN	32909	Scotland East
W736DWX	30881	South Yorkshire	W809PAF	53009	South West	W912VLN	32912	Manchester
W737DWX	30882	South Yorkshire	W809VMA	42350	Hampshire D&B	W913VLN	32913	Manchester
W738DWX	30883	South Yorkshire	W811DWX	60850	West Yorkshire	W914VLN	32914	Scotland East
W739DWX	30884	South Yorkshire	W811EOW	32041	Hampshire D&B	W915VLN	32915	Manchester
W741DWX	30886	Eastern Counties	W811PAE	32011	West of England	W916VLN	32916	Manchester
W742DWX	30887	Essex	W811PAF	53011	South West	W917VLN	32917	Scotland East
W743DWX	30888	Eastern Counties	W811PFB	48211	West of England	W918VLN	32918	Aberdeen
W744DWX	30889	Eastern Counties	W812DWX	60851	West Yorkshire	W919VLN	32919	Scotland East
W745DWX	30890	West Yorkshire	W812EOW	32042	Hampshire D&B	W921VLN	32921	Scotland East
W746DWX	30891	West Yorkshire	W812PAE	32012	West of England	W922VLN	32922	Scotland East
W747DWX	30892	West Yorkshire	W812PAF	53012	Hampshire D&B	W923VLN	32923	Aberdeen
W748DWX	30893	West Yorkshire	W812PFB	48212	West of England	W924VLN	32924	Scotland East
W751DWX	30896	West Yorkshire	W813DWX	60852	West Yorkshire	W926VLN	32926	Manchester
W752DWX	30897	West Yorkshire	W813EOW	32043	Hampshire D&B	W927VLN	32927	Aberdeen
W753DWX	30898	South Yorkshire	W813PAE	32013	West of England	W928VLN	32928	Aberdeen
W754DWX	30899	South Yorkshire	W813PAF	53013	South West	W929VLN	32929	Unallocated
W756DWX	30901	Eastern Counties	W813PFB	48213	West of England	W931ULL	32931	Glasgow
W757DWX	30902	Essex	W814DWX	60853	West Yorkshire	W934JNF	43824	Scotland East
W758DWX	30903	Essex	W814EOW	32044	Hampshire D&B	W934ULL	32934	Scotland East
W759DWX	30904	South Yorkshire	W814PAE	32014	West of England	W935ULL	32935	Glasgow
W761DWX	30906	South Yorkshire	W814PAF	53014	South West	W936ULL	32936	Glasgow
W762DWX	30907	South Yorkshire	W814PFB	48214	West of England	W937ULL	32937	Glasgow
W766HBT	60833	West Yorkshire	W815DWX	60854	West Yorkshire	W939ULL	32939	Glasgow

Registration	Fleet	Area
W941ULL	32941	Glasgow
W942ULL	32942	Glasgow
W946ULL	32946	Glasgow
W947ULL	32947	Glasgow
W948ULL	32948	Scotland East
W949ULL	32949	Scotland East
W951ULL	32951	Scotland East
W952ULL	32952	Glasgow
WA05UNE	20353	Aberdeen
WA05UNF	20352	Aberdeen
WA05UNG	20351	Aberdeen
WA08MVE	33420	South West
WA08MVF	33421	South West
WA08MVG	33422	South West
WA54OLN	32759	South West
WA54OLO	32756	South West
WA54OLP	32757	South West
WA54OLR	32760	South West
WA54OLT	32758	South West
WA56FTK	33414	West of England
WA56FTN	33415	West of England
WA56FTO	33416	West of England
WA56FTP	33417	West of England
WA56FTT	33418	West of England
WA56FTU	33419	West of England
WA56FTV	42946	South West
WA56FTX	42947	West of England
WA56FTY	42948	West of England
WA56FTZ	42969	West of England
WA56FUB	33411	West of England
WA56FUD	33412	West of England
WA56FUE	33413	West of England
WA56OAO	42941	Manchester
WA56OAP	42942	South West
WA56OAS	42943	South West
WA56OAU	42944	Manchester
WA56OAV	42945	Manchester
WJ55CRX	32761	South West
WJ55CRZ	32762	South West
WJ55CSF	32763	Hampshire D&B
WJ55CSO	32764	Hampshire D&B
WJ55CSU	32765	Hampshire D&B
WJ55CSV	32766	Hampshire D&B
WJ55CTE	32767	Hampshire D&B
WJ55CTF	32768	Hampshire D&B
WK02TYD	48270	Hampshire D&B
WK02TYF	48271	South West
WK02TYH	48272	Hampshire D&B
WK06AEE	43850	Cymru
WK06AEF	43851	Cymru
WK06AFU	43852	Cymru
WK06AFV	43853	Cymru
WK08ESV	64049	South West
WK10AZU	64050	South West
WK52SYE	32755	South West
WK52WTV	43811	South West
WK56ABZ	44500	Cymru
WM04NZU	23208	South West
WR03YZL	32279	West of England
WR03YZM	32280	West of England
WR03YZN	32281	West of England
WR03YZP	32282	West of England
WR03YZS	32283	West of England
WR03YZT	32284	West of England
WR03YZU	32285	West of England
WR03YZV	32286	West of England
WR03YZW	32287	West of England
WR03YZX	32288	West of England
WR03ZBC	32291	West of England
WR03ZBD	32292	West of England
WSU489	20205	Aberdeen
WSV408	20416	West of England
WSV409	20108	South West
WU02KVE	30564	South Yorkshire
WU02KVF	30565	South Yorkshire
WU02KVH	30567	South Yorkshire
WU02KVJ	30568	South Yorkshire
WU02KVK	30569	South Yorkshire
WU02KVL	30570	South Yorkshire
WU02KVM	30571	South Yorkshire
WU02KVO	30572	South Yorkshire
WU02KVP	30573	South Yorkshire
WU02KVR	30574	South Yorkshire
WU02KVS	30575	South Yorkshire
WU02KVT	30576	South Yorkshire
WU02KVV	30577	South Yorkshire
WU02KVW	30578	South Yorkshire
WV02EUP	20514	Eastern Counties
WV02EUR	20515	Eastern Counties
WX05OZF	20307	Scotland East
WX05RRV	53802	Cymru
WX05RRY	53803	South West
WX05RRZ	53804	West of England
WX05RSO	53805	West of England
WX05RSU	53806	West of England
WX05RSV	53807	West of England
WX05RSY	53808	West of England
WX05RSZ	53809	West of England
WX05RTO	53810	West of England
WX05RTU	53811	West of England
WX05RTV	53812	West of England
WX05RTZ	53813	West of England
WX05RUA	53814	West of England
WX05RUC	53815	West of England
WX05RUJ	53816	West of England
WX05RUO	53817	West of England
WX05RUR	53818	West of England
WX05RUU	53820	West of England
WX05RUV	53820	West of England
WX05RUW	42895	West of England
WX05RUY	42896	West of England
WX05RVA	42897	West of England
WX05RVC	42898	West of England
WX05RVE	42899	West of England
WX05RVF	42900	West of England
WX05RVJ	42901	West of England
WX05RVK	42902	West of England
WX05RVL	42903	West of England
WX05RVM	42904	West of England
WX05RVN	42905	West of England
WX05RVO	42906	West of England
WX05RVP	42907	West of England
WX05RVR	42908	West of England
WX05RVT	42909	West of England
WX05RVU	42910	West of England
WX05RVV	42911	West of England
WX05RVW	42912	Cymru
WX05RVY	42913	Cymru
WX05RVZ	42914	West of England
WX05RWE	42915	West of England
WX05RWF	42916	West of England
WX05SVD	42938	West of England
WX05SVE	42939	West of England
WX05UAF	32636	West of England
WX05UAG	32637	West of England
WX05UAH	32638	West of England
WX05UAJ	42552	West of England
WX05UAK	42553	West of England
WX05UAL	42554	West of England
WX05UAM	42555	West of England
WX05UAN	42556	West of England
WX05UAO	42557	West of England
WX06OMF	42949	West of England
WX06OMG	42950	West of England
WX06OMH	42951	West of England
WX06OMJ	42952	West of England
WX06OMK	42953	West of England
WX06OML	42954	West of England
WX06OMM	42955	West of England
WX06OMO	42956	West of England
WX06OMP	42957	West of England
WX06OMR	42958	West of England
WX06OMS	42959	West of England
WX06OMT	42960	West of England
WX06OMU	42962	West of England
WX06OMV	42961	West of England
WX06OMW	42963	West of England
WX06OMY	42964	West of England
WX06OMZ	42965	West of England
WX06ONA	42966	West of England
WX06ONB	42967	West of England
WX06ONC	42968	West of England
WX08LNN	44902	West of England
WX08LNO	44903	West of England
WX08LNP	44904	West of England
WX09KBK	37757	West of England
WX09KBN	37758	West of England
WX09KBO	37759	West of England
WX09KBP	37760	West of England
WX09KBU	37761	West of England
WX09KBV	37762	West of England
WX09KBY	37763	West of England
WX09KBZ	37764	West of England
WX09KCA	37765	West of England
WX09KCC	37766	West of England
WX09KCE	37767	West of England
WX09KCF	37768	West of England
WX09KCG	37769	West of England
WX09KCJ	37770	West of England
WX09KCK	37771	West of England
WX09KCN	37772	West of England
WX53UKK	32289	West of England
WX53UKL	32290	West of England
WX54XCM	66727	West of England
WX54XCN	66728	West of England
WX54XCO	66729	West of England
WX54XCP	66730	West of England
WX54XCR	66731	West of England
WX54XCT	66732	West of England
WX54XCU	66733	West of England
WX54XCV	66734	West of England
WX54XCW	66735	Glasgow
WX54XCY	66736	Glasgow
WX54XCZ	66737	Glasgow
WX54XDA	66716	Cymru
WX54XDB	66718	Cymru
WX54XDC	66719	West of England
WX54XDD	66717	Cymru
WX54XDE	66721	West of England
WX54XDF	66720	West of England
WX54XDG	66724	West of England
WX54XDH	66723	West of England
WX54XDJ	66725	West of England
WX54XDK	66726	West of England
WX54XDL	66722	West of England
WX54ZHM	20300	Scotland East
WX54ZHN	20301	Scotland East

Reg	No.	Location	Reg	No.	Location	Reg	No.	Location
WX54ZHO	20302	Scotland East	WX57HKD	37323	West of England	WX58JYE	37619	West of England
WX55HVZ	10174	West of England	WX57HKE	37324	West of England	WX58JYF	37620	West of England
WX55HWA	10175	West of England	WX57HKF	37325	West of England	WX58JYG	37621	West of England
WX55HWB	10176	West of England	WX57HKG	37326	West of England	WX58JYH	37622	West of England
WX55HWC	10177	West of England	WX57HKH	37327	West of England	WX58JYJ	37623	West of England
WX55TYZ	66938	West of England	WX57HKJ	37328	West of England	WX58JYK	37624	West of England
WX55TZA	66939	West of England	WX57HKK	37329	West of England	WX58JYL	37625	West of England
WX55TZB	66940	West of England	WX57HKL	37330	West of England	WX58JYN	37626	West of England
WX55TZC	66941	West of England	WX57HKM	37331	West of England	WX58JYO	37627	West of England
WX55TZD	66942	West of England	WX57HKN	37332	West of England	WX58JYP	37628	West of England
WX55TZE	66943	West of England	WX57HKO	37333	West of England	WX58JYR	37629	West of England
WX55TZF	66944	Hampshire D&B	WX57HKP	37334	West of England	WX58JYS	37630	West of England
WX55TZG	66945	Hampshire D&B	WX57HKT	37335	West of England	WX58JYT	37631	West of England
WX55TZH	66946	Glasgow	WX57HKU	37336	West of England	WX58JYU	37632	West of England
WX55TZJ	66947	Glasgow	WX57HKV	37337	West of England	WX59BYM	69435	West of England
WX55TZK	66948	Glasgow	WX57HKW	37338	West of England	WX59BYN	69436	West of England
WX55TZL	66949	Glasgow	WX57HKY	37339	West of England	WX59BYO	69437	West of England
WX55TZM	66950	Eastern Counties	WX57HKZ	37340	West of England	WX59BYP	69438	West of England
WX55TZN	66951	Glasgow	WX57HLA	37341	West of England	WX59BYR	69439	West of England
WX55TZO	66952	Glasgow	WX57HLC	37342	West of England	WX59BYS	69440	West of England
WX55TZP	66953	Hampshire D&B	WX57HLD	37343	West of England	WX59BYT	69441	West of England
WX55TZR	66954	Glasgow	WX57HLE	37344	West of England	WX59BYU	69442	West of England
WX55TZS	66955	Glasgow	WX57HLF	37345	West of England	WX59BYV	69443	West of England
WX55TZT	66956	West of England	WX57HLG	37346	West of England	WX59BYW	69444	West of England
WX55TZU	66957	Eastern Counties	WX57HLH	37347	West of England	WX59BYY	69445	West of England
WX55TZV	66958	Cymru	WX57HLJ	37348	West of England	WX59BYZ	69446	West of England
WX55TZW	66959	Eastern Counties	WX57HLK	37349	West of England	WX59BZA	69447	West of England
WX55TZY	66960	Cymru	WX57HLM	37350	West of England	WX59BZB	69448	West of England
WX55TZZ	66961	Cymru	WX57HLN	37351	West of England	WX59BZC	69449	West of England
WX55UAA	66934	West of England	WX57HLO	37352	West of England	WX59BZD	69450	West of England
WX55UAB	66935	West of England	WX57HLP	37353	West of England	WX59BZE	69451	West of England
WX55UAC	66936	West of England	WX57HLR	37354	West of England	WX59BZF	69452	West of England
WX55UAD	66937	West of England	WX57HLU	37355	West of England	WX59BZG	69453	West of England
WX55VHK	37001	West of England	WX57HLV	37356	West of England	WX59BZH	69454	West of England
WX55VHL	37002	West of England	WX57HLW	37357	West of England	WX59BZJ	69455	West of England
WX55VHM	37003	West of England	WX57HLY	37358	West of England	WX59BZK	69456	West of England
WX55VHN	37004	West of England	WX57HLZ	37359	West of England	WX59BZL	69457	West of England
WX55VHO	37005	West of England	WX58JWU	37587	West of England	WX59BZM	69458	West of England
WX55VHP	37006	West of England	WX58JWV	37588	West of England	WX59BZN	69459	West of England
WX55VHR	37007	West of England	WX58JWW	37589	West of England	WX59BZO	69460	West of England
WX55VHT	37008	West of England	WX58JWY	37590	West of England	X69NSS	62131	Scotland East
WX55VHU	37009	West of England	WX58JWZ	37591	West of England	X78HLR	41390	Cymru
WX55VHV	37010	West of England	WX58JXA	37592	West of England	X79HLR	41400	Cymru
WX55VHW	37011	West of England	WX58JXB	37593	West of England	X103NSS	31560	Scotland East
WX55VHY	37012	West of England	WX58JXC	37594	West of England	X104NSS	31561	Scotland East
WX55VHZ	37013	West of England	WX58JXD	37595	West of England	X132NSS	31558	Scotland East
WX55VJA	37014	West of England	WX58JXE	37596	West of England	X136FPO	10136	Aberdeen
WX55VJC	37015	West of England	WX58JXF	37597	West of England	X136NSS	31562	Scotland East
WX55VJD	37016	West of England	WX58JXG	37598	West of England	X137NSS	31563	Scotland East
WX55VJE	37017	West of England	WX58JXH	37599	West of England	X138FPO	10138	Aberdeen
WX55VJF	37018	West of England	WX58JXJ	37600	West of England	X141FPO	10141	Aberdeen
WX55VJG	37019	West of England	WX58JXK	37601	West of England	X144FPO	10144	Aberdeen
WX55VJJ	37020	West of England	WX58JXL	37602	West of England	X191HFB	20461	South West
WX56HJZ	32684	West of England	WX58JXM	37603	West of England	X193HFB	20463	Essex
WX56HKA	32685	West of England	WX58JXN	37604	West of England	X201HAE	43821	South West
WX56HKB	32686	West of England	WX58JXO	37605	West of England	X202HAE	43822	South West
WX56HKC	32687	West of England	WX58JXP	37606	West of England	X203HAE	43823	South West
WX56HKD	32688	West of England	WX58JXR	37607	West of England	X238AMO	42338	Hampshire D&B
WX56HKE	32689	West of England	WX58JXS	37608	West of England	X239AMO	42339	Hampshire D&B
WX56HKF	32690	West of England	WX58JXT	37609	West of England	X241AMO	42341	Hampshire D&B
WX56HKG	32691	West of England	WX58JXU	37610	West of England	X243AMO	42343	Hampshire D&B
WX57HJO	37315	West of England	WX58JXV	37611	West of England	X244AMO	42344	Hampshire D&B
WX57HJU	37316	West of England	WX58JXW	37612	West of England	X246AMO	42346	Hampshire D&B
WX57HJV	37317	West of England	WX58JXY	37613	West of England	X247AMO	42347	Hampshire D&B
WX57HJY	37318	West of England	WX58JXZ	37614	West of England	X253USH	60196	Midlands
WX57HJZ	37319	West of England	WX58JYA	37615	West of England	X256USH	60199	Scotland East
WX57HKA	37320	West of England	WX58JYB	37616	West of England	X257USH	60201	Midlands
WX57HKB	37321	West of England	WX58JYC	37617	West of England	X261USH	60205	Midlands
WX57HKC	37322	West of England	WX58JYD	37618	West of England	X269USH	60213	West Yorkshire

Reg	No.	Area	Reg	No.	Area	Reg	No.	Area
X272USH	60204	Scotland East	X476SCY	42476	South West	X737HLF	41737	Essex
X289FFA	40020	Midlands	X477NSS	62153	Aberdeen	X738HLF	41738	Unallocated
X291FFA	40021	Midlands	X477SCY	42477	South West	X749VUA	30894	West Yorkshire
X292FFA	40022	Midlands	X478SCY	42478	Cymru	X751JLO	41751	Scotland East
X293FFA	40023	Midlands	X501BFJ	32751	South West	X752HLR	41752	Scotland East
X294FFA	40024	Midlands	X502BFJ	32752	South West	X753HLR	41753	Scotland East
X295FFA	40025	Midlands	X503BFJ	32753	South West	X754HLR	41754	Scotland East
X296FFA	40026	Midlands	X503JLO	41730	Essex	X756HLR	41756	Scotland East
X297FFA	40027	Midlands	X504BFJ	32754	South West	X761HLR	41761	Essex
X298FFA	40028	Midlands	X506HLR	41755	Scotland East	X762HLR	41762	Essex
X299FFA	40029	Midlands	X511HLR	41775	Glasgow	X763VUA	30908	West Yorkshire
X303JGE	66233	Glasgow	X512HLR	41777	Glasgow	X764VUA	30909	West Yorkshire
X304JGE	66234	Glasgow	X513HLR	41780	Manchester	X766VUA	30911	West Yorkshire
X351VWT	30931	West Yorkshire	X514HLR	41786	Manchester	X767VUA	30912	West Yorkshire
X352VWT	30932	West Yorkshire	X578RJW	32052	Glasgow	X771NSO	31559	Scotland East
X353VWT	30933	West Yorkshire	X601NSS	62122	Aberdeen	X773HLR	41773	Glasgow
X354VWT	30934	West Yorkshire	X602NSS	62123	Aberdeen	X776HLR	41776	Glasgow
X356VWT	30935	West Yorkshire	X603NSS	62124	Aberdeen	X778HLR	41778	Glasgow
X357VWT	30936	West Yorkshire	X604NSS	62125	Aberdeen	X779HLR	41779	Glasgow
X358VWT	30937	South Yorkshire	X605NSS	62126	Aberdeen	X779VUA	30915	West Yorkshire
X359VWT	30938	South Yorkshire	X606NSS	62127	Aberdeen	X781HLR	41781	Manchester
X381HLR	41381	Cymru	X606RFS	62224	Scotland East	X782HLR	41782	Manchester
X382HLR	41382	Cymru	X607NSS	62128	Aberdeen	X783HLR	41783	Manchester
X383HLR	41383	Cymru	X608NSS	62129	Glasgow	X784HLR	41784	Manchester
X384HLR	41384	Cymru	X609NSS	62130	Glasgow	X785HLR	41785	Manchester
X385HLR	41385	Cymru	X611HLT	32955	South Yorkshire	X787HLR	41787	Manchester
X386HLR	41386	Cymru	X611NSS	62132	Aberdeen	X788HLR	41788	Manchester
X387HLR	41387	Hampshire D&B	X611OBN	40308	Manchester	X791NWR	30923	West Yorkshire
X388HLR	41388	Cymru	X612HLT	32960	Glasgow	X792NWR	30924	West Yorkshire
X389HLR	41389	Cymru	X612NSS	62133	Aberdeen	X793NWR	30925	West Yorkshire
X391HLR	41391	Cymru	X613HLT	32970	Aberdeen	X794NWR	30926	West Yorkshire
X392HLR	41392	Cymru	X613NSS	62134	Aberdeen	X795NWR	30927	West Yorkshire
X393HLR	41393	Cymru	X614HLT	32980	Glasgow	X796NWR	30928	West Yorkshire
X394HLR	41394	Cymru	X614NSS	62135	Aberdeen	X797NWR	30929	West Yorkshire
X395HLR	41395	Cymru	X615NSS	62136	Aberdeen	X798NWR	30930	West Yorkshire
X397HLR	41397	Cymru	X615OBN	40312	Manchester	X856UOK	30561	South Yorkshire
X398HLR	41398	Cymru	X616NSS	62137	Aberdeen	X857UOK	30562	South Yorkshire
X399HLR	41399	Cymru	X616OBN	40313	Manchester	X858UOK	30563	South Yorkshire
X401CSG	10017	Manchester	X617NSS	62138	Aberdeen	X944NSO	62141	Aberdeen
X424UMS	61675	Glasgow	X617OBN	40314	Manchester	X954HLT	32954	South West
X425UMS	61676	Glasgow	X618NSS	62139	Aberdeen	X956HLT	32956	Glasgow
X426UMS	61677	Glasgow	X618OBN	40315	Manchester	X957HLT	32957	South Yorkshire
X427UMS	61678	Glasgow	X619NSS	62140	Aberdeen	X958HLT	32958	Glasgow
X429UMS	61679	Glasgow	X619OBN	40316	Manchester	X959HLT	32959	Manchester
X431UMS	61680	Glasgow	X621NSS	62149	Aberdeen	X961HLT	32961	Glasgow
X432UMS	61681	Glasgow	X622NSS	62150	Aberdeen	X962HLT	32962	Aberdeen
X433UMS	61682	Glasgow	X623NSS	62151	Aberdeen	X963HLT	32963	Unallocated
X434UMS	61683	Glasgow	X624NSS	62152	Aberdeen	X964HLT	32964	Glasgow
X435UMS	61684	Glasgow	X627OBN	40317	Manchester	X965HLT	32965	Aberdeen
X436UMS	61685	Glasgow	X683ADK	62182	Aberdeen	X967HLT	32967	Scotland East
X437UMS	61686	Glasgow	X684ADK	62183	Aberdeen	X968HLT	32968	Scotland East
X438UMS	61687	Glasgow	X685ADK	62191	Aberdeen	X969HLT	32969	Glasgow
X439UMS	61688	Glasgow	X686ADK	62192	Aberdeen	X971HLT	32971	Glasgow
X441UMS	61689	Glasgow	X687ADK	62193	West of England	X972HLT	32972	Manchester
X442UMS	61690	Glasgow	X688ADK	62194	West of England	X973HLT	32973	Aberdeen
X443UMS	61691	Glasgow	X689ADK	62195	Aberdeen	X974HLT	32974	Aberdeen
X446UMS	61693	Glasgow	X691ADK	62196	Aberdeen	X975HLT	32975	Aberdeen
X447UMS	61694	Glasgow	X692ADK	62197	Aberdeen	X977HLT	32977	Glasgow
X448UMS	61695	Glasgow	X693ADK	62198	Aberdeen	X978HLT	32978	Glasgow
X449UMS	61696	Glasgow	X694ADK	62199	Aberdeen	X981HLT	32981	Glasgow
X451UMS	61697	Glasgow	X695ADK	62200	Aberdeen	X993FFA	40150	Midlands
X452UMS	61698	Glasgow	X696ADK	62201	Aberdeen	X994FFA	40151	Midlands
X453UMS	61699	Glasgow	X697ADK	62202	Aberdeen	XFF283	40581	South West
X454UMS	61700	Glasgow	X698ADK	62203	Aberdeen	XSS344Y	31577	Aberdeen
X457UMS	61701	Glasgow	X699ADK	60405	Manchester	Y1EDN	42801	South West
X458UMS	61702	Glasgow	X729HLF	41729	Cymru	Y2EDN	42802	South West
X461UMS	61704	Glasgow	X732HLF	41732	Essex	Y148ROT	10148	Aberdeen
X474SCY	42474	South West	X735HLF	41735	Essex	Y181BGB	66281	Glasgow
X475SCY	42475	South West	X736HLF	41736	Essex	Y182BGB	66282	Glasgow

Y186HNH	66358	Scotland East	Y942CSF	62233	Manchester	YG02DLZ	60915	South West
Y223NLF	32976	Aberdeen	Y943CSF	62234	South Yorkshire	YJ04FYB	32432	West Yorkshire
Y224NLF	32979	Glasgow	Y944CSF	62236	Manchester	YJ04FYC	32433	West Yorkshire
Y251HHL	50232	South Yorkshire	Y945CSF	62237	South Yorkshire	YJ04FYD	32434	West Yorkshire
Y252HHL	50233	South Yorkshire	Y946CSF	62235	South Yorkshire	YJ04FYE	32435	West Yorkshire
Y253HHL	50234	South Yorkshire	Y947CSF	62238	West of England	YJ04FYF	32436	West Yorkshire
Y254HHL	50235	South Yorkshire	Y948CSF	62239	South Yorkshire	YJ04FYG	32437	West Yorkshire
Y256HHL	50236	South Yorkshire	Y949CSF	62240	South Yorkshire	YJ04FYH	32438	West Yorkshire
Y301RTD	61705	Glasgow	Y949RTD	61710	Glasgow	YJ04FYK	32439	West Yorkshire
Y302RTD	61706	Glasgow	Y951CSF	62241	Manchester	YJ04FYL	32440	West Yorkshire
Y303RTD	61707	Glasgow	Y952CSF	62244	South Yorkshire	YJ04FYM	32441	West Yorkshire
Y304RTD	61708	Glasgow	Y953CSF	62243	South Yorkshire	YJ04FYN	32442	West Yorkshire
Y307RTD	61709	Glasgow	Y984NLP	32984	Glasgow	YJ04FYP	32443	West Yorkshire
Y343XBN	60195	Scotland East	Y985NLP	32985	Glasgow	YJ04FYR	32444	West Yorkshire
Y344NLF	32983	Glasgow	Y986NLP	32986	Glasgow	YJ04FYS	32445	West Yorkshire
Y344XBN	60198	Scotland East	Y987NLP	32987	Glasgow	YJ04FYT	32446	West Yorkshire
Y346NLF	32982	Glasgow	Y988NLP	32988	Glasgow	YJ04FYU	32447	West Yorkshire
Y346XBN	60202	Midlands	Y989NLP	32989	Glasgow	YJ04FYV	32448	West Yorkshire
Y347XBN	60208	Midlands	Y991NLP	32991	Glasgow	YJ04FYW	32449	West Yorkshire
Y351AUY	42351	Midlands	Y992NLP	32992	Glasgow	YJ04FYX	32450	West Yorkshire
Y352AUY	42352	Midlands	Y993NLP	32993	Glasgow	YJ04FYY	32451	West Yorkshire
Y353AUY	42353	Midlands	Y994NLP	32994	Aberdeen	YJ04FYZ	32452	West Yorkshire
Y354AUY	42354	Midlands	Y995NLP	32995	Scotland East	YJ04FZH	32460	West Yorkshire
Y356AUY	42356	Midlands	Y996NLP	32996	Glasgow	YJ04FZK	32461	West Yorkshire
Y445CUB	60876	York	Y997NLP	32997	Glasgow	YJ04FZL	32462	West Yorkshire
Y446CUB	60877	West Yorkshire	Y998NLP	32998	Glasgow	YJ04FZM	32463	West Yorkshire
Y447CUB	60878	West Yorkshire	YA05SOJ	66792	West Yorkshire	YJ04FZN	32464	West Yorkshire
Y449CUB	60880	York	YA05SOU	66790	West Yorkshire	YJ04FZP	32465	West Yorkshire
Y451CUB	60881	York	YA13AAF	64507	Cymru	YJ04FZR	32466	West Yorkshire
Y546XNW	53034	South Yorkshire	YA13AAJ	64508	Cymru	YJ04FZS	32467	West Yorkshire
Y547XNW	53035	South Yorkshire	YA54WBK	68528	West Yorkshire	YJ04FZT	32468	West Yorkshire
Y597KNE	60197	Scotland East	YA54WBL	68527	West Yorkshire	YJ04FZU	32469	West Yorkshire
Y598KNE	60206	Essex	YA54WBN	68530	West Yorkshire	YJ04FZV	32470	West Yorkshire
Y626RSA	62154	Aberdeen	YA54WBO	68529	West Yorkshire	YJ04FZX	32471	West Yorkshire
Y627RSA	62155	Aberdeen	YD63UZM	64509	Cymru	YJ04FZY	32472	West Yorkshire
Y628RSA	62163	Aberdeen	YG02DGY	60926	York	YJ04FZZ	32473	West Yorkshire
Y629RSA	62164	Aberdeen	YG02DGZ	60909	York	YJ05KNV	66754	York
Y631RSA	62166	Aberdeen	YG02DHA	60908	West Yorkshire	YJ05KNW	66755	West Yorkshire
Y632RSA	62167	Aberdeen	YG02DHC	60927	York	YJ05KNX	66756	West Yorkshire
Y632RTD	60203	Scotland East	YG02DHD	60925	West Yorkshire	YJ05KNY	66757	West Yorkshire
Y633RSA	62168	Aberdeen	YG02DHE	60924	West Yorkshire	YJ05KNZ	66758	West Yorkshire
Y633RTD	60212	West Yorkshire	YG02DHF	60923	West Yorkshire	YJ05KOB	66750	West Yorkshire
Y634RSA	62169	Aberdeen	YG02DHJ	60922	York	YJ05KOD	66751	West Yorkshire
Y634RTD	60214	West Yorkshire	YG02DHK	60902	York	YJ05KOE	66752	West Yorkshire
Y635RSA	62177	Aberdeen	YG02DHL	60904	West Yorkshire	YJ05KOH	66753	West Yorkshire
Y636RSA	62178	Aberdeen	YG02DHM	60903	West Yorkshire	YJ05VUW	32538	West Yorkshire
Y637RSA	62179	Aberdeen	YG02DHN	60906	West Yorkshire	YJ05VUX	32537	West Yorkshire
Y638RSA	62180	Aberdeen	YG02DHO	60905	West Yorkshire	YJ05VUY	32532	West Yorkshire
Y639RSA	62181	Aberdeen	YG02DHP	40592	West of England	YJ05VVA	66759	York
Y661UKU	60703	South Yorkshire	YG02DHU	60928	York	YJ05VVB	66760	West Yorkshire
Y701RSA	62165	Aberdeen	YG02DHV	60907	West Yorkshire	YJ05VVC	66761	West Yorkshire
Y774TNC	60406	South Yorkshire	YG02DHX	40599	South Yorkshire	YJ05VVD	66762	West Yorkshire
Y794XNW	30939	West Yorkshire	YG02DHY	40593	West of England	YJ05VVE	66763	York
Y795XNW	30940	West Yorkshire	YG02DKO	60914	South West	YJ05VVF	66764	West Yorkshire
Y796XNW	30941	West Yorkshire	YG02DKU	60916	South West	YJ05VVG	66765	West Yorkshire
Y797XNW	30942	West Yorkshire	YG02DKV	60917	South West	YJ05VVH	66766	West Yorkshire
Y798XNW	30943	West Yorkshire	YG02DKX	40598	South Yorkshire	YJ05VVK	66767	West Yorkshire
Y901KND	40318	Manchester	YG02DKY	40597	South Yorkshire	YJ05VVL	66768	West Yorkshire
Y902KND	40319	Manchester	YG02DLD	60912	South West	YJ05VVM	66769	West Yorkshire
Y903KND	40320	Manchester	YG02DLE	40596	South Yorkshire	YJ05VVN	66770	Glasgow
Y904KND	40321	Manchester	YG02DLF	40595	South Yorkshire	YJ05VVO	66771	Glasgow
Y905KND	40322	Manchester	YG02DLJ	60918	South West	YJ05VVP	66772	West Yorkshire
Y932NLP	32990	Glasgow	YG02DLK	40594	West of England	YJ05VVR	66773	West Yorkshire
Y933NLP	32999	Glasgow	YG02DLN	60921	York	YJ05VVS	66774	West Yorkshire
Y934NLP	33000	Glasgow	YG02DLO	60911	South West	YJ05VVT	66775	West Yorkshire
Y937CSF	62232	South Yorkshire	YG02DLU	60920	York	YJ05VVU	66776	West Yorkshire
Y938CSF	62245	West of England	YG02DLV	48273	Hampshire D&B	YJ05VVW	66777	West Yorkshire
Y939CSF	62242	West of England	YG02DLX	60919	York	YJ05VVX	66778	West Yorkshire
Y941CSF	62231	Manchester	YG02DLY	60913	South West	YJ05VVY	66779	West Yorkshire

The 2014 First Bus Handbook

Reg	Fleet	Operator	Reg	Fleet	Operator	Reg	Fleet	Operator
YJ05VVZ	66780	West Yorkshire	YJ07LVN	19021	West Yorkshire	YJ08GVY	37086	West Yorkshire
YJ05VWA	68545	West Yorkshire	YJ07LVO	19022	West Yorkshire	YJ08GVZ	37087	West Yorkshire
YJ05VWE	32540	West Yorkshire	YJ07LVR	19023	West Yorkshire	YJ08GWA	37088	West Yorkshire
YJ05VWF	32541	West Yorkshire	YJ07LVS	19024	West Yorkshire	YJ08GWC	37089	West Yorkshire
YJ05VWG	32539	West Yorkshire	YJ07LVT	19025	West Yorkshire	YJ08GWD	37090	West Yorkshire
YJ05VWH	32542	West Yorkshire	YJ07LVU	19026	West Yorkshire	YJ08GWE	37091	West Yorkshire
YJ05XOP	53140	Hampshire D&B	YJ07LVV	19027	West Yorkshire	YJ08GWF	37092	West Yorkshire
YJ06WTV	68628	West Yorkshire	YJ07LVW	19028	West Yorkshire	YJ08GWG	37093	West Yorkshire
YJ06WTX	68626	West Yorkshire	YJ07LWC	66995	York	YJ08GWK	37094	West Yorkshire
YJ06WTZ	68630	West Yorkshire	YJ07LWD	66996	York	YJ08GWL	37095	West Yorkshire
YJ06WUA	68631	West Yorkshire	YJ07LWE	66997	West Yorkshire	YJ08GWM	37096	West Yorkshire
YJ06XEK	68640	West Yorkshire	YJ07LWF	66998	West Yorkshire	YJ08GWN	37097	West Yorkshire
YJ06XEL	68641	West Yorkshire	YJ07WBK	68711	West Yorkshire	YJ08GWO	37098	West Yorkshire
YJ06XFR	68608	West Yorkshire	YJ07WBL	68700	West Yorkshire	YJ08GWP	37099	West Yorkshire
YJ06XKK	37021	South Yorkshire	YJ07WFM	69245	Hampshire D&B	YJ08GWU	37100	West Yorkshire
YJ06XKL	37022	South Yorkshire	YJ07WFN	69246	Hampshire D&B	YJ08GWV	37101	West Yorkshire
YJ06XKM	37023	South Yorkshire	YJ07WFO	69247	Hampshire D&B	YJ08GWW	37102	West Yorkshire
YJ06XKN	37024	South Yorkshire	YJ07WFP	69248	Hampshire D&B	YJ08GWX	69299	West Yorkshire
YJ06XKO	37025	South Yorkshire	YJ07WFR	69249	Cymru	YJ08GWY	69300	West Yorkshire
YJ06XKP	37026	South Yorkshire	YJ07WFS	69250	Cymru	YJ08XCN	68692	West Yorkshire
YJ06XKS	37027	South Yorkshire	YJ07WFT	69251	Cymru	YJ08XCO	68690	West Yorkshire
YJ06XKT	37028	South Yorkshire	YJ07WFU	69252	Cymru	YJ08XCP	68691	West Yorkshire
YJ06XKU	37029	South Yorkshire	YJ07WFV	69253	West of England	YJ08XCR	68689	West Yorkshire
YJ06XKV	37030	South Yorkshire	YJ07WFW	69270	West Yorkshire	YJ08XCS	68693	West Yorkshire
YJ06XKW	37031	South Yorkshire	YJ07WFX	69271	West Yorkshire	YJ08XXW	69379	York
YJ06XKX	37032	South Yorkshire	YJ07WFY	69272	West Yorkshire	YJ08XYB	69363	York
YJ06XKY	37033	South Yorkshire	YJ07WFZ	69273	West Yorkshire	YJ08XYC	69364	York
YJ06XKZ	37034	South Yorkshire	YJ07WGA	69274	West Yorkshire	YJ08XYD	69365	York
YJ06XLA	37035	South Yorkshire	YJ07XMB	68697	West Yorkshire	YJ08XYE	69366	York
YJ06XLB	37036	West Yorkshire	YJ07XND	68708	West Yorkshire	YJ08XYF	69367	York
YJ06XLC	37037	West Yorkshire	YJ07XWF	68710	West Yorkshire	YJ08XYG	69368	York
YJ06XLD	37038	West Yorkshire	YJ07XWG	68698	West Yorkshire	YJ08XYH	69369	York
YJ06XLE	37039	West Yorkshire	YJ08CDE	69329	West Yorkshire	YJ08XYK	69370	York
YJ06XLF	37040	West Yorkshire	YJ08CDF	69330	West Yorkshire	YJ08XYL	69371	York
YJ06XLG	37041	West Yorkshire	YJ08CDK	69331	West Yorkshire	YJ08XYM	69372	York
YJ06XLH	37042	West Yorkshire	YJ08CDN	69332	West Yorkshire	YJ08XYN	69373	York
YJ06XLK	32692	West Yorkshire	YJ08CDO	69333	West Yorkshire	YJ08XYO	69374	York
YJ06XLL	32693	West Yorkshire	YJ08CDU	69334	West Yorkshire	YJ08XYP	69375	York
YJ06XLM	32694	West Yorkshire	YJ08CDV	69335	West Yorkshire	YJ08XYR	69376	York
YJ06XLN	32695	West Yorkshire	YJ08CDX	69336	West Yorkshire	YJ08XYS	69377	York
YJ06XLO	32696	West Yorkshire	YJ08CDY	69337	West Yorkshire	YJ08XYT	69378	York
YJ06XLP	32697	West Yorkshire	YJ08CDZ	69338	West Yorkshire	YJ08ZGL	69358	York
YJ06XLR	19012	West Yorkshire	YJ08CEA	69339	West Yorkshire	YJ08ZGM	69359	York
YJ06XLS	19013	West Yorkshire	YJ08CEF	69340	West Yorkshire	YJ08ZGN	69360	York
YJ06XLT	37043	West Yorkshire	YJ08CEK	69341	West Yorkshire	YJ08ZGO	69361	York
YJ06XLU	37044	West Yorkshire	YJ08CEN	69342	West Yorkshire	YJ08ZGP	69362	York
YJ06XLV	37045	York	YJ08CEO	69343	West Yorkshire	YJ09FVE	37684	West Yorkshire
YJ06XLW	37046	West Yorkshire	YJ08CEU	69344	West Yorkshire	YJ09FVF	37685	West Yorkshire
YJ06XLX	37047	West Yorkshire	YJ08CEV	69345	West Yorkshire	YJ09FVG	37676	West Yorkshire
YJ06XLY	37048	West Yorkshire	YJ08CEX	69346	West Yorkshire	YJ09FVH	37677	West Yorkshire
YJ06XLZ	37049	West Yorkshire	YJ08CEY	69347	West Yorkshire	YJ09FVK	37678	West Yorkshire
YJ06XMA	37050	West Yorkshire	YJ08CFA	69348	West Yorkshire	YJ09FVL	37679	West Yorkshire
YJ06XMB	37051	West Yorkshire	YJ08CFD	69349	West Yorkshire	YJ09FVM	37680	West Yorkshire
YJ06XMC	37052	West Yorkshire	YJ08CFE	69350	West Yorkshire	YJ09FVN	37681	West Yorkshire
YJ06XMD	37053	West Yorkshire	YJ08GVE	37071	West Yorkshire	YJ09FVO	37682	West Yorkshire
YJ06XME	37054	West Yorkshire	YJ08GVF	37072	West Yorkshire	YJ09FVP	37683	West Yorkshire
YJ06XMF	37055	West Yorkshire	YJ08GVG	37073	West Yorkshire	YJ09FWA	69306	York
YJ06XMG	37056	West Yorkshire	YJ08GVK	37074	West Yorkshire	YJ09FWB	69307	West Yorkshire
YJ06XMH	37057	West Yorkshire	YJ08GVL	37075	West Yorkshire	YJ09FWC	69308	West Yorkshire
YJ06XMK	37058	West Yorkshire	YJ08GVM	37076	West Yorkshire	YJ09FWL	69316	West Yorkshire
YJ06XML	37059	West Yorkshire	YJ08GVN	37077	West Yorkshire	YJ09FWM	69317	West Yorkshire
YJ06XMM	37060	West Yorkshire	YJ08GVO	37078	West Yorkshire	YJ09FWN	69318	West Yorkshire
YJ06XMO	37061	West Yorkshire	YJ08GVP	37079	West Yorkshire	YJ09FWO	69319	West Yorkshire
YJ06XMP	37062	West Yorkshire	YJ08GVR	37080	West Yorkshire	YJ09FWP	69320	West Yorkshire
YJ07EHO	53907	West Yorkshire	YJ08GVT	37081	West Yorkshire	YJ09FWR	69321	West Yorkshire
YJ07EHR	53909	West Yorkshire	YJ08GVU	37082	West Yorkshire	YJ09FWS	69322	West Yorkshire
YJ07FLP	68709	West Yorkshire	YJ08GVV	37083	West Yorkshire	YJ09FWT	69323	West Yorkshire
YJ07LVL	19019	West Yorkshire	YJ08GVW	37084	West Yorkshire	YJ09FWU	69324	West Yorkshire
YJ07LVM	19020	West Yorkshire	YJ08GVX	37085	West Yorkshire	YJ09FWV	69325	Manchester

Reg	No.	Location	Reg	No.	Location	Reg	No.	Location
YJ09FWW	69326	Manchester	YJ09OBU	37723	West Yorkshire	YJ51RDV	30961	York
YJ09FWX	69327	Manchester	YJ09OBV	37724	West Yorkshire	YJ51RDX	30962	York
YJ09FWY	69328	Manchester	YJ09OBW	37725	West Yorkshire	YJ51RDY	30963	York
YJ09FWZ	69412	West Yorkshire	YJ09OBX	37726	West Yorkshire	YJ51RDZ	60888	South Yorkshire
YJ09FXA	69413	West Yorkshire	YJ09OBY	37727	West Yorkshire	YJ51REU	60894	South Yorkshire
YJ09FXB	69414	West Yorkshire	YJ09OBZ	37728	West Yorkshire	YJ51RFE	60895	South West
YJ09FXC	69415	West Yorkshire	YJ09OCA	37729	West Yorkshire	YJ51RFF	60896	York
YJ09FXD	69416	West Yorkshire	YJ09OCB	37730	West Yorkshire	YJ51RFK	60910	South West
YJ09FXE	69417	West Yorkshire	YJ09OCC	37731	West Yorkshire	YJ51RFL	60899	York
YJ09FXF	69418	West Yorkshire	YJ09OCD	37732	West Yorkshire	YJ51RFN	60900	York
YJ09FXG	69419	West Yorkshire	YJ09OCE	37733	West Yorkshire	YJ51RFO	60901	York
YJ09FXH	69420	Manchester	YJ09OCF	37734	West Yorkshire	YJ51RFX	60898	York
YJ09NYA	69466	West Yorkshire	YJ09OCG	37735	West Yorkshire	YJ51RFY	60897	York
YJ09NYB	69467	West Yorkshire	YJ12GXV	49228	Manchester	YJ51RFZ	40587	West Yorkshire
YJ09NYC	69468	West Yorkshire	YJ12GXZ	49227	Manchester	YJ51RGO	40588	West of England
YJ09NYD	69469	West Yorkshire	YJ12MYF	49202	Manchester	YJ51RGU	40589	West of England
YJ09NYF	69470	West Yorkshire	YJ12MYG	49203	Manchester	YJ51RGV	40590	West of England
YJ09NYG	69471	West Yorkshire	YJ12MYH	49204	Manchester	YJ51RGX	40591	West of England
YJ09NYH	69472	West Yorkshire	YJ12MYK	49205	Manchester	YJ51RGY	60893	South Yorkshire
YJ09NYK	69473	West Yorkshire	YJ12MYL	49206	Manchester	YJ51RGZ	60891	South Yorkshire
YJ09NYM	69474	West Yorkshire	YJ12MYN	49208	Manchester	YJ51RHE	60889	South Yorkshire
YJ09NYN	69475	West Yorkshire	YJ12MYO	49209	Manchester	YJ51RHF	60892	South Yorkshire
YJ09NYO	69476	West Yorkshire	YJ12MYP	49210	Manchester	YJ51RHK	60890	South Yorkshire
YJ09NYP	69477	West Yorkshire	YJ12MYR	49211	Manchester	YJ51RHO	40577	West Yorkshire
YJ09NYR	69478	West Yorkshire	YJ12MYS	49212	Manchester	YJ51RHU	40578	West Yorkshire
YJ09NYS	69479	West Yorkshire	YJ12MYT	49213	Manchester	YJ51RHV	40579	West Yorkshire
YJ09NYT	69480	West Yorkshire	YJ12MYU	49214	Manchester	YJ51RJV	40585	South West
YJ09NYU	69481	West Yorkshire	YJ12MYV	49215	Manchester	YJ51RJX	40586	South West
YJ09NYV	69482	West Yorkshire	YJ12MYW	49216	Manchester	YJ51RKO	40571	York
YJ09NYW	69483	West Yorkshire	YJ12MYX	49217	Manchester	YJ51RKU	40572	York
YJ09NYX	69484	West Yorkshire	YJ12MYY	49218	Manchester	YJ51RKV	40573	York
YJ09NYY	69485	West Yorkshire	YJ12MZD	49220	Manchester	YJ51RPY	30944	West Yorkshire
YJ09NZY	37686	West Yorkshire	YJ12MZF	49222	Manchester	YJ51RPZ	30945	West Yorkshire
YJ09OAA	37687	West Yorkshire	YJ13GUE	29006	Aberdeen	YJ51RRO	30946	West Yorkshire
YJ09OAB	37688	West Yorkshire	YJ13GUF	29007	Aberdeen	YJ51RRU	30947	West Yorkshire
YJ09OAC	37689	West Yorkshire	YJ13HLR	49301	Cymru	YJ51RRV	30948	West Yorkshire
YJ09OAD	37690	West Yorkshire	YJ13HLU	49302	Cymru	YJ51RRX	30949	West Yorkshire
YJ09OAE	37691	West Yorkshire	YJ13HLV	49303	Cymru	YJ51RRY	30950	West Yorkshire
YJ09OAG	37692	West Yorkshire	YJ13HLW	49304	Cymru	YJ51RRZ	30951	West Yorkshire
YJ09OAH	37693	West Yorkshire	YJ13HLX	49305	Cymru	YJ51RSO	30952	West Yorkshire
YJ09OAL	37694	West Yorkshire	YJ13HLY	49306	Cymru	YJ51RSU	30953	West Yorkshire
YJ09OAM	37695	West Yorkshire	YJ13HLZ	49307	Cymru	YJ51RSV	40574	York
YJ09OAN	37696	West Yorkshire	YJ13HMA	49308	Cymru	YJ51RSX	40575	York
YJ09OAO	37697	West Yorkshire	YJ13HMC	49309	Cymru	YJ51RSY	40576	West Yorkshire
YJ09OAP	37698	West Yorkshire	YJ13HMD	49002	Cymru	YJ54BSV	53201	Glasgow
YJ09OAS	37699	West Yorkshire	YJ13HME	49003	Cymru	YJ54BVA	53301	West Yorkshire
YJ09OAU	37700	West Yorkshire	YJ13HMF	49004	Cymru	YJ54BVB	53302	West Yorkshire
YJ09OAV	37701	West Yorkshire	YJ13HMG	49005	Cymru	YJ54BVC	53303	West Yorkshire
YJ09OAW	37702	West Yorkshire	YJ13HMH	49006	Cymru	YJ54XTO	32503	West Yorkshire
YJ09OAX	37703	West Yorkshire	YJ13HMK	49007	Cymru	YJ54XTP	32504	West Yorkshire
YJ09OAY	37704	West Yorkshire	YJ13HMU	49008	Cymru	YJ54XTR	32505	West Yorkshire
YJ09OAZ	37705	West Yorkshire	YJ13HMV	49009	Cymru	YJ54XTT	32506	West Yorkshire
YJ09OBA	37706	West Yorkshire	YJ13HMX	49010	Cymru	YJ54XTU	32507	West Yorkshire
YJ09OBB	37707	West Yorkshire	YJ51PZT	60882	York	YJ54XTV	32508	West Yorkshire
YJ09OBC	37708	West Yorkshire	YJ51PZU	60883	York	YJ54XTW	32509	West Yorkshire
YJ09OBD	37709	West Yorkshire	YJ51PZV	60884	York	YJ54XTX	32510	West Yorkshire
YJ09OBE	37710	West Yorkshire	YJ51PZW	60885	South Yorkshire	YJ54XTZ	32511	West Yorkshire
YJ09OBF	37711	West Yorkshire	YJ51PZX	60886	South Yorkshire	YJ54XUA	32512	West Yorkshire
YJ09OBG	37712	West Yorkshire	YJ51PZY	60887	South Yorkshire	YJ54XUB	32513	West Yorkshire
YJ09OBH	37713	West Yorkshire	YJ51PZZ	40570	South West	YJ54XUC	32514	West Yorkshire
YJ09OBK	37714	West Yorkshire	YJ51RAU	30964	York	YJ54XUD	32515	West Yorkshire
YJ09OBL	37715	West Yorkshire	YJ51RAX	30965	York	YJ54XUE	32516	West Yorkshire
YJ09OBM	37716	West Yorkshire	YJ51RCO	30959	York	YJ54XUF	32517	West Yorkshire
YJ09OBN	37717	West Yorkshire	YJ51RCU	30955	York	YJ54XUG	32518	West Yorkshire
YJ09OBO	37718	West Yorkshire	YJ51RCV	30956	York	YJ54XUH	32519	West Yorkshire
YJ09OBP	37719	West Yorkshire	YJ51RCX	30957	York	YJ54XUK	32520	West Yorkshire
YJ09OBR	37720	West Yorkshire	YJ51RCZ	30958	York	YJ54XUM	32521	West Yorkshire
YJ09OBS	37721	West Yorkshire	YJ51RDO	30954	York	YJ54XUN	32522	West Yorkshire
YJ09OBT	37722	West Yorkshire	YJ51RDU	30960	York	YJ54XUO	32523	West Yorkshire

Reg	No	Location	Reg	No	Location	Reg	No	Location
YJ54XUP	32524	West Yorkshire	YJ58CDV	53910	West Yorkshire	YJ61FAF	29004	Aberdeen
YJ54XUR	32525	West Yorkshire	YJ58CDX	53911	West Yorkshire	YJ61JDO	59009	Manchester
YJ54XUT	32526	West Yorkshire	YJ58CDY	53912	West Yorkshire	YJ61JDU	59010	Manchester
YJ54XUU	32527	West Yorkshire	YJ58CEV	53065	Hampshire D&B	YJ61JDX	59011	Manchester
YJ54XUV	32528	West Yorkshire	YJ58GMO	37361	West Yorkshire	YJ61JDZ	59012	Manchester
YJ54XUW	32529	West Yorkshire	YJ58GMU	37363	West Yorkshire	YJ61JEO	59013	Manchester
YJ54XUX	32530	West Yorkshire	YJ58GMV	37365	West Yorkshire	YJ61JEU	59014	Manchester
YJ54XUY	32531	West Yorkshire	YJ58GNP	37360	West Yorkshire	YJ61JFA	59015	Manchester
YJ54XVA	32533	West Yorkshire	YJ58GNU	37362	West Yorkshire	YJ61JFE	59016	Manchester
YJ54XVB	32534	West Yorkshire	YJ58GNV	37364	West Yorkshire	YJ61JFU	49117	Manchester
YJ54XVC	32535	West Yorkshire	YJ58GNX	37366	West Yorkshire	YJ61JFV	49118	Manchester
YJ54XVD	32536	West Yorkshire	YJ58RNN	37645	West Yorkshire	YJ61JFX	49119	Manchester
YJ54XVM	66738	West Yorkshire	YJ58RNO	37646	West Yorkshire	YJ61JHK	49113	Manchester
YJ54XVN	66739	West Yorkshire	YJ58RNU	37647	West Yorkshire	YJ61JHL	49114	Manchester
YJ54XVO	66740	West Yorkshire	YJ58RNV	37648	West Yorkshire	YJ61JHO	49115	Manchester
YJ54XVP	66741	West Yorkshire	YJ58RNX	37649	West Yorkshire	YJ61JHU	49116	Manchester
YJ54XVR	66742	West Yorkshire	YJ58RNY	37650	West Yorkshire	YJ61MMA	64504	Cymru
YJ54XVT	66743	West Yorkshire	YJ58RNZ	37651	West Yorkshire	YJ61MME	64505	Cymru
YJ54XVU	66744	West Yorkshire	YJ58ROH	37652	West Yorkshire	YJ61MMF	64506	Cymru
YJ54XVW	66745	West Yorkshire	YJ58ROU	37653	West Yorkshire	YJ62FAM	59100	West of England
YJ54XVX	66746	West Yorkshire	YJ58RPO	37654	West Yorkshire	YJ62FLD	49300	West of England
YJ54XVY	66747	West Yorkshire	YJ58RPU	37655	West Yorkshire	YK04EZG	66713	West Yorkshire
YJ54XVZ	66748	West Yorkshire	YJ58RPV	37656	West Yorkshire	YK04EZH	66715	West Yorkshire
YJ54XWA	66749	West Yorkshire	YJ58RPX	37657	West Yorkshire	YK04EZJ	66711	West Yorkshire
YJ54YCO	68515	West Yorkshire	YJ58RPY	37658	West Yorkshire	YK04EZL	66712	West Yorkshire
YJ54YCP	68516	West Yorkshire	YJ58RPZ	37659	West Yorkshire	YK04EZM	66714	West Yorkshire
YJ55CAO	68546	West Yorkshire	YJ58RRO	37660	West Yorkshire	YK04KWR	53801	South West
YJ55CAU	68548	West Yorkshire	YJ58RRU	37661	West Yorkshire	YK05CDN	53826	South West
YJ55CAV	68547	West Yorkshire	YJ58RRV	37662	West Yorkshire	YK05CDO	53827	South West
YJ56EAA	19014	West Yorkshire	YJ58RRX	37663	West Yorkshire	YK05FJE	66784	West Yorkshire
YJ56EAC	19015	West Yorkshire	YJ58RRY	37664	West Yorkshire	YK05FJF	66783	West Yorkshire
YJ56EAE	19016	West Yorkshire	YJ58RRZ	37665	West Yorkshire	YK05FJJ	66781	West Yorkshire
YJ56EAF	19017	West Yorkshire	YJ58RSO	37666	West Yorkshire	YK05FLB	66782	West Yorkshire
YJ56EAG	19018	West Yorkshire	YJ58RSU	37667	West Yorkshire	YK05FLC	66786	West Yorkshire
YJ56LJE	68651	West Yorkshire	YJ58RSV	37668	West Yorkshire	YK05FOP	66791	West Yorkshire
YJ56LJF	68652	West Yorkshire	YJ58RSX	37669	West Yorkshire	YK05FOT	66789	West Yorkshire
YJ56LJK	68653	West Yorkshire	YJ58RSY	37670	West Yorkshire	YK05FOU	66788	West Yorkshire
YJ56LJL	68655	West Yorkshire	YJ58RSZ	37671	West Yorkshire	YK05FOV	66787	West Yorkshire
YJ56LJN	68654	West Yorkshire	YJ58RTO	37672	West Yorkshire	YK05FPA	66785	West Yorkshire
YJ56LJY	68664	West Yorkshire	YJ58RTU	37673	West Yorkshire	YK06AOU	19001	West Yorkshire
YJ56LKC	68667	West Yorkshire	YJ58RTV	37674	West Yorkshire	YK06ATO	68642	West Yorkshire
YJ56LKD	68668	West Yorkshire	YJ58RTX	37675	West Yorkshire	YK06ATU	19003	West Yorkshire
YJ56LKE	68663	West Yorkshire	YJ58RVA	69315	West Yorkshire	YK06ATV	19002	West Yorkshire
YJ56LLG	68656	West Yorkshire	YJ59KSO	37752	West Yorkshire	YK06ATX	19005	West Yorkshire
YJ56LLK	68657	West Yorkshire	YJ59KSU	37753	West Yorkshire	YK06ATY	19007	West Yorkshire
YJ56LLN	68659	West Yorkshire	YJ59KSV	37754	West Yorkshire	YK06ATZ	19008	West Yorkshire
YJ56LLO	68660	West Yorkshire	YJ59KSY	37755	West Yorkshire	YK06AUA	19010	West Yorkshire
YJ56LMX	68669	West Yorkshire	YJ59KSZ	37756	West Yorkshire	YK06AUC	19011	West Yorkshire
YJ56LNA	68662	West Yorkshire	YJ60KCA	59001	Manchester	YK06AUL	19009	West Yorkshire
YJ56LRL	68672	West Yorkshire	YJ60KCC	59002	Manchester	YK06CZZ	68643	West Yorkshire
YJ56LRN	68671	West Yorkshire	YJ60KCE	59003	Manchester	YK06DAA	68646	West Yorkshire
YJ56LRU	68670	West Yorkshire	YJ60KCF	59004	Manchester	YK06DNN	68638	West Yorkshire
YJ56WGA	68674	West Yorkshire	YJ60KCG	59005	Manchester	YK06DTZ	68639	West Yorkshire
YJ56ZMU	68675	West Yorkshire	YJ60KCK	59006	Manchester	YK06DYJ	68635	West Yorkshire
YJ56ZTM	68704	West Yorkshire	YJ60KCN	59007	Manchester	YK06EFR	68702	West Yorkshire
YJ57NFF	68705	West Yorkshire	YJ60KCO	59008	Manchester	YK06EFS	68703	West Yorkshire
YJ57VTV	68685	West Yorkshire	YJ60KCU	49101	Manchester	YK06EHE	68648	West Yorkshire
YJ57VVA	68686	West Yorkshire	YJ60KCV	49102	Manchester	YK07AYA	37103	South Yorkshire
YJ57VYX	68684	West Yorkshire	YJ60KCX	49103	Manchester	YK07AYB	37104	South Yorkshire
YJ57VYY	68687	West Yorkshire	YJ60KCY	49104	Manchester	YK07AYC	37105	South Yorkshire
YJ57WKB	68707	West Yorkshire	YJ60KCZ	49105	Manchester	YK07AYD	37106	South Yorkshire
YJ57WKC	68706	West Yorkshire	YJ60KDF	49106	Manchester	YK07AYE	37107	South Yorkshire
YJ57YSK	69268	York	YJ60KDK	49107	Manchester	YK07AYF	37108	South Yorkshire
YJ57YSL	69269	York	YJ60KDN	49108	Manchester	YK07AYG	37109	South Yorkshire
YJ57YSM	69276	York	YJ60KDO	49109	Manchester	YK07AYH	37110	South Yorkshire
YJ57YSN	69275	York	YJ60KDU	49110	Manchester	YK07AYJ	37111	South Yorkshire
YJ57YSO	69277	York	YJ60KDV	49111	Manchester	YK07AYL	37112	South Yorkshire
YJ57YSP	69278	York	YJ60KDX	49112	Manchester	YK07AYM	37113	South Yorkshire
YJ57YSR	69279	York	YJ61FAA	29005	Aberdeen	YK07AYN	37114	South Yorkshire

Reg	No.	Location	Reg	No.	Location	Reg	No.	Location
YK07AYO	37115	South Yorkshire	YM52UVW	61223	Scotland East	YN06TDV	65030	Essex
YK07AYP	37116	South Yorkshire	YM52UVZ	61224	Scotland East	YN06TDX	65031	Essex
YK07AYS	37117	South Yorkshire	YM52UWA	61225	Scotland East	YN06TDZ	65032	Essex
YK07AYT	37118	South Yorkshire	YM52UWB	61226	Scotland East	YN06UPZ	37146	Midlands
YK07AYU	37119	South Yorkshire	YM52UWD	61227	Scotland East	YN06URA	37147	Glasgow
YK07AYV	37120	South Yorkshire	YM52UWF	61228	Scotland East	YN06URB	37148	Glasgow
YK07AYW	37121	South Yorkshire	YM52UWG	61229	Scotland East	YN06URC	37149	Glasgow
YK07AYX	37122	South Yorkshire	YM52UWH	61230	Scotland East	YN06URD	37150	Glasgow
YK07AYY	37123	West Yorkshire	YM52UWJ	61231	Scotland East	YN06URE	37151	Glasgow
YK07AYZ	37124	West Yorkshire	YM52UWK	61232	Scotland East	YN06URF	37152	Glasgow
YK07BJX	68694	West Yorkshire	YM52UWN	61233	Scotland East	YN06URG	37153	Glasgow
YK07BJY	68695	West Yorkshire	YN03ZVW	53151	Hampshire D&B	YN06URH	37154	Glasgow
YK07BJZ	68696	West Yorkshire	YN03ZVX	50407	West Yorkshire	YN06URJ	37155	Glasgow
YK07FTP	68682	West Yorkshire	YN04AJU	23013	South West	YN06WME	65033	Midlands
YK07FTT	68683	West Yorkshire	YN04AJV	23015	Hampshire D&B	YN06WMF	65034	Midlands
YK07FTU	68676	West Yorkshire	YN04AJX	23014	South West	YN06WMG	65035	Midlands
YK07FTX	68699	West Yorkshire	YN04GLV	36005	Hampshire D&B	YN06WMJ	65036	Midlands
YK07FUA	68680	West Yorkshire	YN04GME	65705	Midlands	YN06WMK	65037	Midlands
YK07FUD	68677	West Yorkshire	YN04GMF	65706	Midlands	YN06WML	65038	Midlands
YK53GXR	66707	West Yorkshire	YN04GNV	36001	Hampshire D&B	YN06WMM	65039	Midlands
YK53GXT	66708	West Yorkshire	YN04GNX	36002	Hampshire D&B	YN06WMO	65040	Midlands
YK53GXU	66709	West Yorkshire	YN04GNY	36003	Hampshire D&B	YN06WMP	65041	Midlands
YK53GXV	66710	West Yorkshire	YN04GNZ	36004	Hampshire D&B	YN06WMT	65042	Midlands
YK54ENL	69001	York	YN04YHW	23202	South West	YN07MKD	37246	York
YK54ENM	69002	York	YN04YHY	23201	South West	YN07MKE	37247	York
YK54ENN	69003	York	YN04YHZ	23204	Cymru	YN07MKF	37248	York
YK54ENO	69004	York	YN04YJC	65001	Midlands	YN07MKG	37249	York
YK54ENP	69000	York	YN04YJD	65002	Midlands	YN07MKJ	37250	York
YK55AAJ	68603	West Yorkshire	YN04YJE	65003	Midlands	YN07MKK	37251	York
YK55AAN	68610	West Yorkshire	YN04YJF	65004	Midlands	YN07MKL	37252	York
YK55AUE	68614	West Yorkshire	YN04YJG	65005	Midlands	YN07MKM	37253	York
YK55AUF	68615	West Yorkshire	YN05GXF	65759	South West	YN07MKO	37254	York
YK55AUH	68616	West Yorkshire	YN05GXG	65760	South West	YN07MKP	37255	York
YK55AUP	68606	West Yorkshire	YN05GYA	12001	Manchester	YN07MKV	37256	York
YK55AUU	68609	West Yorkshire	YN05GYB	12002	Manchester	YN07MKX	37257	South Yorkshire
YK55AVF	68621	West Yorkshire	YN05GYC	12005	Manchester	YN07MKZ	37258	South Yorkshire
YK55AVG	68622	West Yorkshire	YN05GYD	12006	Manchester	YN07MLE	37259	South Yorkshire
YK55AVJ	68623	West Yorkshire	YN05GYE	12007	Manchester	YN07MLJ	37261	South Yorkshire
YK55AVM	68625	West Yorkshire	YN05GYF	12008	Manchester	YN07MLK	37262	South Yorkshire
YK55ENM	53905	West Yorkshire	YN05GYG	12009	Manchester	YN07MLL	37263	South Yorkshire
YK55ENN	53906	West Yorkshire	YN05GYH	12003	Manchester	YN07MLO	37264	South Yorkshire
YK55ENR	53904	West Yorkshire	YN05GYJ	12004	Manchester	YN07MLU	37265	South Yorkshire
YK55JCN	68701	West Yorkshire	YN05GYK	12010	Manchester	YN08LCK	37230	South Yorkshire
YK57CJF	37125	West Yorkshire	YN05GYO	12011	Manchester	YN08LCL	37231	South Yorkshire
YK57CJJ	37126	West Yorkshire	YN05GYP	12014	Manchester	YN08LCM	37234	South Yorkshire
YK57CJO	37127	West Yorkshire	YN05GYR	12015	Manchester	YN08LCO	37235	South Yorkshire
YK57CJU	37128	West Yorkshire	YN05GYS	12016	Manchester	YN08LCP	37237	South Yorkshire
YK57CJV	37129	West Yorkshire	YN05GYT	12017	Manchester	YN08LCT	37238	Glasgow
YK57CJX	37130	West Yorkshire	YN05GYU	12013	Manchester	YN08LCU	37239	Glasgow
YK57CJY	37131	West Yorkshire	YN05GYV	12012	Manchester	YN08LCV	37240	Glasgow
YK57CJZ	37132	West Yorkshire	YN05GYW	12018	Manchester	YN08LCW	37241	Glasgow
YK57EZS	37063	West Yorkshire	YN05HCL	65027	Midlands	YN08LCY	37242	Glasgow
YK57EZT	37064	West Yorkshire	YN05HCO	65727	Midlands	YN08LCZ	37243	Glasgow
YK57EZU	37065	West Yorkshire	YN05HCP	65728	Midlands	YN08LDA	37244	Glasgow
YK57EZW	37066	West Yorkshire	YN05HCU	65729	Midlands	YN08LDC	37245	Glasgow
YK57EZW	37067	West Yorkshire	YN05HCV	65730	Midlands	YN08LDD	37278	Glasgow
YK57EZX	37068	West Yorkshire	YN05HCX	65731	Midlands	YN08NLL	37472	South Yorkshire
YK57EZZ	37069	West Yorkshire	YN05HCY	65732	Midlands	YN08NLM	37473	South Yorkshire
YK57FAA	37070	West Yorkshire	YN05HCZ	65733	Midlands	YN08NLO	37474	South Yorkshire
YK57FCL	66999	West Yorkshire	YN05HGA	36006	Hampshire D&B	YN08NLP	37475	South Yorkshire
YM52UVK	61214	Scotland East	YN06CGU	23321	Cymru	YN08NLR	37476	South Yorkshire
YM52UVL	61215	Scotland East	YN06CGV	23322	Cymru	YN08NLT	37477	South Yorkshire
YM52UVN	61216	Scotland East	YN06CGX	23323	Cymru	YN08NLU	37478	South Yorkshire
YM52UVO	61217	Scotland East	YN06CGY	23324	Cymru	YN08NLV	37479	South Yorkshire
YM52UVP	61218	Scotland East	YN06CGZ	23325	Cymru	YN08NLX	37480	South Yorkshire
YM52UVR	61219	Scotland East	YN06NXP	65761	South West	YN08NLY	37481	South Yorkshire
YM52UVS	61220	Scotland East	YN06NXW	65762	South West	YN08NLZ	37482	South Yorkshire
YM52UVT	61221	Scotland East	YN06TDO	65028	Essex	YN08NMA	37483	Manchester
YM52UVU	61222	Scotland East	YN06TDU	65029	Essex	YN08NME	37484	South Yorkshire

Code	No.	Region	Code	No.	Region	Code	No.	Region
YN08NMF	37485	South Yorkshire	YN54NXO	23308	Cymru	YN58ETT	37525	South Yorkshire
YN08NMJ	37486	South Yorkshire	YN54NXR	23309	Cymru	YN58ETU	37526	South Yorkshire
YN08NMK	37487	South Yorkshire	YN54NXT	23310	Cymru	YN58ETV	37527	South Yorkshire
YN08NMM	37488	South Yorkshire	YN54NXU	23302	Cymru	YN58ETX	37528	South Yorkshire
YN08NMU	37489	South Yorkshire	YN54NXV	23303	Cymru	YN58ETY	37529	South Yorkshire
YN08NMV	37490	South Yorkshire	YN54NXW	23304	Cymru	YN62GXS	20809	Hampshire D&B
YN08NMX	37491	South Yorkshire	YN54NXZ	23307	Cymru	YN62GYR	20808	Hampshire D&B
YN08NMY	37492	South Yorkshire	YN54NYR	23311	Cymru	YP02ABN	65678	Essex
YN08OWO	20801	Essex	YN54NYT	23312	Cymru	YR02UVU	50239	South Yorkshire
YN08OWP	20802	Essex	YN54NYU	23313	Cymru	YR52VEH	65679	Essex
YN08OWR	20803	Essex	YN54NYV	23314	Cymru	YR52VEK	65680	Essex
YN08OWU	20804	Essex	YN54NZA	65006	Hampshire D&B	YR52VEL	65681	Essex
YN08OWV	20805	Essex	YN54NZC	65007	Hampshire D&B	YR52VEP	65682	Essex
YN08PLF	37493	South Yorkshire	YN54NZD	65008	Hampshire D&B	YR52VEU	65683	Essex
YN08PLO	37495	South Yorkshire	YN54NZE	65009	Hampshire D&B	YR52VEY	65684	Essex
YN08PLU	37496	South Yorkshire	YN54NZF	65010	Hampshire D&B	YR52VFO	65685	Essex
YN08PLX	37498	South Yorkshire	YN54NZG	65011	Hampshire D&B	YS03ZKA	62406	Essex
YN08PLZ	37499	South Yorkshire	YN54NZH	65012	Hampshire D&B	YS03ZKB	62407	Essex
YN08PMO	37500	South Yorkshire	YN54NZJ	65013	Hampshire D&B	YS03ZKC	65686	Essex
YN08PMU	37501	South Yorkshire	YN54NZK	65014	Hampshire D&B	YS03ZKD	62409	Essex
YN08PMV	37502	South Yorkshire	YN54NZM	65015	Hampshire D&B	YS03ZKE	62408	Essex
YN08PMX	37503	South Yorkshire	YN54NZO	65016	Hampshire D&B	YS03ZKF	62410	Essex
YN08PMY	37504	South Yorkshire	YN54NZP	65017	Hampshire D&B	YS03ZKG	65687	Essex
YN08PNE	37505	South Yorkshire	YN54NZR	65018	Hampshire D&B	YS03ZKH	65688	Essex
YN08PNF	37506	South Yorkshire	YN54NZT	65019	Hampshire D&B	YS03ZKJ	65689	Essex
YN08PNJ	37507	South Yorkshire	YN54NZU	65020	Hampshire D&B	YS03ZKK	65690	Eastern Counties
YN08PNK	37508	South Yorkshire	YN54NZV	65021	Hampshire D&B	YS03ZKL	65691	Eastern Counties
YN09HFH	69461	South Yorkshire	YN54NZW	65022	Hampshire D&B	YS03ZKM	65692	Eastern Counties
YN09HFJ	69462	South Yorkshire	YN54NZX	65023	Hampshire D&B	YS51JVA	61135	Hampshire D&B
YN09HFK	69463	South Yorkshire	YN54NZY	65024	Hampshire D&B	YS51JVD	62228	Aberdeen
YN09HFL	69464	South Yorkshire	YN54NZZ	65025	Hampshire D&B	YS51JVE	68005	Hampshire D&B
YN09HFM	69465	South Yorkshire	YN54OCK	65026	Midlands	YS51JVH	68006	Hampshire D&B
YN53EFE	31787	Glasgow	YN55PXF	23315	Cymru	YS51JVK	61136	Hampshire D&B
YN53EFF	31788	Glasgow	YN55PXG	23316	Cymru	YT51EZW	50237	South Yorkshire
YN53EFG	31789	Glasgow	YN55PXH	23317	Cymru	YT51EZX	50238	South Yorkshire
YN53EFH	31790	Scotland East	YN55PXJ	23318	Cymru	YU52VXH	61192	South Yorkshire
YN53EFJ	31791	Scotland East	YN55PXK	23319	Cymru	YU52VXJ	61193	South Yorkshire
YN53EFK	31792	Scotland East	YN55PXL	23320	Cymru	YU52VXK	61194	South Yorkshire
YN53EFL	31793	Glasgow	YN56NHE	57001	Scotland East	YU52VXL	61195	South Yorkshire
YN53EFM	31794	Glasgow	YN56NHF	57002	Scotland East	YU52VXM	61196	South Yorkshire
YN53EFO	31795	Glasgow	YN57BVU	20321	Cymru	YU52VXN	61197	South Yorkshire
YN53EFP	31796	Glasgow	YN57BVV	20322	Cymru	YU52VXO	61198	South Yorkshire
YN53EFR	31797	Glasgow	YN57BVW	20323	Cymru	YU52VXP	61199	South Yorkshire
YN53EFT	31798	Glasgow	YN57BVX	20324	Cymru	YU52VXR	61200	South Yorkshire
YN53EFU	31799	Glasgow	YN57BVY	20325	Cymru	YU52VXS	61201	South Yorkshire
YN53EFV	31800	Glasgow	YN57BVZ	20326	Scotland East	YU52VXT	61202	South Yorkshire
YN53EFW	31801	Glasgow	YN57BWU	20327	Scotland East	YU52VXV	61203	South Yorkshire
YN53EFX	31802	Glasgow	YN57RJU	37228	South Yorkshire	YU52VXW	61204	South Yorkshire
YN53EFZ	31803	Glasgow	YN57RJZ	37232	South Yorkshire	YU52VXX	61205	South Yorkshire
YN53EGC	31804	Glasgow	YN57RKA	37233	South Yorkshire	YU52VXY	61206	South Yorkshire
YN53ELJ	50319	West Yorkshire	YN57RKJ	37236	South Yorkshire	YU52VYE	31129	South Yorkshire
YN53ELO	50318	West of England	YN58ERX	37494	South Yorkshire	YU52VYF	31130	South Yorkshire
YN53EOA	31776	South Yorkshire	YN58ERY	37497	South Yorkshire	YU52VYG	31131	South Yorkshire
YN53EOB	31777	South Yorkshire	YN58ERZ	37509	South Yorkshire	YU52VYH	31132	South Yorkshire
YN53EOC	31778	South Yorkshire	YN58ESF	37510	South Yorkshire	YU52VYJ	31133	South Yorkshire
YN53EOD	31779	South Yorkshire	YN58ESG	37511	South Yorkshire	YU52VYK	31134	South Yorkshire
YN53EOE	31780	South Yorkshire	YN58ESO	37512	South Yorkshire	YU52VYL	31135	South Yorkshire
YN53EOF	31781	South Yorkshire	YN58ESU	37513	South Yorkshire	YU52VYM	32278	West of England
YN53EOG	31782	South Yorkshire	YN58ESV	37514	South Yorkshire	YU52VYN	31137	South Yorkshire
YN53EOH	31783	South Yorkshire	YN58ESY	37515	South Yorkshire	YU52VYO	31138	South Yorkshire
YN53EOJ	31784	South Yorkshire	YN58ETA	37516	South Yorkshire	YU52VYP	31139	South Yorkshire
YN53EOK	31785	South Yorkshire	YN58ETD	37517	South Yorkshire	YU52VYR	31140	South Yorkshire
YN53EOL	31786	South Yorkshire	YN58ETE	37518	South Yorkshire	YU52VYS	31141	South Yorkshire
YN53VBT	56001	Aberdeen	YN58ETF	37519	South Yorkshire	YU52VYT	31142	South Yorkshire
YN53VBU	56002	Scotland East	YN58ETJ	37520	South Yorkshire	YU52VYV	31143	West Yorkshire
YN53VBV	56003	Scotland East	YN58ETK	37521	South Yorkshire	YU52VYW	31144	South Yorkshire
YN54APF	23021	Aberdeen	YN58ETL	37522	South Yorkshire	YU52VYX	31145	South Yorkshire
YN54APK	23020	Cymru	YN58ETO	37523	South Yorkshire	YU52VYY	31146	West Yorkshire
YN54APX	23019	South West	YN58ETR	37524	South Yorkshire	YU52VYZ	31147	West Yorkshire

Reg	No	Location	Reg	No	Location	Reg	No	Location
YU52VZA	31148	South Yorkshire	YX13AEF	44537	Essex	YX62DXF	44525	West of England
YV03UBA	23008	South West	YX13AEV	44552	Cymru	YX62DXH	44526	West of England
YV03UBB	23009	South West	YX13AEW	44553	Cymru	YX63LHK	44591	Cymru
YV03UBC	23010	South West	YX13AEY	44554	Cymru	YX63LHL	44592	Cymru
YV03UBD	23011	Hampshire D&B	YX13AEZ	44555	Cymru	YX63LHM	44593	Cymru
YV03UBE	23012	South West	YX13AFA	44556	Cymru	YX63LHR	44594	Cymru
YV03UOU	40976	South Yorkshire	YX13AFE	44557	Cymru	YX63LHS	44595	Cymru
YV03UOW	40975	South Yorkshire	YX13AHN	44538	Essex	YX63LJF	33803	Eastern Counties
YV03UOX	40974	South Yorkshire	YX13AHO	44539	Essex	YX63LJJ	33804	Eastern Counties
YV03UOY	40973	South Yorkshire	YX13AHP	44540	Essex	YX63LJK	33805	Eastern Counties
YW04VAU	32431	West Yorkshire	YX13AHU	44541	Essex	YX63LJL	33806	Eastern Counties
YX05AVV	56501	Aberdeen	YX13AHV	44542	Essex	YX63LJN	33807	Eastern Counties
YX08HJF	44599	Essex	YX13AHZ	44543	Essex	YX63LJO	33808	Eastern Counties
YX09ACV	44516	Essex	YX13AKF	44544	Essex	YX63LJU	33809	Eastern Counties
YX09ACY	44517	Essex	YX13AKG	44545	Essex	YX63LJV	33810	Eastern Counties
YX09ACZ	44518	Essex	YX13AKJ	44546	Essex	YX63LJY	33811	Eastern Counties
YX09ADO	44519	Essex	YX13AKK	44547	Essex	YX63LJZ	33812	Eastern Counties
YX09ADU	44921	West of England	YX13AKN	44548	Essex	YX63LKA	33813	Eastern Counties
YX09ADV	44922	South West	YX13AKO	44549	Essex	YX63LKC	33814	Eastern Counties
YX09ADZ	44923	South West	YX13AKP	44550	Essex	YX63LKD	33815	Eastern Counties
YX09AFN	44905	West of England	YX13AKU	44558	Cymru	YX63LKE	33816	Eastern Counties
YX09AFO	44906	West of England	YX13AKV	44559	Cymru	YX63LKF	33817	Eastern Counties
YX09AFU	44907	West of England	YX13AKY	44551	Essex	YX63LKG	33818	Eastern Counties
YX09AFV	44908	West of England	YX13BNA	44573	Cymru	YX63LKJ	33819	Eastern Counties
YX09AFY	44909	West of England	YX13BNB	44574	Cymru	YX63LKK	33820	Eastern Counties
YX09AFZ	44910	West of England	YX13BND	44575	Cymru	YX63LKL	33821	Eastern Counties
YX09AGO	44911	West of England	YX13BNE	44576	Cymru	YX63LKM	33822	Eastern Counties
YX09AGU	44912	West of England	YX13BNF	44577	Cymru	YX63LKN	33823	Eastern Counties
YX09AGV	44913	West of England	YX13BNJ	44578	Cymru	YX63LKO	33824	Eastern Counties
YX09AGZ	44914	West of England	YX13BNK	44579	Cymru	YX63LKR	44569	Cymru
YX09AHA	44915	West of England	YX13BNL	44580	Cymru	YX63LKU	44570	Cymru
YX09AHC	44916	West of England	YX13BNN	44581	Cymru	YX63LKV	44560	Hampshire D&B
YX09AHD	44917	West of England	YX58FRJ	45111	South West	YX63LKY	44561	Hampshire D&B
YX09AHE	44918	West of England	YX58FRK	45112	South West	YX63LKZ	44562	Hampshire D&B
YX09AHF	44919	West of England	YX58FRL	45113	South West	YX63LLC	44563	Hampshire D&B
YX09AHG	44920	West of England	YX58FRN	45114	South West	YX63LLD	44564	Hampshire D&B
YX09AHK	44924	South West	YX58FRP	45115	South West	YX63LLE	44565	Hampshire D&B
YX10AXP	54302	Glasgow	YX58HVF	44076	Essex	YX63LLF	44566	Hampshire D&B
YX10AXT	54307	Glasgow	YX58HVG	44077	Essex	YX63LLG	44567	Hampshire D&B
YX10AYL	54304	Glasgow	YX58HVH	44078	Essex	YX63LLJ	44568	Hampshire D&B
YX11HNW	44925	South Yorkshire	YX58HVJ	44079	Essex	YX63ZUD	44582	Cymru
YX11HNY	44926	South Yorkshire	YX58HVK	44080	Essex	YX63ZVA	44583	Cymru
YX11HNZ	44927	South Yorkshire	YX58HVL	44081	Essex	YX63ZVB	44584	Cymru
YX11HPO	20806	Hampshire D&B	YX58HWF	44507	Hampshire D&B	YX63ZVC	44585	Cymru
YX11HPP	20807	Hampshire D&B	YX58HWG	44508	Hampshire D&B	YX63ZVD	44586	Cymru
YX12CHK	54401	Glasgow	YX58HWH	44509	Hampshire D&B	YX63ZVE	44587	Cymru
YX12CHL	54402	Glasgow	YX58HWJ	44510	Hampshire D&B	YX63ZVF	44588	Cymru
YX12CHO	54403	Glasgow	YX62DVM	44520	West of England	YX63ZVG	44589	Cymru
YX12CJF	54404	Glasgow	YX62DWG	44521	West of England	YX63ZVH	44590	Cymru
YX12CJJ	54405	Glasgow	YX62DWM	44522	West of England	YY63WBT	20810	Hampshire D&B
YX12CJO	54406	Glasgow	YX62DWO	44523	West of England	YY63WBU	20811	Hampshire D&B
YX12CJU	54407	Glasgow	YX62DXC	44524	West of England			

ISBN 9781904875246

© Published by British Bus Publishing Ltd, March 2014

British Bus Publishing Ltd, 16 St Margaret's Drive, Telford, TF1 3PH

Telephone: 01952 255669

web; www.britishbuspublishing.co.uk
e-mail: sales@britishbuspublishing.co.uk